# ANALYTIC GEOMETRY

# ANALYTIC GEOMETRY

BY

ROSS R. MIDDLEMISS
*Professor of Applied Mathematics*
*Washington University*

FIRST EDITION
SEVENTH IMPRESSION

McGRAW-HILL BOOK COMPANY, INC.
NEW YORK AND LONDON
1945

# PREFACE

In writing this book the author has attempted to present a brief course in analytic geometry that is more in keeping with the actual needs of scientific and technical students than that offered by most of the available texts. The choice of subject matter and methods has been influenced by the fact that most students study analytic geometry primarily as a preparation for calculus and the various sciences. In content the book differs from the average text in the following ways:

The treatment of conic sections has been shortened by omitting topics that contribute little or nothing to the training of the student for scientific work. The space thus gained has been utilized by providing a brief chapter on the polynomial curves and by devoting more attention to the exponential, logarithmic, trigonometric, and inverse trigonometric functions and their graphs. The chapter on polynomial curves includes subject matter that advances the student's preparation for calculus. The chapter on exponential and logarithmic curves contains a brief section on the hyperbolic functions and also includes instruction in the use of tables of natural logarithms.

The discussion of curves as to intercepts, symmetry, and asymptotes is introduced in Chap. V on Rational Fractional Functions. Horizontal asymptotes are found here by investigating the behavior of the function when $x$ increases beyond bound. This method introduces the student to ideas that are valuable in the study of calculus. Later on, in Chap. IX on Other Algebraic Curves, the topic of curve discussion is extended to include investigations that are valuable in connection with the general problem of sketching algebraic curves.

The idea of addition of ordinates is introduced early and mentioned rather often. This topic probably deserves somewhat more attention than it usually receives. It would certainly seem, for example, that a student of calculus should be able to visualize immediately the general shape of the graph of an equation such as $y = ax^2 + \dfrac{b}{x}$ by thinking of the result of sketching the separate graphs of $y = ax^2$ and $y = b/x$ and adding ordinates. Multiplication of ordinates is discussed in the chapter on exponential and logarithmic curves.

The concept of moment of a force is introduced, and a few simple problems of mechanics are solved as an application of the procedure for computing the distance from a line to a point. The section on direction numbers of a line in space includes problems on the computation of components of forces.

An effort has been made to present the subject in such a way as to make a maximum contribution to the general mathematical training of the student. Whether or not a sophomore studying engineering or some other science can locate the radical center of three circles, or whether or not he has heard of the ovals of Cassini and the conchoid of Nicomedes, is unimportant. It *is* important, on the other hand, that he should have a clear understanding of the fundamental *methods* of analytic geometry and that he should have in mind the most essential of the fundamental facts. The necessary instruction should be given in such a way as to stimulate the interest of the student and give him valuable training in clear and accurate thinking. It is hoped that in this task the book will prove helpful.

The author is indebted to his present colleagues Profs. P. R. Rider, S. E. Warschawski, and G. C. Helme, and to his former colleagues Profs. C. A. Hutchinson and J. R. Britton of the University of Colorado for many useful suggestions.

Ross R. Middlemiss.

St. Louis, Missouri,
July. 1945.

# CONTENTS

# INTRODUCTION

## REVIEW OF ESSENTIAL DEFINITIONS AND FORMULAS FROM ALGEBRA AND TRIGONOMETRY

**1. The quadratic equation.**—The two roots of the quadratic equation

(1) $$ax^2 + bx + c = 0 \qquad (a \neq 0)$$

are

$$x_1 = \frac{-b + \sqrt{b^2 - 4ac}}{2a} \quad \text{and} \quad x_2 = \frac{-b - \sqrt{b^2 - 4ac}}{2a}.$$

If $a$, $b$, and $c$ are real numbers, these roots are

Real and unequal if $b^2 - 4ac > 0$;
Real and equal if $b^2 - 4ac = 0$;
Imaginary and unequal if $b^2 - 4ac < 0$.

The formula

(2) $$x = \frac{-b \pm \sqrt{b^2 - 4ac}}{2a},$$

which gives both roots, is called the *quadratic formula*. It is derived by solving the equation $ax^2 + bx + c = 0$ by completing the square.

**2. Determinants.**—The symbol

(3) $$\begin{vmatrix} a_1 & b_1 \\ a_2 & b_2 \end{vmatrix}$$

is called a *determinant of second order;* the numbers $a_1$, $a_2$, $b_1$, $b_2$ are called its *elements*. The determinant has a value that is defined by the equation

(4) $$\begin{vmatrix} a_1 & b_1 \\ a_2 & b_2 \end{vmatrix} \equiv a_1 b_2 - a_2 b_1.$$

1

*Example*

$$\begin{vmatrix} 3 & -2 \\ 4 & 5 \end{vmatrix} = 3 \cdot 5 - 4 \cdot (-2) = 15 + 8 = 23.$$

The *determinant of third order*, which contains nine elements, is denoted by the symbol

(5)
$$\begin{vmatrix} a_1 & b_1 & c_1 \\ a_2 & b_2 & c_2 \\ a_3 & b_3 & c_3 \end{vmatrix}.$$

Its value is defined to be equal to

(6)
$$a_1 \begin{vmatrix} b_2 & c_2 \\ b_3 & c_3 \end{vmatrix} - a_2 \begin{vmatrix} b_1 & c_1 \\ b_3 & c_3 \end{vmatrix} + a_3 \begin{vmatrix} b_1 & c_1 \\ b_2 & c_2 \end{vmatrix}$$

which in turn is equal to

$$a_1 b_2 c_3 + a_2 b_3 c_1 + a_3 b_1 c_2 - a_1 b_3 c_2 - a_2 b_1 c_3 - a_3 b_2 c_1.$$

*Example*

$$\begin{vmatrix} 3 & 6 & 4 \\ 2 & -2 & 1 \\ 3 & 5 & 2 \end{vmatrix} = 3 \begin{vmatrix} -2 & 1 \\ 5 & 2 \end{vmatrix} - 2 \begin{vmatrix} 6 & 4 \\ 5 & 2 \end{vmatrix} + 3 \begin{vmatrix} 6 & 4 \\ -2 & 1 \end{vmatrix}$$
$$= 3(-4 - 5) - 2(12 - 20) + 3(6 + 8) = 31.$$

By the *minor* of an element of a determinant we mean the determinant that remains when the row and column in which the element occurs are struck out. Thus the minor of the element $a_1$ in the determinant (5) is $\begin{vmatrix} b_2 & c_2 \\ b_3 & c_3 \end{vmatrix}$, and the minor of $b_1$ is $\begin{vmatrix} a_2 & c_2 \\ a_3 & c_3 \end{vmatrix}$. In the above definition (6) we have expressed the value of (5) in terms of the minors of elements of the first column.

Determinants of order higher than the third are defined in a similar way.

**3. Linear equations.**—Consider the pair of linear equations

(7)
$$\begin{aligned} a_1 x + b_1 y &= c_1 \\ a_2 x + b_2 y &= c_2. \end{aligned}$$

By multiplying the top equation by $b_2$ and the bottom

one by $b_1$, and subtracting, we can easily eliminate $y$ and solve for $x$. In a similar way we may solve for $y$. The results are

$$x = \frac{c_1 b_2 - c_2 b_1}{a_1 b_2 - a_2 b_1}; \qquad y = \frac{a_1 c_2 - a_2 c_1}{a_1 b_2 - a_2 b_1}.$$

Using the determinant notation, we have

$$(8) \qquad x = \frac{\begin{vmatrix} c_1 & b_1 \\ c_2 & b_2 \end{vmatrix}}{\begin{vmatrix} a_1 & b_1 \\ a_2 & b_2 \end{vmatrix}}; \qquad y = \frac{\begin{vmatrix} a_1 & c_1 \\ a_2 & c_2 \end{vmatrix}}{\begin{vmatrix} a_1 & b_1 \\ a_2 & b_2 \end{vmatrix}}.$$

The determinant $\begin{vmatrix} a_1 & b_1 \\ a_2 & b_2 \end{vmatrix}$, which appears in both denominators, is called the *determinant of the coefficients* of (7) and is denoted by $D$. The equations (7) have the unique simultaneous solution given by (8) if $D \neq 0$. If $D = 0$, and if the numerators in (8) are not both zero, the equations have no common solution. If all three determinants in (8) are equal to zero, then every solution of either equation is also a solution of the other.

The solution of the set of three simultaneous equations

$$(9) \qquad \begin{aligned} a_1 x + b_1 y + c_1 z &= d_1 \\ a_2 x + b_2 y + c_2 z &= d_2 \\ a_3 x + b_3 y + c_3 z &= d_3 \end{aligned} \Bigg\}$$

is similarly found to be

$$(10) \qquad x = \frac{\begin{vmatrix} d_1 & b_1 & c_1 \\ d_2 & b_2 & c_2 \\ d_3 & b_3 & c_3 \end{vmatrix}}{D}; \qquad y = \frac{\begin{vmatrix} a_1 & d_1 & c_1 \\ a_2 & d_2 & c_2 \\ a_3 & d_3 & c_3 \end{vmatrix}}{D};$$

$$z = \frac{\begin{vmatrix} a_1 & b_1 & d_1 \\ a_2 & b_2 & d_2 \\ a_3 & b_3 & d_3 \end{vmatrix}}{D}; \qquad \text{if } D = \begin{vmatrix} a_1 & b_1 & c_1 \\ a_2 & b_2 & c_2 \\ a_3 & b_3 & c_3 \end{vmatrix} \neq 0.$$

The *homogeneous* equations

$$(11) \qquad \begin{aligned} a_1 x + b_1 y &= 0 \\ a_2 x + b_2 y &= 0 \end{aligned} \Bigg\}$$

obviously have the "trivial" solution $x = 0$, $y = 0$. They have solutions other than this if and only if

$$\begin{vmatrix} a_1 & b_1 \\ a_2 & b_2 \end{vmatrix} = 0.$$

Similar considerations apply to the case of three homogeneous linear equations in $x$, $y$, and $z$ (see Prob. 7, page 6).

**4. Exponents.**—We at first define the symbol $a^n$ *for n a positive integer only* as follows:

$$a^1 = a$$
$$a^2 = a \cdot a$$
$$a^3 = a \cdot a \cdot a$$
$$\cdots \cdots \cdots$$
$$a^n = a \cdot a \cdot a \cdots \text{ to } n \text{ factors.}$$

This definition assigns no meaning whatever to $a^x$ if $x$ is not a positive integer.

From the above definition one can easily deduce the following rules which govern the use of positive integral exponents:

(1)     $a^m \cdot a^n = a^{m+n}$

(2)     $\dfrac{a^m}{a^n} = a^{m-n}$     if     $m > n$,     $a \neq 0.$

(3)     $(a^m)^n = a^{mn}$

(4)     $(a \cdot b)^n = a^n \cdot b^n$

(5)     $\left(\dfrac{a}{b}\right)^n = \dfrac{a^n}{b^n}$     if     $b \neq 0.$

We next extend our definition in order to assign meanings to symbols such as $a^0$, $a^{-3}$, and $a^{\frac{2}{3}}$. In making this extension we impose the requirement that the same rules which govern the use of positive integral exponents shall apply in all cases. Thus if we wish that

$$a^m \cdot a^0 = a^{m+0} = a^m \qquad (a \neq 0)$$

we must *assign* the value *one* to the symbol $a^0$ if $a \neq 0$. Note also that with this definition of $a^0$ rule (2) holds if $m = n$. We do not here assign any meaning to $a^0$ if $a = 0$; *i.e.*, $0^0$ remains a meaningless symbol.

Considering negative exponents next, we require that

$$a^m \cdot a^{-m} = a^{m-m} = a^0 = 1.$$

Hence we must *define* the symbol $a^{-m}$ to mean $1/a^m$.

Similarly, for fractional exponents, if we wish that

$$a^{\frac{1}{2}} a^{\frac{1}{2}} = a^{\frac{1}{2}+\frac{1}{2}} = a, \qquad (a > 0)$$

we must define $a^{\frac{1}{2}}$ to stand for a square root of $a$. To avoid ambiguity we define it to stand for the *positive* square root. In general we define the symbol $a^{\frac{1}{q}}$ $(a > 0)$ to stand for the positive $q$th root of $a$. Then of course $a^{\frac{p}{q}}$ denotes the $p$th power of this root.

**5. Logarithms.**—*The logarithm of a number* $N$ *to the base* $a$ *is the exponent of the power to which* $a$ *must be raised to obtain* $N$; *i.e.*, if

$$a^x = N \qquad \text{then} \qquad x = \log_a N.$$

The base may be any positive number except 1. The bases usually used are 10, in which case the corresponding logarithms are called *common logarithms*, and the irrational number $e = 2.71828$; logarithms to this base are called *natural logarithms*.

Logarithms are exponents, and their fundamental properties follow from the laws governing the use of exponents. They are

$$\log_a (MN) = \log_a M + \log_a N;$$
$$\log_a \left(\frac{M}{N}\right) = \log_a M - \log_a N;$$
$$\log_a N^q = q \log_a N;$$
$$\log_b N = \frac{\log_a N}{\log_a b}.$$

As a special case of the last formula, we have

$$\log_e N = \frac{\log_{10} N}{\log_{10} e};$$

since $\log_{10} e = \log_{10} 2.71828 \doteq 0.43429$, this becomes

$$\log_e N = \frac{\log_{10} N}{0.43429} = 2.3026 \log_{10} N.$$

## PROBLEMS

**1.** Solve each of the following quadratic equations by completing the square:

(a) $x^2 - 7x + 10 = 0.$        (b) $x^2 - x - 20 = 0.$
(c) $2x^2 - 5x - 3 = 0.$        (d) $3x^2 - x - 4 = 0.$

**2.** Derive the quadratic formula.

**3.** Use the quadratic formula to solve the following equations:

(a) $2x^2 - x - 15 = 0.$        (b) $x^2 + x + 1 = 0.$
(c) $x^2 - 4x + 20 = 0.$        (d) $2x^2 + 6x + 3 = 0.$

**4.** Evaluate the following determinants:

(a) $\begin{vmatrix} 4 & 1 \\ 8 & 5 \end{vmatrix}$    (b) $\begin{vmatrix} -3 & 6 \\ 2 & 1 \end{vmatrix}$    (c) $\begin{vmatrix} 6 & 3 & 1 \\ -2 & 4 & 1 \\ 2 & 1 & 0 \end{vmatrix}$    (d) $\begin{vmatrix} 4 & 0 & 5 \\ 3 & 1 & 0 \\ 2 & 2 & 1 \end{vmatrix}.$

**5.** Solve the given pair of equations simultaneously using determinants:

(a) $3x + 4y = 13$
    $x + y = 3.$
(c) $5x - y = 5.2$
    $2x + 5y = 17.2.$

(b) $x - 3u = 7$
    $3x - 9y = 12.$
(d) $5x + 2y = 4$
    $15x + 6y = 12.$

**6.** Solve the given set of equations simultaneously using determinants:

(a) $2x - 3y + 3z = 16$
    $5x + 4y - z = 3$
    $3x + y - 7z = -16.$

(b) $x - 4y + z = 7$
    $3x - 6y - z = -3$
    $y + z = 1.$

**7.** The equations

$$5x + 2y + z = 0$$
$$x - 3y + 7z = 0$$
$$4x + 5y - 6z = 0$$

have the trivial solution $x = 0$, $y = 0$, $z = 0$. They have other solutions if and only if the determinant $D$ of the coefficients is zero. Show that $D = 0$, and then show that if $z = k$, where $k$ is any number, the equations are satisfied if $x = -k$ and $y = 2k$.

**8.** Evaluate:  $32^{\frac{1}{5}} + \frac{1}{5}(32)^{-\frac{4}{5}}$.

**9.** Evaluate:  $[4(8)^{-\frac{2}{3}} - 3(2)^0 + 2(27)^{\frac{2}{3}}]^{-\frac{1}{2}}$.

**10.** Solve for $x$:    $x^{-\frac{3}{2}} - 27 = 0$.

**11.** Solve for $x$:    $25(x^{-\frac{2}{3}}) = 1$.

**12.** Using the definition of a logarithm show that

$$\log_a (MN) = \log_a M + \log_a N.$$

HINT: Let $\log_a M = x$ and $\log_a N = y$; then $M = a^x$, $N = a^y$, and $MN = a^{x+y}$. It follows that $x + y = \log_a (MN)$.  Why?

**13.** Prove the formula: $\log_a \dfrac{M}{N} = \log_a M - \log_a N$.

**14.** Prove the formula: $\log_a N^q = q \log_a N$.

**15.** Calculate $\log_e 165$ using a table of common logarithms.  Check by using a table of natural logarithms.

**16.** To what power must 17 be raised to obtain 643?

### 6. Angles.

—In trigonometry an angle is assumed to be generated by revolving a line called a *generating line* about a point called a *vertex*.  The initial position of the generating line is called the *initial side* of the angle, and its final position is called the *terminal side* (Fig. *A*).  If the rotation is counterclockwise, the angle is called positive; if clockwise, it is called negative.

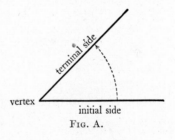

FIG. A.

### 7. Measurement of angles.

—The common unit of angle measurement in elementary mathematics is the *degree* which is one-ninetieth part of a right angle.  The degree is further divided into minutes and seconds as follows:

**1 right angle = 90 degrees,**
**1 degree = 60 minutes,**
**1 minute = 60 seconds.**

In advanced mathematics it is usually desirable to

measure angles in *radians*. A radian, as indicated in Fig. *B*, is the angle subtended at the center of a circle by an arc whose length is equal to the radius. Since the radius of a circle is contained in the circumference $2\pi$ times, we have

$$2\pi \text{ radians} = 360 \text{ degrees;}$$

$$1 \text{ radian} = \frac{360}{2\pi} = 57.296 \text{ degrees;}$$

$$1 \text{ degree} = \frac{2\pi}{360} = 0.017453 \text{ radian.}$$

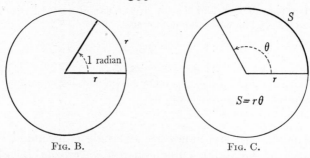

FIG. B.          FIG. C.

If $\theta$ is the number of radians subtended at the center of a circle of radius $r$ by an arc whose length is $S$ (Fig. *C*), then

$$\theta = \frac{S}{r} \quad \text{or} \quad S = r\theta.$$

**8. The trigonometric functions.**—It is assumed in the following paragraphs that the student is familiar with the rectangular coordinate system (see page 17 to 19).

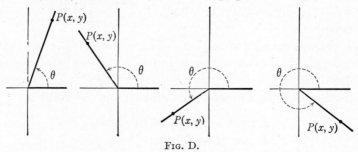

FIG. D.

If $\theta$ is any *number*, the trigonometric functions of $\theta$ are defined as follows: Construct an angle of $\theta$ radians with vertex at the origin and initial side along the positive $x$-axis, measuring the angle counterclockwise if $\theta$ is positive and clockwise if negative. Choose any point $P(x, y)$ on the terminal side of $\theta$; denote its distance from the origin by $r$, it being agreed that $r$ is to be regarded as positive. Then (Fig. $D$)

$$\sin \theta = \frac{y}{r} \qquad \csc \theta = \frac{r}{y}$$

$$\cos \theta = \frac{x}{r} \qquad \sec \theta = \frac{r}{x}$$

$$\tan \theta = \frac{y}{x} \qquad \cot \theta = \frac{x}{y}$$

**9. The signs of the functions.**—We agree to consider that $x$ is positive when $P$ is to the right and negative when $P$ is to the left of the $y$-axis; $y$ is positive when $P$ is above and negative when $P$ is below the $x$-axis.

These conventions as to the signs of $x$ and $y$, and the above agreement as to the sign of $r$, fix the signs of the trigonometric functions of $\theta$. Thus if $\theta$ is an angle whose terminal side lies in the second quadrant, $\cos \theta$ is negative; for $\cos \theta = x/r$ and $x$ is negative while $r$ is positive.

**10. Values of the functions for certain angles.**—In order to find the value of any function of any angle that is a

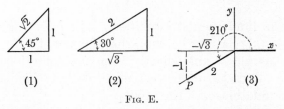

(1)      (2)      (3)

Fig. E.

multiple of 30° or 45°, one has only to remember that in the 45° right triangle the two legs are equal and in the 30°–60° right triangle the shortest leg is exactly equal to one-half the hypotenuse [Fig. $E$ (1) and (2)]. Thus to find $\sin 210°$ (or $7\pi/6$ radians) one draws Fig. $E$ (3) and writes down from it

$$\sin 210° = -\tfrac{1}{2}.$$

The values of the functions for the quadrantal angles 0, 90, 180, and 270° can also be easily found. For this, one needs only to note that for such angles either $x$ or $y$ is zero and the other equals $\pm r$. Thus for $\theta = 270°$, $x = 0$, and $y = -r$; hence (Fig. $F$)

$$\sin 270° = \frac{-r}{r} = -1;$$

$$\cos 270° = \frac{0}{r} = 0.$$

FIG. F.

It is essential in the study of analytic geometry, and particularly in connection with the sketching of curves in polar coordinates, that the student be able to find quickly and without tables the values of the functions for these special angles.

**11. The values of the functions when that of one is known.**—If, for a certain angle, the value of one of the six trigonometric functions and the quadrant in which the terminal side lies are known, the values of the other five functions can be found easily. Thus if it is known that $\sin \alpha$

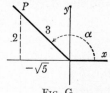

FIG. G.

$= \frac{2}{3}$ and the terminal side of $\alpha$ lies in the second quadrant, we deduce by drawing Fig. $G$ that $\cos \alpha = -\sqrt{5}/3$, $\tan \alpha = -2/\sqrt{5}$ etc.

**12. The fundamental identities.**—The following are the fundamental relations between the trigonometric functions. The proofs follow immediately from the definitions of the functions, and the student should be entirely familiar with both the relations and the proofs:

($a$) $\sin^2 \theta + \cos^2 \theta = 1.$

($b$) $1 + \tan^2 \theta = \sec^2 \theta.$

($c$) $1 + \cot^2 \theta = \csc^2 \theta.$

($d$) $\tan \theta = \dfrac{\sin \theta}{\cos \theta}.$

($e$) $\begin{cases} \csc \theta = \dfrac{1}{\sin \theta}. \\[2mm] \sec \theta = \dfrac{1}{\cos \theta}. \\[2mm] \cot \theta = \dfrac{1}{\tan \theta}. \end{cases}$

**13. The functions of $-\theta$.**—By comparing the values of $x$,

$y$, and $r$ for any angle $\theta$ with those for $-\theta$ (an angle equal to $\theta$ but measured clockwise from the positive $x$-axis), it is easy to show that:

$$\sin(-\theta) = -\sin\theta;$$
$$\cos(-\theta) = \cos\theta;$$
$$\tan(-\theta) = -\tan\theta.$$

**14. Reduction formulas.**—By comparing the values of $x$, $y$, and $r$ for an angle $\theta$ with those for the angles $90° \pm \theta$ and $180° \pm \theta$, one can show that

$$\sin(90° - \theta) = \cos\theta \qquad \sin(90° + \theta) = \cos\theta$$
$$\cos(90° - \theta) = \sin\theta \qquad \cos(90° + \theta) = -\sin\theta$$
$$\tan(90° - \theta) = \cot\theta \qquad \tan(90° + \theta) = -\cot\theta$$

$$\sin(180° - \theta) = \sin\theta \qquad \sin(180° + \theta) = -\sin\theta$$
$$\cos(180° - \theta) = -\cos\theta \qquad \cos(180° + \theta) = -\cos\theta$$
$$\tan(180° - \theta) = -\tan\theta \qquad \tan(180° + \theta) = \tan\theta$$

**15. Functions of the sum and difference of two angles. Double and half-angle formulas.**—From the definitions of the functions, it can be shown that if one adds two angles $\alpha$ and $\beta$, the sine, cosine, and tangent of the sum are given by

$(a)$ $\qquad \sin(\alpha + \beta) = \sin\alpha\cos\beta + \cos\alpha\sin\beta;$

$(b)$ $\qquad \cos(\alpha + \beta) = \cos\alpha\cos\beta - \sin\alpha\sin\beta;$

$(c)$ $\qquad \tan(\alpha + \beta) = \dfrac{\tan\alpha + \tan\beta}{1 - \tan\alpha\tan\beta}.$

Replacing $\beta$ by $-\beta$ in $(a)$, $(b)$, and $(c)$, we have for the difference of two angles

$(d)$ $\qquad \sin(\alpha - \beta) = \sin\alpha\cos\beta - \cos\alpha\sin\beta;$

$(e)$ $\qquad \cos(\alpha - \beta) = \cos\alpha\cos\beta + \sin\alpha\sin\beta;$

$(f)$ $\qquad \tan(\alpha - \beta) = \dfrac{\tan\alpha - \tan\beta}{1 + \tan\alpha\tan\beta}.$

If $\beta = \alpha$, formulas $(a)$, $(b)$, and $(c)$ reduce to

$(g)$ $\qquad \sin 2\alpha = 2\sin\alpha\cos\alpha;$

$(h)$ $\qquad \cos 2\alpha = \cos^2\alpha - \sin^2\alpha;$

(*i*)
$$\tan 2\alpha = \frac{2 \tan \alpha}{1 - \tan^2 \alpha}.$$

From formula (*h*) it can easily be shown that

(*j*)  $\sin \frac{1}{2}\alpha = \pm \sqrt{\dfrac{1 - \cos \alpha}{2}};$

(*k*)  $\cos \frac{1}{2}\alpha = \pm \sqrt{\dfrac{1 + \cos \alpha}{2}};$

(*l*)  $\tan \frac{1}{2}\alpha = \pm \sqrt{\dfrac{1 - \cos \alpha}{1 + \cos \alpha}} = \dfrac{1 - \cos \alpha}{\sin \alpha} = \dfrac{\sin \alpha}{1 + \cos \alpha}.$

It should be observed that the $\pm$ sign does not appear in the last two forms of the formula for tan $\frac{1}{2}\alpha$. This is because $1 \pm \cos \alpha$ is never negative and tan $\frac{1}{2}\alpha$ always has the same sign as sin $\alpha$.

**16. Sine and cosine laws.**—SINE LAW: *In any triangle the sides are proportional to the sines of the opposite angles; i.e.,* (Fig. *H*),

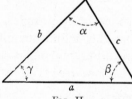

FIG. H.

$$\frac{a}{\sin \alpha} = \frac{b}{\sin \beta} = \frac{c}{\sin \gamma}.$$

COSINE LAW: *The square of any side of a triangle is equal to the sum of the squares of the other two sides minus twice the product of these sides and the cosine of the included angle.* Thus, in Fig. *H*,

$$c^2 = a^2 + b^2 - 2ab \cos \gamma.$$

**17. Greek alphabet.**

| LETTERS | | NAMES | LETTERS | | NAMES | LETTERS | | NAMES |
|---|---|---|---|---|---|---|---|---|
| A | $\alpha$ | Alpha | I | $\iota$ | Iota | P | $\rho$ | Rho |
| B | $\beta$ | Beta | K | $\kappa$ | Kappa | $\Sigma$ | $\sigma$ | Sigma |
| $\Gamma$ | $\gamma$ | Gamma | $\Lambda$ | $\lambda$ | Lambda | T | $\tau$ | Tau |
| $\Delta$ | $\delta$ | Delta | M | $\mu$ | Mu | $\Upsilon$ | $\upsilon$ | Upsilon |
| E | $\epsilon$ | Epsilon | N | $\nu$ | Nu | $\Phi$ | $\phi$ | Phi |
| Z | $\zeta$ | Zeta | $\Xi$ | $\xi$ | Xi | X | $\chi$ | Chi |
| H | $\eta$ | Eta | O | $o$ | Omicron | $\Psi$ | $\psi$ | Psi |
| $\Theta$ | $\theta$ | Theta | $\Pi$ | $\pi$ | Pi | $\Omega$ | $\omega$ | Omega |

## PROBLEMS

**1.** Change the following from degrees to radians:

(a) 88°.        (b) 240°.        (c) 400°.        (d) 7° 10′.

**2.** Change the following from radians to degrees:

(a) 1.4.        (b) $5\pi/6$.        (c) 2.1.        (d) $-3.6$.

**3.** Show that $30° = \pi/6$ radians, $45° = \pi/4$ radians, $60° = \pi/3$ radians.

**4.** Find the angle subtended at the center of a circle of radius 24 ft. by an arc whose length is 16 ft. 3 in.

Evaluate the following expressions without using tables:

**5.** $\cos 135° + \sin 60° - \sin 315° + \cos 150°$.

**6.** $\sec 0° + 2 \cos 90° - 3 \sin 270° + \cos 180°$.

**7.** $\tan 495° + \sec 540° - 3 \cos 420°$.

**8.** $4 \sin \dfrac{\pi}{6} - 2 \tan \dfrac{7\pi}{4} + \sin \dfrac{5\pi}{6}$.

**9.** Using tables find $\sin 485°$, $\cos(-604°)$, $\tan 820°$.

**10.** Draw a figure and from it show that $\sin(-\theta) = -\sin\theta$ and $\cos(-\theta) = \cos\theta$ when the terminal side of $\theta$ lies in the first quadrant; the third quadrant.

**11.** Prove the fundamental identities listed in Art. 12.

**12.** Prove the formulas for $\sin(x+y)$ and $\cos(x+y)$ assuming that $x$ and $y$ are positive angles such that $(x+y) < \frac{1}{2}\pi$. How may the proof be extended to cover all values of $x$ and $y$?

**13.** Show how all the rest of the formulas concerning the functions of the sum and difference of two angles, and the double and half-angle formulas [formulas (c) to (l)], are derived from those for $\sin(x+y)$ and $\cos(x+y)$.

**14.** If $\tan \theta = \frac{3}{4}$, $\theta$ being a positive angle $< \pi/2$, find $\sin 2\theta$, $\cos 2\theta$, and $\tan \frac{1}{2}\theta$.

**15.** If $\tan \theta = -\frac{5}{12}$ and the terminal side of $\theta$ lies in the second quadrant, find $\sin 2\theta$, $\cos 2\theta$, and $\tan 2\theta$.

**16.** If $\cos x = \frac{5}{13}$ and $\sin y = \frac{3}{5}$, the terminal side of $x$ being in the fourth quadrant and that of $y$ in the second, find $\sin(x+y)$ and $\tan(x-y)$.

**17.** If $\tan 2\theta = \frac{24}{7}$, $2\theta$ being a positive angle $< 90°$, find $\sin\theta$ and $\cos\theta$.

**18.** If $\tan 2\theta = -\frac{4}{3}$, $2\theta$ being a positive angle between 90 and 180°, find $\sin\theta$ and $\cos\theta$.

By using the fundamental identities reduce

**19.** $\sec\theta - \sin\theta \tan\theta$ to $\cos\theta$.

**20.** $1 - \dfrac{\sin^2\theta}{1 + \cos\theta}$ to $\cos\theta$.

**21.** $\dfrac{\sin \theta}{1 + \cos \theta} + \dfrac{1 + \cos \theta}{\sin \theta}$ to $\dfrac{2}{\sin \theta}$.

**22.** $\dfrac{\cos \theta + \cot \theta}{1 + \sin \theta}$ to $\cot \theta$.

In each of the following, find all positive values of $\theta < 360°$ that satisfy the given equation:

**23.** $\cos \theta - \sin 2\theta = 0.$      **24.** $6 \cos^2 \theta - 5 \cos \theta + 1 = 0.$

**25.** $\tan 2\theta - 2 \sin \theta = 0.$

**26.** $\sin 3\theta = \sin 2\theta + \sin \theta.$

**27.** $3 \sin \theta = 5 - 4 \cos \theta.$

**28.** $\sin 2\theta = \cos \theta - 2 \cos^2 \frac{1}{2}\theta.$

Prove the following identities:

**29.** $\cos^4 \theta - \sin^4 \theta = \cos 2\theta.$      **30.** $\sin 3\theta = 3 \sin \theta - 4 \sin^3 \theta.$

**31.** $(\sin \frac{1}{2}x - \cos \frac{1}{2}x)^2 = 1 - \sin x.$

**32.** $\cos 3\theta = 4 \cos^3 \theta - 3 \cos \vartheta.$

**33.** $\dfrac{2 \sin \theta - \sin 2\theta}{2 \sin \theta + \sin 2\theta} = \tan^2 \frac{1}{2}\theta.$

**34.** $\sin 2\theta \tan \frac{1}{2}\theta + \cos 2\theta = 2 \cos \theta - 1.$

**35.** $\dfrac{\sin 3x - \sin x}{\cos 3x + \cos x} = \tan x.$

**36.** $\sec^6 \theta - \tan^6 \theta = 3 \tan^4 \theta + 3 \tan^2 \theta + 1.$

**37.** From the formulas for the sine and cosine of $(\alpha + \beta)$ and $(\alpha - \beta)$ derive the following formulas:

(a) $\sin A + \sin B = 2 \sin \frac{1}{2}(A + B) \cos \frac{1}{2}(A - B).$

(b) $\sin A - \sin B = 2 \cos \frac{1}{2}(A + B) \sin \frac{1}{2}(A - B).$

(c) $\cos A + \cos B = 2 \cos \frac{1}{2}(A + B) \cos \frac{1}{2}(A - B).$

(d) $\cos A - \cos B = -2 \sin \frac{1}{2}(A + B) \sin \frac{1}{2}(A - B).$

**38.** Using the formulas of Prob. 37 show that

$$\frac{\sin 2x + \sin 4x}{\cos 2x + \cos 4x} = \tan 3x.$$

# PLANE
# ANALYTIC GEOMETRY

# CHAPTER I

## FUNCTIONS AND GRAPHS

**1. Introduction.**—Analytic geometry is a branch of mathematics in which problems of geometry are solved by the use of algebra and a coordinate system, and problems of algebra are simplified and clarified by interpreting equations geometrically as representing lines, curves, or surfaces. A beginning has already been made by the student in his study of algebra; for he has no doubt interpreted a pair of given linear equations in $x$ and $y$ as representing two straight lines in a plane, and their common solution as representing the point of intersection.

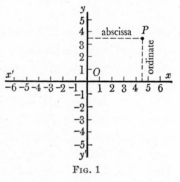

Fig. 1

The idea of combining the analytical methods of algebra with the concepts of geometry, by means of a coordinate system, was due largely to René Descartes, a French mathematician. In 1637 he published the first systematic work on the subject under the title of "La Géometrie." Because of this the subject is sometimes called *Cartesian geometry.* The rectangular coordinates with which the student has had some experience in algebra and trigonometry are sometimes called *Cartesian* coordinates. They are discussed in the next section.

**2. Rectangular coordinates.**—Let $x'x$ and $y'y$ be two mutually perpendicular lines intersecting at 0 (Fig. 1). For the present we may regard $x'x$ as a "horizontal" line and $y'y$ as a "vertical" line. On each line we choose a unit of measurement and mark off a scale with the zero point

17

at 0. On the horizontal line we put positive numbers to the right and negative numbers to the left of 0; on the vertical line we put positive numbers above and negative numbers below 0. This amounts to choosing the positive direction on the horizontal line as being to the right and that on the vertical line as being upward.* The lines $x'x$ and $y'y$ are called the *coordinate axes*, $x'x$ being the *x-axis* and $y'y$ the *y-axis*. Point 0 is called the *origin*.

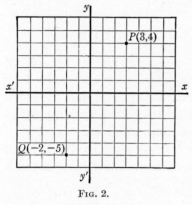

Fig. 2.

Consider now any point $P$ in the plane of the axes. Its distance from the $y$-axis is called its *abscissa*, or *x-coordinate;* this distance is *positive* if $P$ is to the *right* of the $y$-axis and *negative* if to the *left*. Its distance from the $x$-axis is called its *ordinate*, or *y-coordinate;* this distance is *positive* if $P$ is *above* the $x$-axis and *negative* if *below*. The abscissa and ordinate together are called the *rectangular coordinates* (or simply coordinates) of $P$. In writing down the coordinates of a point we put them in parentheses, putting the abscissa first. Thus the coordinates of $P$ and $Q$ in Fig. 2 are written, respectively, as $P(3, 4)$ and $Q(-2, -5)$.

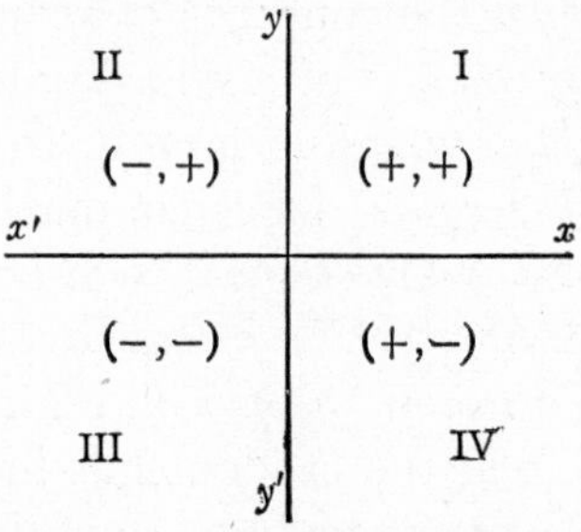

The process of locating and marking a point whose coordinates are given is called *plotting* the point. Plotting is facilitated by the use of paper that is ruled

|  | $y$ |  |
|---|---|---|
| II |  | I |
| $(-,+)$ |  | $(+,+)$ |
| $x'$ |  | $x$ |
| $(-,-)$ |  | $(+,-)$ |
| III |  | IV |
|  | $y'$ |  |

Fig. 3.

off into small squares as in Fig. 2. Such paper is called *rectangular coordinate paper*.

It is assumed that to every point in the plane there corresponds one and only one pair of real numbers and that

* A general discussion of directed lines is given in the next chapter.

to every pair of real numbers, taken in a given order, there corresponds a single point. This is stated briefly by saying that there is a *one-to-one correspondence* between the points of the plane and the pairs of real numbers $(x, y)$.

The coordinates axes divide the plane into four portions called *quadrants* which are numbered just as in trigonometry. Figure 3 shows the numbering and indicates the signs of the coordinates for each quadrant.

### PROBLEMS

**1.** Plot the points: $A(3, 2)$, $B(-\frac{1}{2}, 4)$, $C(2, 0)$, $D(-1, -3)$, $E(0, -1)$, $F(6, -2)$.

**2.** Plot the points: $A(3, 4)$, $B(-2, 6)$, $C(-1, -1)$, $D(0, 5)$, $E(-3, 0)$, $F(2, -3)$.

**3.** Draw the triangle whose vertices are

(*a*) $A(3, 5)$ $B(-3, 2)$ $C(1, -4)$.

(*b*) $D(4, 0)$ $E(0, -2)$ $F(-2, 5)$.

**4.** Draw the triangle $ABC$ and find its area.

(*a*) $A(0, 0)$ $\qquad B(8, 0)$ $\qquad C(0, -6)$.

(*b*) $A(-4, -3)$ $B(4, -3)$ $\qquad C(0, -8)$.

(*c*) $A(2, 2)$ $\qquad B(-2, -2)$ $C(4, -4)$.

**5.** The line segment from $(1, 0)$ to $(6, 0)$ is one side of a parallelogram, and the segment from $(1, 0)$ to $(3, 4)$ is another side. Find the fourth vertex.

**6.** In each of the following, three vertices of a parallelogram are given. Draw the figure and find three possible sets of coordinates for the fourth vertex; find the area of the parallelogram:

(*a*) $A(0, 0)$ $\qquad B(3, 4)$ $\qquad C(8, 0)$.

(*b*) $A(-6, -2)$ $B(-4, 2)$ $C(3, 2)$.

**7.** A line is drawn from the origin to $P(-8, 6)$. What are the coordinates of its mid-point?

**8.** The center of a square is at the origin, and its sides are parallel to the coordinate axes. If each diagonal of the square is 12 units long, Ind the coordinates of the vertices.

**9.** Find the length of the hypotenuse of a right triangle whose vertices are

(*a*) $A(1, 0)$ $\qquad B(5, 0)$ $\qquad C(5, 3)$.

(*b*) $A(1, -2)$ $B(6, -2)$ $C(6, 10)$.

**10.** For what points is the ordinate equal to zero? For what points is it equal to 2?

**11.** For what points is the abscissa equal to zero? For what points is it equal to $-3$?

**12.** For what points is the abscissa equal to the ordinate?

**13.** For what points is the sum of the ordinate and abscissa equal to zero?

**14.** A 50-lb. rectangular plate having the dimensions indicated in Fig. 4 is held in the position shown by a horizontal force $P$ applied at $A$. In order to calculate the magnitude of the force $P$, it would be necessary to know the coordinates of $A$ with respect to the axes shown. Find these coordinates.

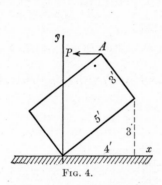
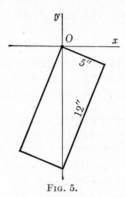

Fig. 4.                    Fig. 5.

**15.** A rectangular plate having the dimensions shown is suspended from $O$ and hangs in the $xy$-plane as illustrated in Fig. 5. Find the coordinates of its vertices and its "center of gravity." HINT: The center of gravity is at the intersection of the diagonals and will be directly below the point $O$.

**3. Functions.**—*A variable* $y$ *is said to be a* **function** *of a second variable* $x$ *if a relation exists between them such that to each of a certain set of values of* $x$ *there corresponds one or more values of* $y$. If there is just *one* value of $y$ for each value of $x$, $y$ is said to be a *single-valued* function of $x$.

The student is familiar with countless examples. The volume of a cube is a single-valued function of the length $x$ of its edge, the relation being $V = x^3$. For each (positive) value of $x$ there is a definite value of $V$. The equation $2x - 3y = 6$ yields a definite value of $y$ for each value assigned to $x$, so we say that it "defines" $y$ as a single-valued function of $x$ for all values of $x$. It also, of course, defines $x$ as a function of $y$; *i.e.*, we may assign values to $y$

and the equation determines corresponding values of $x$. The variable to which we assign values is called the *independent variable;* the other is called the *dependent variable.*

When two variables are connected by a simple equation like $2x - 3y = 6$, we may ordinarily choose either as the independent variable; in some cases, however, one choice may be more desirable than the other. Consider, for example, the equation $y = x^2 + 4$. Any real value whatever may be assigned to $x$, and a single real value of $y$ results. The equation therefore defines $y$ as a single-valued function of $x$ for all (real) values of $x$. If, on the other hand, $y$ is taken as the independent variable, the situation is somewhat more complicated; only values equal to or greater than 4 for $y$ will result in real values of $x$—and for each value of $y > 4$* there will be *two* values of $x$. In the field of real numbers we say that the equation defines $x$ as a double-valued function of $y$ for $y \geqq 4$.

In analytic geometry we shall deal only with real values of the variables. We shall say, for example, that the equation $x^2 + y^2 = 25$ defines $y$ as a function of $x$ only for $-5 \leqq x \leqq 5$; for it is only for such values of $x$ that the equation yields real values of $y$.

The statement "$y$ is a function of $x$" is abbreviated by writing $y = f(x)$. We shall also use symbols such as $f(x)$, $g(x)$, and $\phi(x)$ to denote specific functions of $x$. Thus if we are concerned in a particular problem with the functions $x^2 - 4x + 2$ and $4x^3 - 7x$, we may find it convenient to designate one of them by the symbol $f(x)$ and the other by $g(x)$.

If $f(x)$ denotes a certain function of $x$, then $f(a)$ denotes the value of $f(x)$ when $x$ has the value $a$; it is found by substituting $a$ for $x$ in the expression for $f(x)$. Thus if

$$f(x) = x^2 - 4x + 2,$$

---

* The abbreviation $M > N$ means that $M$ is greater than $N$; $M < N$ means that $M$ is less than $N$; $a < M < b$ means that $M$ is greater than $a$ and less than $b$, so that $M$ is between $a$ and $b$. The symbol $\leqq$ means "less than or equal to."

then
$$f(0) = 0^2 - 4(0) + 2 = 2,$$
$$f(1) = 1^2 - 4(1) + 2 = -1,$$
$$f(-2) = (-2)^2 - 4(-2) + 2 = 14,$$
$$f(n) = n^2 - 4(n) + 2.$$

It should be remarked here that $y$ may be defined as a function of $x$ by some means other than a simple equation. Thus, the temperature in a room may be "exhibited" as a function of the time by placing a thermometer and a clock side by side. Corresponding values of the two variables may be obtained by taking simultaneous readings of the two instruments. Whether or not a simple equation could be devised that would "fit" at least approximately a set of data so obtained is a question that is studied under the heading of Curve Fitting.

**4. Graphs.**—By means of a coordinate system we have associated a point in the $xy$-plane with a pair of values of $x$ and $y$. We may now associate a line, curve, or other geometrical figure with an *equation* in $x$ and $y$. For if all points whose coordinates satisfy the equation are plotted, they will in general form such a figure. We now set up the following:

**Definition:** *The graph or locus of an equation, or other relation between two variables, is the totality of all points whose coordinates satisfy the equation or relation.*

In making the graph of an equation we actually plot only as many points as are deemed necessary to indicate the graph with sufficient accuracy for the purpose at hand, and then draw a smooth curve through them.

If the known relation between the variables consists only of a table of corresponding values, obtained perhaps by observation or experiment, the graph as defined above consists only of the corresponding set of isolated points. If, however, the variables are known to vary "continuously," one often draws a curve to show the variation. This might be done, for example, in making a graph showing how the temperature in a room varies with the time.

It should be observed that we have made no provision for plotting points corresponding to imaginary values of the variables.* If a given equation is satisfied only by such values, it has no graph. Thus the equation

$$2x^2 + y^2 + 4 = 0$$

has no graph. The graph of $x^2 + y^2 = 0$ consists of the one point $(0, 0)$.

The following examples will acquaint the student with the fundamental process of making a graph by plotting points and connecting them.

### Example 1

Make the graph of the equation $y = x^2 - 3x - 4$.

### Solution

Substituting for $x$ all integers from $-2$ to $+5$, we obtain the following table of corresponding values:

| $x$ | $-2$ | $-1$ | 0 | 1 | 2 | 3 | 4 | 5 |
|---|---|---|---|---|---|---|---|---|
| $y$ | 6 | 0 | $-4$ | $-6$ | $-6$ | $-4$ | 0 | 6 |

Plotting the points and connecting them with a smooth curve, we have the graph shown in Fig. 6. The curve is called a *parabola*. It has important properties that will be discussed later.

### Example 2

Make the graph of the equation $x^2 + y^2 = 25$.

### Solution

Solving for $y$ in terms of $x$ we get

$$y = \pm \sqrt{25 - x^2}.\dagger$$

It is obvious that real values of $y$

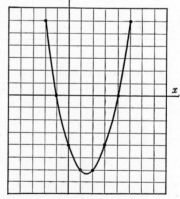

Fig. 6.

* Provision for this is made in the study of functions of a complex variable. Two planes are used, one for plotting the values of the independent variable, and the other for the dependent variable.

† The symbol $\sqrt{\phantom{x}}$ is defined to stand for the *positive* square root only.

are obtained only for values of $x$ from $-5$ to $+5$ and that to each such value of $x$ there corresponds *two* values of $y$. We easily obtain the following table:

| $x$ | $-5$ | $-4$ | $-3$ | $-2$ | $-1$ | 0 | 1 | 2 | 3 | 4 | 5 |
|---|---|---|---|---|---|---|---|---|---|---|---|
| $y$ | 0 | $\pm 3$ | $\pm 4$ | $\pm \sqrt{21}$ | $\pm 2\sqrt{6}$ | $\pm 5$ | $\pm 2\sqrt{6}$ | $\pm \sqrt{21}$ | $\pm 4$ | $\pm 3$ | 0 |

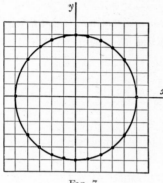

FIG. 7.

The graph (Fig. 7) is a circle with center at the origin and radius 5. This is evident even without plotting the points; for the equation requires that the sum of the squares of the $x$- and $y$-coordinates of any point on the graph shall be 25, and this is obviously true for all points on this circle and for no other points.

### Example 3

The table shown below gives the daily maximum temperatures in a certain city for the first 10 days of July, 1944. Construct the corresponding graph.

| Date (July)........... | 1 | 2 | 3 | 4 | 5 | 6 | 7 | 8 | 9 | 10 |
|---|---|---|---|---|---|---|---|---|---|---|
| Max. temp.......... | 100° | 96° | 88° | 86° | 88° | 82° | 84° | 90° | 90° | 92° |

*Solution*

It is convenient in this case to draw a horizontal line through the 80° mark on the temperature scale ($y$-axis) and use this as the $x$-axis,

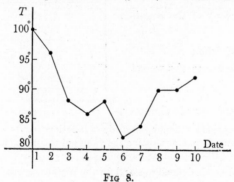

FIG 8.

or date scale (Fig. 8).   Also, although the graph consists only of the plotted points, it is customary in plotting data of this kind to draw in the connecting line segments.   We would not ordinarily draw a smooth curve because this is not a case of continuous variation.

**5. Interpretation of the graph.**—In accordance with our definition of the graph of an equation, we must always interpret the graph as the locus of all points whose coordinates satisfy the equation.   Thus, when we say that the circle (Fig. 7) with center at the origin and radius 5 units is the graph of the equation $x^2 + y^2 = 25$, we mean that this equation is satisfied by the coordinates $(x, y)$ of every point on the circle and is not satisfied by the coordinates of any other point in the plane.

In applied mathematics particularly, it is often useful also to regard the graph of a single-valued function as a picture showing how the value of the function (dependent variable) varies with that of the independent variable. This interpretation of the graph will be made clear by the following:

*Example*

A piece of tin is 20 in. square.   A box is to be made from it by cutting a small square from each corner and turning up the sides (Fig. 9).   Express the volume $V$ of the box obtained as a function of the length $x$ of the side of the square cut out.   From the graph of this equation study the way in which $V$ varies with $x$.

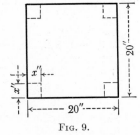

Fig. 9.

*Solution*

The length and width of the box are each $20 - 2x$, and the depth is $x$.   Hence $V = x(20 - 2x)^2$, or

$$V = 4x(10 - x)^2.$$

This equation gives the volume of the box (in cubic inches) for any value of $x$ (in inches).   Physical considerations restrict $x$ to values from 0 to 10.   Substituting the integers in this interval for $x$ we easily get the following table from which the graph can be made:

| $x$ | 0 | 1 | 2 | 3 | 4 | 5 | 6 | 7 | 8 | 9 | 10 |
|---|---|---|---|---|---|---|---|---|---|---|---|
| $V$ | 0 | 324 | 512 | 588 | 576 | 500 | 384 | 252 | 128 | 36 | 0 |

The graph (Fig. 10) shows the relation between $V$ and $x$ pictorially. It shows that $V$ increases as $x$ increases until $x$ reaches a value $x_1$ between 3 and 4 for which $V$ appears to be largest. From here on, an increase in $x$ results in a smaller value of $V$; and finally if $x = 10$, $V = 0$. The

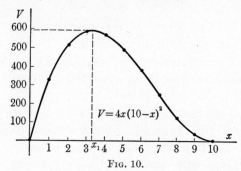

$$V = 4x(10-x)^2$$

FIG. 10.

precise value of $x$ for which $V$ is largest can be found by a method that requires the use of calculus. It amounts to finding the point where the tangent line to the curve is parallel to the $x$-axis.

## PROBLEMS

In each of the following, make a graph of the given equation for the given range of values of $x$. Mark the scale on both axes and show the table of values.

1. $x + y = 5$,      $-1 \leqq x \leqq 6$.
2. $2y = x + 2$,      $-4 \leqq x \leqq 4$.
3. $\dfrac{x}{4} - \dfrac{y}{6} = 1$,      $-7 \leqq x \leqq 5$.
4. $2x + 7 = 0$.
5. $y + 2 = 0$.
6. $y = \frac{1}{4}x^2$,      $-4 \leqq x \leqq 4$.
7. $y = 4x - x^2$,      $-1 \leqq x \leqq 5$.
8. $y = x^2 - 6x + 5$,    $0 \leqq x \leqq 6$.
9. $y = x^2 + 3x$,      $-5 \leqq x \leqq 2$.
10. $y = x^3 - 4x^2$,      $-1 \leqq x \leqq 5$.
11. $y^2 = 4x$,      $0 \leqq x \leqq 8$.
12. $x^2 + y^2 = 36$,      $-6 \leqq x \leqq 6$.
13. $9x^2 + 25y^2 = 225$,   $-5 \leqq x \leqq 5$.
14. $xy = 4$,      $-4 \leqq x \leqq 4$.

**15.** $x^2y + 4y - 8 = 0$, $-4 \leqq x \leqq 4$.

**16.** Taking $y$ as the independent variable, make a graph of the equation $y^2 - 2y = x - 3$. Assign to $y$ values from $-3$ to $+5$.

**17.** Make a graph of $y^2 = x^3$. Does the equation define $y$ as a single- or double-valued function of $x$, and what, if any, are the restrictions on $x$? What is the situation if $y$ is taken as the independent variable?

**18.** Same as Prob. 17 for the equation $y^2 = 4 - x$.

**19.** Express the area of a circle as a function of its radius and make a graph of this function.

**20.** Express the surface area $S$ and volume $V$ of a cube as functions of the length $x$, of its edge. Plot both graphs on the same axes. What is the significance of the abscissa of the point of intersection?

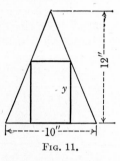

**21.** A rectangle is inscribed in an isosceles triangle as shown in Fig. 11. Express the area of the rectangle as a function of its height $y$. Draw the graph of this function. What value of $y$ appears to give the largest rectangle? HINT: Find the other dimension of the rectangle in terms of $y$ by using similar triangles.

FIG. 11.

**22.** A chord is drawn in a circle of radius 6 in. Express the length $L$ of the chord as a function of its distance $x$ from the center of the circle. Make a graph of the function.•

**23.** A right circular cylinder of radius $x$ is inscribed in a right circular cone of radius 6 in. and height 12 in., as indicated in Fig. 12. Express the volume of the cylinder as a function of $x$ and make a graph of the function. What value of $x$ appears to give the largest cylinder? In making the graph it is convenient to let a unit on the "volume" axis represent $\pi$ cu. in.

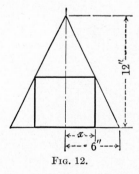

FIG. 12.

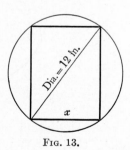

FIG. 13.

**24.** A rectangle is inscribed in a circle of radius 6 in. Express the area $A$ of the rectangle as a function of the length $x$ of its base (Fig. 13).

Make a graph of this function and estimate the value of $x$ for which $A$ is largest.

**25.** The following experimentally determined data give the length $L$ of a certain spring (inches) when subjected to a pull of $x$ pounds. Make the corresponding graph showing how the length varies with the load.

| $x$ | 0 | 1 | 2 | 3 | 4 | 5 | 6 | 7 | 8 |
|---|---|---|---|---|---|---|---|---|---|
| $L$ | 13.10 | 14.32 | 15.56 | 16.82 | 18.04 | 19.30 | 20.58 | 21.88 | 23.18 |

**26.** The following data give the period $T$ (seconds) of a simple pendulum of length $L$ (feet). Make the corresponding graph showing how the period varies with the length. The period is the time required for the pendulum to make one complete swing (over and back).

| $L$ | 0.50 | 1.0 | 1.5 | 2.0 | 2.5 | 3.0 | 3.5 | 4.0 |
|---|---|---|---|---|---|---|---|---|
| $T$ | 0.78 | 1.11 | 1.35 | 1.56 | 1.75 | 1.92 | 2.07 | 2.21 |

**6. Intersections of graphs.**—In Fig. 14 the graphs of the equations $3y - x = 5$ and $x^2 + y^2 = 25$ are drawn on the same coordinate axes. The first is a straight line,* and the second is a circle.

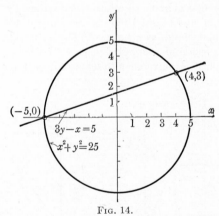

FIG. 14.

From our definition of the graph of an equation it is clear that the equation $3y - x = 5$ is satisfied by the

---

* In Chap. III it will be proved that the graph of any equation of first degree in $x$ and $y$ is a straight line.

coordinates of every point on the line and is not satisfied by the coordinates of any other point in the plane. Similarly, the equation $x^2 + y^2 = 25$ is satisfied by the coordinates of every point on the circle and is not satisfied by the coordinates of any other point. It is therefore evident that the *two* equations

$$\begin{cases} 3y - x = 5 \\ x^2 + y^2 = 25, \end{cases}$$

regarded as a simultaneous system, are *both* satisfied by the coordinates of those points which lie on both the line and the circle, and are not satisfied by any other real pairs of values of $x$ and $y$. Thus the coordinates of the points of intersection of the graphs are the pairs of real values of $x$ and $y$ that satisfy both equations "simultaneously."

These coordinates can be found analytically in simple cases by the usual algebraic methods of solving systems of equations. Thus in the above case we proceed as follows:

(1)                 $3y - x = 5$
(2)                 $x^2 + y^2 = 25.$

From (1), $x = 3y - 5$; substituting this for $x$ in (2), simplifying, and solving we have

$$(3y - 5)^2 + y^2 = 25;$$
$$9y^2 - 30y + 25 + y^2 = 25;$$
$$y^2 - 3y = 0;$$
$$y = 0 \text{ or } 3.$$

Substituting these values for $y$ in (1) we find that the corresponding values of $x$ are, respectively, $-5$ and $4$. The coordinates of the points of intersection are then $(-5, 0)$ and $(4, 3)$.

If the graphs of the equations do not intersect, it can be concluded that there is no

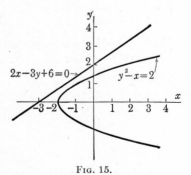

FIG. 15.

pair of real values of $x$ and $y$ that satisfies the equations simultaneously. Figure 15 shows the graphs of

$$\begin{cases} y^2 - x = 2 \\ 2x - 3y + 6 = 0. \end{cases}$$

The student may verify algebraically that the equations are not satisfied simultaneously by any pair of real values of $x$ and $y$.

### PROBLEMS

In each of the following, draw both graphs on the same axes and find or estimate the coordinates of the points of intersection; then check by solving the equations algebraically:

**1.** $x + 2y = 10$
$2x - 3y = -1.$

**2.** $2x + 3y = -4$
$5x - 2y = 9.$

**3.** $x - 2y = 12$
$3x - 6y = 4.$

**4.** $3x - y = 3$
$6x - 2y = 6.$

**5.** $y = x^2 - 5x$
$y + 4 = 0.$

**6.** $y = x^2 - 3x - 4$
$3y + 4x = 0.$

**7.** $y^2 - 4x = 0$
$y - 2x + 4 = 0.$

**8.** $xy = 12$
$3y - 2x + 6 = 0.$

**9.** $y = x^2 - x - 6.$
$2x - y = 8.$

**10.** $x^2 + y^2 = 16$
$6y = x^2.$

**11.** $x^2 + y^2 = 1$
$x + y = \sqrt{2}.$

**12.** $y = x(x - 4)^2$
$y - x = 0.$

**13.** $y = 4x - x^2$
$y - x = 2.$

**14.** $y = \dfrac{8}{x^2 + 4}$
$2y = x.$

**15.** $y^3 - x^2 = 0$
$y^2 - 2x = 0.$

**16.** $y = 2x^3$
$y - x = 1.$

**17.** $y - x^3 = 0$
$y - 4 = x^2.$

**18.** $y + 16 = x^4$
$5x^2 + y = 10x.$

Show by making the graphs that the following systems of equations have no real solutions:

**19.** $x^2 + y^2 = 16$
$x + y = 6.$

**20.** $y = x^2 + 1$
$y = x - 1.$

**21.** $y = 4x - x^2$
$y - x = 4.$

**22.** $x^2 + y^2 = 4$
$9x^2 + 25y^2 = 225.$

## CHAPTER II

## FUNDAMENTAL THEOREMS
## AND METHODS

**7. Directed lines.**—A *directed line* is simply a line on which a positive direction or sense has been designated. The $x$- and $y$- axes are examples. Segments on a directed line are regarded as positive or negative according to the way in which they are read. Thus if the positive direction on the line in Fig. 16 is upward to the right, as indicated by the arrowhead, then the segment $AB$ is positive while $BA$ is negative. If the distance from $A$ to $B$ is 2 units, then $AB = +2$ and $BA = -2$. That is, $BA = -AB$.

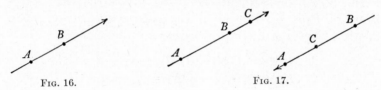

FIG. 16.              FIG. 17.

A fundamental property of a directed line is that if $A$, $B$, and $C$ are three points on it, then

$$AC = AB + BC$$

regardless of the positions of these points (Fig. 17). This property results also in the following important fact:

*If $A$ and $B$ are any two points on a directed line, and if $O$ is a reference point (or origin) on the line, then*

$$AB = OB - OA.$$

The reader should study the cases shown in Fig. 18.

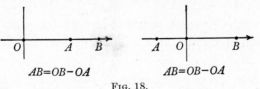

$AB = OB - OA$              $AB = OB - OA$

FIG. 18.

31

**8. Projections.**—The projection of a point on a line is the foot of the perpendicular drawn from the point to the line. In Fig. 19 the projection of the point $A$ on the line $l$ is the point $A'$; the projection of $B$ is $B'$. The projection of the segment $AB$ is the segment $A'B'$; the projection of $BA$ is $B'A'$.

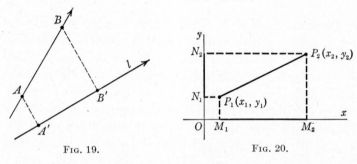

FIG. 19.                    FIG. 20.

In Fig. 20 the segments $M_1M_2$ and $N_1N_2$ are the projections of $P_1P_2$ on the $x$- and $y$-axes, respectively. The *directed lengths* of these projections are obviously

$$M_1M_2 = OM_2 - OM_1 = x_2 - x_1;$$
$$N_1N_2 = ON_2 - ON_1 = y_2 - y_1.$$

These formulas hold for all positions of $P_1$ and $P_2$. Thus, the length of the projection on the $x$-axis of the segment

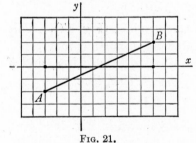

FIG. 21.

$A(-3, -2)$ $B(6, 2)$ is $6 - (-3) = 9$ (Fig. 21).

**9. Length of a line segment parallel to a coordinate axis.**—It is convenient to take the positive direction on a segment parallel to a coordinate axis the same as that of the axis. The directed length of such a segment is then the same as that of its projection on the axis. Thus in Fig. 22 the directed length of $P_1P_2$ is

$$P_1P_2 = M_1M_2 = OM_2 - OM_1 = x_2 - x_1.$$

Similarly, the directed length $P_3P_4$ is

$$P_3P_4 = N_3N_4 = ON_4 - ON_3 = y_4 - y_3.$$

Of course the directed length $P_2P_1$ is $x_1 - x_2$, while

$$P_4P_3 = y_3 - y_4.$$

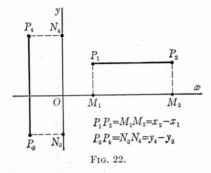

$$P_1P_2 = M_1M_2 = x_2 - x_1$$
$$P_3P_4 = N_3N_4 = y_4 - y_3$$

Fig. 22.

**10. The distance formula.**—Let $P_1(x_1, y_1)$ and $P_2(x_2, y_2)$ be any two given points, and let it be required to find the distance $d$ between them (Fig. 23). Through $P_1$ draw

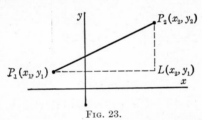

Fig. 23.

$P_1L$ parallel to the $x$-axis, and through $P_2$ draw $P_2L$ parallel to the $y$-axis, thus forming the right triangle $P_1LP_2$. It is clear that $P_1P_2$ is the hypotenuse of a right triangle whose legs are $P_1L = x_2 - x_1$, and $LP_2 = y_2 - y_1$. Therefore

$$(P_1P_2)^2 = (x_2 - x_1)^2 + (y_2 - y_1)^2.$$

If we denote by $d$ the *undirected* distance between the two points, we may write

$$d = \sqrt{(x_2 - x_1)^2 + (y_2 - y_1)^2}.$$

By drawing figures showing the points $P_1$ and $P_2$ in various positions, the student may verify that the formula holds for all positions of these points.

### Example 1

Find the distance from $A(-3, 6)$ to $B(3, -2)$.

*Solution* (Fig. 24)

Using the formula $d = \sqrt{(x_2 - x_1)^2 + (y_2 - y_1)^2}$ we have in this case

$$d = \sqrt{[3 - (-3)]^2 + [-2 - 6]^2}$$
$$= \sqrt{6^2 + 8^2} = \sqrt{100} = 10.$$

Thus the undirected distance is 10 units. If we wish to designate $B$ to $A$ as the positive direction on the line, then $BA = 10$ and $AB = -10$.

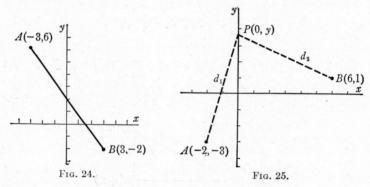

FIG. 24.                    FIG. 25.

### Example 2

Find the point on the $y$-axis that is equidistant from $A(-2, -3)$ and $B(6, 1)$.

*Solution* (Fig. 25)

Since the required point is on the $y$-axis, *its abscissa is zero;* its ordinate $y$ is the unknown to be found. Call the point $P(0, y)$ and let its undirected distances from $A$ and $B$ be $d_1$ and $d_2$, respectively. Then

$$d_1 = \sqrt{(0 + 2)^2 + (y + 3)^2}; \qquad d_2 = \sqrt{(0 - 6)^2 + (y - 1)^2}$$

Equating these distances and solving for $y$ we have

$$\sqrt{(0 + 2)^2 + (y + 3)^2} = \sqrt{(0 - 6)^2 + (y - 1)^2}$$
$$4 + y^2 + 6y + 9 = 36 + y^2 - 2y + 1$$
$$8y = 24$$
$$y = 3.$$

The required point is then $P(0, 3)$.

## PROBLEMS

**1.** In each of the following, draw the given segments and find the directed lengths of their projections on the coordinate axes:

(a) $A(1, 1)$   $B(4, 2)$; $C(2, -3)$   $D(-3, 4)$; $E(-6, -7)$ $F(-2, -4)$.

(b) $A(1, -1)$ $B(8, 3)$; $C(-8, 6)$   $D(1, -2)$; $E(-3, -6)$ $F(2, -2)$.

(c) $A(-4, 0)$ $B(0, 6)$; $C(10, -2)$ $D(3, 2)$;   $E(-6, -1)$ $F(0, -3)$.

**2.** Each of the following segments is parallel to the $x$-axis; draw each segment and find the corresponding directed distance from the first point to the second:

(a) $A(3, 1)$   $B(5, 1)$; $C(-6, -2)$ $D(2, -2)$; $E(2, 4)$   $F(-4, 4)$.

(b) $A(4, 2)$   $B(2, 2)$; $C(-1, -1)$ $D(5, -1)$; $E(2, -3)$ $F(-4, -3)$.

(c) $A(-1, 0)$ $B(6, 0)$; $C(-8, 5)$   $D(-2, 5)$; $E(3, -3)$ $F(-5, -3)$.

**3.** As in Prob. 2 for the following segments parallel to the $y$-axis:

(a) $A(4, 2)$   $B(4, 8)$; $C(-1, -3)$ $D(-1, 2)$; $E(-4, -1)$ $F(-4, -5)$.

(b) $A(3, -3)$ $B(3, 4)$; $C(0, 2)$   $D(0, 6)$;   $E(-2, 4)$   $F(-2, -2)$.

(c) $A(5, -5)$ $B(5, 1)$; $C(2, 2)$   $D(2, -1)$; $E(-3, -4)$ $F(-3, 0)$.

**4.** Show that the directed distance from $A(2, 4)$ to $B(x, 4)$ is $x - 2$ for *all* values of $x$. What is the directed distance $BA$?

**5.** Show that the triangle whose vertices are $(1, 3)$, $(3, -1)$, and $(-5, -5)$ is a right triangle.

**6.** Show that the triangle whose vertices are $(-1, 0)$, $(7, -8)$, and $(-2, -9)$ is isosceles.

**7.** Show that a circle could be drawn with its center at $(4, 3)$ and passing through $(7, -1)$, $(8, 0)$, and the origin.

**8.** Show that a circle could be drawn with its center at $(-2, -3)$ and passing through the points $(10, 2)$, $(3, 9)$, and $(-2, 10)$.

**9.** Find the point on the $x$-axis that is equidistant from $A(-2, 3)$ and $B(10, -6)$.

**10.** Find the point equidistant from the three points $A(0, 2)$, $B(0, -8)$, $C(-3, 6)$.

**11.** Find the center and radius of the circle that passes through $A(0, 0)$, $B(1, 7)$, $C(7, -1)$.

**12.** Two vertices of an equilateral triangle are $(0, 6)$ and $(10, -4)$. Find the third vertex.

**13.** Write down an expression for the undirected distance from the fixed point $A(2, 1)$ to a variable point $P(x, y)$. Set this distance equal to 5 and simplify the resulting equation after squaring both

Fig. 26.

sides. Why is this the equation of a circle with center at $A$ and radius 5 (Fig. 26)?

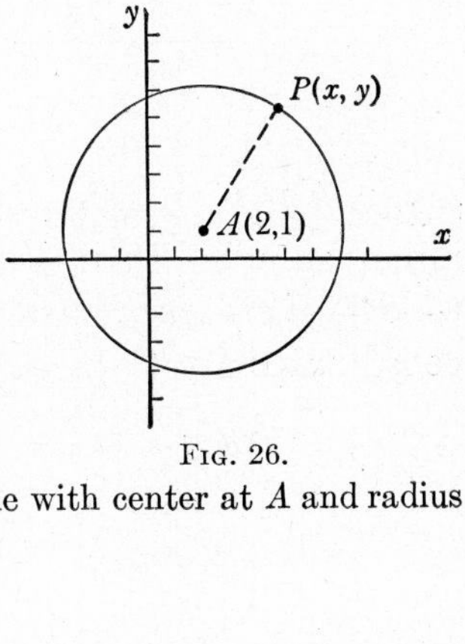

**14.** Write down expressions for the undirected distances $d_1$ and $d_2$ of a variable point $P(x, y)$ from the two fixed points $A(1, -2)$ and $B(7, 2)$. Equate these expressions and simplify the equation after squaring both sides. Why is this the equation of the perpendicular bisector of the line segment $AB$? Draw the graph.

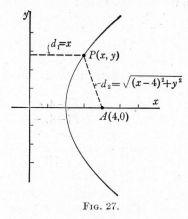

Fig. 27.

**15.** Same as Prob. 14 using $P(-4, 0)$ and $Q(2, -6)$ instead of $A$ and $B$.

**16.** The distance of the point $P(x, y)$ in Fig. 27 from the $y$-axis is obviously equal to $x$ while its distance from $A(4, 0)$ is $\sqrt{(x-4)^2 + y^2}$. By equating these distances find the equation of the path in which $P$ can move if its distance from the $y$-axis is to be always equal to its distance from $A$. (The path of a point that moves in a plane so that its undirected distances from a fixed point and fixed line in the plane are equal is called a *parabola*.)

**11. Division of a line segment.**—It is frequently necessary to find the coordinates of the point $P_0$ on a segment $P_1P_2$ such that $P_1P_0$ is some given fraction of the whole

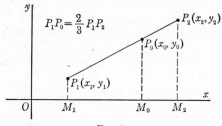

Fig. 28.

segment $P_1P_2$. As an example, let it be required to determine the point $P_0$ in Fig. 28 that is $\frac{2}{3}$ of the way from $P_1$ to $P_2$; *i.e., such that* $P_1P_0 = \frac{2}{3}P_1P_2$. If the required coordinates are $(x_0, y_0)$, we have immediately

$$
\begin{aligned}
x_0 = OM_0 &= OM_1 + \tfrac{2}{3}(M_1M_2) \\
&= OM_1 + \tfrac{2}{3}(OM_2 - OM_1) \\
&= x_1 + \tfrac{2}{3}(x_2 - x_1).
\end{aligned}
$$

Using the projections on the $y$-axis one can similarly show that

$$y_0 = y_1 + \tfrac{2}{3}(y_2 - y_1).$$

The more general situation in which $\tfrac{2}{3}$ is replaced by any number $k$ is covered by the following:

**Theorem :** *If $P_0(x_0, y_0)$ is the point on $P_1(x_1, y_1) P_2(x_2, y_2)$ such that $P_1P_0/P_1P_2 = k$, then*

$$x_0 = x_1 + k(x_2 - x_1);$$
$$y_0 = y_1 + k(y_2 - y_1).$$

The theorem is used most often where $k$ is a fraction between 0 and 1; for a suitable value of $k$ in this range, any

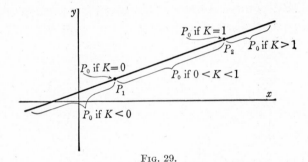

FIG. 29.

point on the segment between $P_1$ and $P_2$ can be obtained. The theorem is however valid in a broader sense. In fact (see Fig. 29),

(a) *If $0 < k < 1$, $P_0$ is between $P_1$ and $P_2$.*

(b) *If $k = 0$ or $1$, $P_0$ coincides with $P_1$ or $P_2$, respectively.*

(c) *If $k > 1$, $P_0$ lies on $P_1P_2$ extended beyond $P_2$.*

(d) *If $k < 0$, $P_0$ lies on $P_1P_2$ extended in the opposite direction beyond $P_1$. In this case the directed segments $P_1P_0$ and $P_1P_2$ have opposite signs.*

### Example

Find the coordinates of the point $P_0$ that is $\tfrac{2}{3}$ of the way from $A(-2, 5)$ to $B(10, 1)$.

*Solution* (Fig. 30)

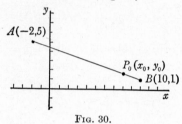

FIG. 30.

Here $k = \frac{5}{6}$ and we have

$$x_0 = -2 + \tfrac{5}{6}[10 - (-2)] = 8;$$
$$y_0 = 5 + \tfrac{5}{6}[1 - 5] = \tfrac{5}{3}.$$

The required point is then $P_0(8, \frac{5}{3})$.

**12. Mid-point.**—As a special case of the preceding theorem we may find the coordinates of the mid-point of a given segment $P_1P_2$ by taking $k = \frac{1}{2}$. We get

$$x_0 = x_1 + \tfrac{1}{2}(x_2 - x_1) = \tfrac{1}{2}(x_1 + x_2);$$
$$y_0 = y_1 + \tfrac{1}{2}(y_2 - y_1) = \tfrac{1}{2}(y_1 + y_2).$$

That is, *if $P_0(x_0, y_0)$ is the mid-point of a segment $P_1(x_1, y_1)$ $P_2(x_2, y_2)$, then*

$$x_0 = \frac{x_1 + x_2}{2}; \qquad y_0 = \frac{y_1 + y_2}{2}.$$

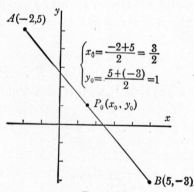

FIG. 31.

Thus the coordinates of the mid-point of the segment

$A(-2, 5)$ $B(5, -3)$ are (Fig. 31)

$$x_0 = \frac{-2 + 5}{2} = \tfrac{3}{2}; \qquad y_0 = \frac{5 + (-3)}{2} = 1.$$

**13. Inclination. Slope.**—A line $l$, not parallel to the x-axis, intersects this axis at some point $Q$ (Fig. 32). The direction of the line, relative to the coordinate axes, is specified by giving the counterclockwise angle $\alpha < 180°$ through which $QX$ would have to be rotated to bring it into coincidence with $l$. *This angle is called the inclination of $l$.* The inclination of a line parallel to the x-axis is defined to be zero.

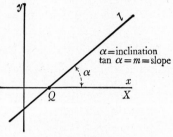

FIG. 32.

The *slope* of a line, usually denoted by the letter $m$, is defined as the *tangent of the angle $\alpha$ of inclination:*

*If $0 < \alpha < 90°$, $m$ is a positive number;*
*If $90° < \alpha < 180°$, $m$ is a negative number;*
*If $\alpha = 0$, $m = 0$;*
*If $\alpha = 90°$, the line has no slope. Why?*

**14. Slope in terms of coordinates.**—We wish now to express the slope of a line $l$ in terms of the coordinates of

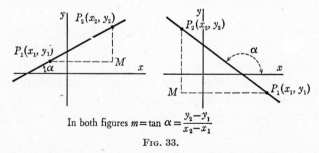

In both figures $m = \tan \alpha = \dfrac{y_2 - y_1}{x_2 - x_1}$

FIG. 33.

two points $P_1(x_1, y_1)$ and $P_2(x_2, y_2)$ on it. The student can readily see that for either of the cases shown in Fig. 33

$$\tan \alpha = \frac{MP_2}{P_1M} = \frac{y_2 - y_1}{x_2 - x_1}.$$

This formula holds for all positions of $P_1$ and $P_2$ provided $x_1 \neq x_2$. We may therefore state the following:

**Theorem:** *If $P_1(x_1, y_1)$ and $P_2(x_2, y_2)$ are any two points on a line $l$ not perpendicular to the x-axis, then the slope of $l$ is*

$$m = \frac{y_2 - y_1}{x_2 - x_1}.$$

It of course makes no difference which of two given points is called $P_1$. The slope of the line through $(1, -3)$ and $(5, 7)$ is (Fig. 34)

$$\frac{7 - (-3)}{5 - 1} = \tfrac{5}{2} \quad \text{or} \quad \frac{-3 - 7}{1 - 5} = \tfrac{5}{2}.$$

If a point moves along the line, it will move 5 units in the

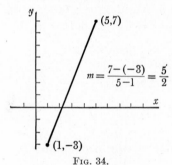

FIG. 34.

$y$-direction for every 2 units in the $x$-direction—or $2\frac{1}{2}$ units in the $y$-direction for each unit in the $x$-direction. The slope is thus a measure of the steepness of the line.

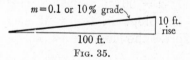

FIG. 35.

The slope of a road is called its *grade*, a 10 per cent grade meaning a slope of 0.10; this indicates a rise of 10 ft. for each 100 ft. of horizontal distance (Fig. 35).

**15. Parallel and perpendicular lines.**—Two lines $l_1$ and $l_2$ are parallel if and only if their inclinations are equal. If the lines have slopes $m_1$ and $m_2$, the condition for parallelism is that

$$m_1 = m_2.$$

If the lines $l_1$ and $l_2$ are mutually perpendicular, the inclination of one of them exceeds that of the other by $90°$; *i.e.*, either $\alpha_1 = \alpha_2 + 90°$, or $\alpha_2 = \alpha_1 + 90°$ (Fig. 36).

In either case

$$\tan \alpha_1 = - \cot \alpha_2 = - \frac{1}{\tan \alpha_2};$$

or, since $\tan \alpha_1 = m_1$, and $\tan \alpha_2 = m_2$,

$$m_1 = - \frac{1}{m_2}, \quad \text{or} \quad m_1 m_2 = -1.$$

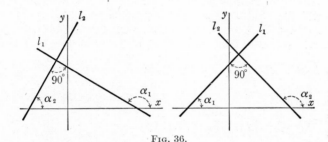

FIG. 36.

Conversely, if $m_1 = -1/m_2$, $\tan \alpha_1 = - \cot \alpha_2$ and $\alpha_1 = \alpha_2 \pm 90°$; from this it follows that the lines are perpendicular. We have then the following:

**Theorem**: *Two lines having slopes $m_1$ and $m_2$ are mutually perpendicular if and only if*

$$\boldsymbol{m_1 = - \frac{1}{m_2}} \quad or \quad \boldsymbol{m_1 m_2 = -1.}$$

The only case not covered by the theorem is that of two lines parallel to the $x$- and $y$-axes, respectively. They are of course mutually perpendicular; the slope of one of them is zero, and the other has no slope.

### PROBLEMS

**1.** In each of the following, find the coordinates of the point $P$ on $AB$ such that $AP$ is the given fractional part of $AB$. Draw the line and show the required point.

(a) $A(-2, 2)$   $B(6, 10)$; $\frac{3}{4}$.       (b) $A(-1, 6)$ $B(5, -6)$; $\frac{2}{3}$.

(c) $A(-7, -3)$ $B(3, 2)$; $\frac{1}{5}$.       (d) $A(6, 4)$   $B(0, -2)$; $\frac{5}{12}$.

(e) $A(1, -4)$   $B(9, 2)$; $\frac{1}{4}$.       (f) $A(-2, 6)$ $B(8, 4)$; $\frac{3}{5}$.

**2.** In each of the following, find the coordinates of the mid-point of $AB$. Draw the line segment and show the required point.

(a) $A(4, -6)$    $B(6, 2)$.        (b) $A(0, 6)$    $B(6, 0)$.
(c) $A(-8, -12)$ $B(-2, -1)$.      (d) $A(-3, 5)$ $B(9, 10)$.
(e) $A(6, 1)$       $B(-2, -1)$.   (f) $A(2, -8)$ $B(-3, 8)$.

**3.** In each of the following, find the coordinates of $P$ so that $AP/AB = k$. Draw $AB$ and extend it as required to show $P$.

(a) $A(0, 0)$    $B(2, 3)$;    $k = 2$.    (b) $A(-2, -2)$ $B(2, 0)$; $k = \frac{3}{2}$.
(c) $A(-4, 6)$ $B(5, 9)$;    $k = \frac{1}{3}$.    (d) $A(2, -1)$    $B(6, 7)$; $k = -\frac{3}{2}$.
(e) $A(3, -6)$ $B(-3, 3)$; $k = -\frac{4}{3}$. (f) $A(0, -10)$    $B(2, 0)$; $k = -\frac{3}{4}$.

**4.** A point $P_0(x_0, y_0)$ is said to divide $P_1(x_1, y_1)$ $P_2(x_2, y_2)$ in the ratio $r_1 : r_2$ if $P_1P_0/P_0P_2 = r_1/r_2$ (Fig. 37). Show that the coordinates of $P_0$ are

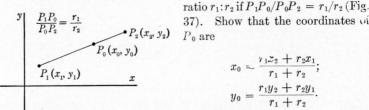

$$x_0 = \frac{r_1x_2 + r_2x_1}{r_1 + r_2};$$

$$y_0 = \frac{r_1y_2 + r_2y_1}{r_1 + r_2}.$$

Fig. 37.

**5.** Find the coordinates of the point dividing the line segment $A(2, 1)$ $B(12, 6)$ in the ratio $2.3$. This point is two-fifths of the way from $A$ to $B$.

**6.** Find the coordinates of the points that divide the segment $A(-2, 6)$ $B(10, -2)$ into four equal parts.

**7.** Draw the triangle $A(-2, -3)$ $B(8, 7)$ $C(10, -9)$. Find the coordinates of the point on each median* which is at a distance from the vertex equal to two-thirds the length of the median.

**8.** Draw the triangle $A(x_1, y_1)$ $B(x_2, y_2)$ $C(x_3, y_3)$. Show that the point on each median which is at a distance from the vertex equal to two-thirds the length of the median has coordinates

$$\left(\frac{x_1 + x_2 + x_3}{3}, \frac{y_1 + y_2 + y_3}{3}\right).$$

**9.** Draw the quadrilateral $A(0, 0)$ $B(4, 12)$ $C(12, 7)$ $D(9, 3)$. Show that the line joining the mid-points of $AB$ and $BC$ is parallel to that joining the mid-points of $AD$ and $DC$.

**10.** Draw the triangle $A(-2, -4)$ $B(8, 1)$ $C(2, 12)$. Show that the

* The medians are the lines drawn from the vertices to the mid-points of the opposite sides.

line joining the mid-points of $AC$ and $BC$ is parallel to $AB$ and equal to $\frac{1}{2}AB$.

**11.** In Fig. 38, $L$ and $M$ are the mid-points of $BC$ and $CD$, respectively; the distance $AP = \frac{2}{3}AL$ and $AQ = \frac{2}{3}AM$. Show that $P$ and $Q$ lie on the diagonal $BD$ and that they divide it into three equal parts. $ABCD$ is any parallelogram.

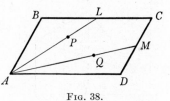

Fig. 38.

**12.** Draw the triangle $A(-3, 8)$ $B(12, 2)$ $C(-1, -2)$. Find the slopes of its altitudes and medians.

**13.** Show that the triangle $A(-8, 3)$ $B(9, 2)$ $C(6, -4)$ is a right triangle.

**14.** Show that the quadrilateral with vertices at $(8, 8)$, $(9, -5)$, $(-4, -6)$, and $(-5, 7)$ is a square.

**15.** Show that the points $(-2, -4)$, $(4, -1)$, and $(8, 1)$ lie on the same straight line.

**16.** A line is drawn through $A(4, 6)$ perpendicular to the line from the origin to $B(6, 1)$. What is its slope?

**17.** What is the slope of the shortest line segment that can be drawn from the origin to the line $A(4, -1)$ $B(-1, 6)$?

**18.** Show that the points $(-5, 0)$, $(1, 9)$, $(2, 4)$, and $(0, 1)$ are the vertices of an isosceles trapezoid.

**19.** A wedge $ABC$ rests on an inclined plane as shown in Fig. 39. Find the slope (to the horizontal) of faces $AB$ and $BC$.

**20.** Find the slope (to the horizontal)

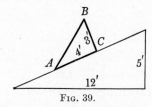

Fig. 39.

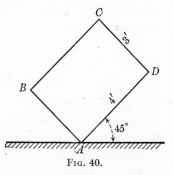

Fig. 40.

of the diagonal $AC$ of the box $ABCD$ when the box is held in the position shown in Fig. 40.

**16. Area of a triangle.**—In Fig. 41, $P_1$, $P_2$, and $P_3$ are the vertices of a triangle lettered so that if one traverses the perimeter from $P_1$ to $P_2$ to $P_3$ to $P_1$ the area lies always to his left. This counterclockwise way of traversing the area is sometimes called *positive* because the formula that we shall now develop for the area of the triangle gives a positive

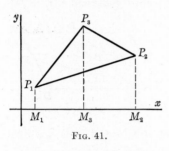

FIG. 41.

result if the points are taken in this order—and a negative result if taken in the clockwise order.

For the case shown it is obvious that the area of the triangle $P_1P_2P_3$ can be obtained by adding the trapezoids $M_1M_3P_3P_1$ and $M_3M_2P_2P_3$ and subtracting the trapezoid $M_1M_2P_2P_1$.   Now,

$$M_1M_3P_3P_1 = \tfrac{1}{2}(y_1 + y_3)(x_3 - x_1);$$
$$M_3M_2P_2P_3 = \tfrac{1}{2}(y_3 + y_2)(x_2 - x_3);$$
$$M_1M_2P_2P_1 = \tfrac{1}{2}(y_1 + y_2)(x_2 - x_1);$$

hence,

$$P_1P_2P_3 = \tfrac{1}{2}(y_1 + y_3)(x_3 - x_1) + \tfrac{1}{2}(y_3 + y_2)(x_2 - x_3)$$
$$- \tfrac{1}{2}(y_1 + y_2)(x_2 - x_1)$$
$$= \tfrac{1}{2}[y_1x_3 - y_3x_1 + y_3x_2 - y_2x_3 + y_2x_1 - y_1x_2].$$

The quantity in the bracket is precisely the expansion of the determinant

$$\begin{vmatrix} x_1 & y_1 & 1 \\ x_2 & y_2 & 1 \\ x_3 & y_3 & 1 \end{vmatrix}$$

so that, at least for the case shown in the figure, *the area of the triangle is equal to one-half the value of this determinant.* For other arrangements of $P_1$, $P_2$, and $P_3$, relative to the coordinate system, the proof may differ somewhat in the details but the result is the same.   In fact, for all positions of the vertices we have the following:

**Theorem:** *The area of the triangle whose vertices are* $P_1(x_1, y_1)$, $P_2(x_2, y_2)$, $P_3(x_3, y_3)$ *is given by the formula*

$$A = \tfrac{1}{2} \begin{vmatrix} x_1 & y_1 & 1 \\ x_2 & y_2 & 1 \\ x_3 & y_3 & 1 \end{vmatrix}.$$

*The result is positive if the order of the points is such that a traverse from $P_1$ to $P_2$ to $P_3$ to $P_1$ is counterclockwise, and negative if clockwise.*

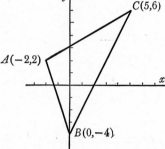

### Example

The area of the triangle $ABC$ in Fig. 42 is,

$$\frac{1}{2}\begin{vmatrix} -2 & 2 & 1 \\ 0 & -4 & 1 \\ 5 & 6 & 1 \end{vmatrix} = 25 \text{ square units.}$$

FIG. 42.

**17. Applications to elementary geometry.**—The methods of analytic geometry can frequently be used to obtain simple proofs of theorems of elementary geometry. The procedure will be illustrated by two examples.

### Example 1

Prove that the diagonals of a parallelogram bisect each other.

*Solution* (Fig. 43)

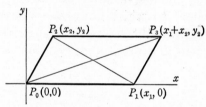

FIG. 43.

After drawing the parallelogram we may choose the coordinate system relative to it in such a manner as to make the coordinates to be used as simple as possible. Thus we may choose one vertex as the origin and let the $x$-axis coincide with one side. The coordinates of three vertices are then obviously

$$P_0(0, 0); \qquad P_1(x_1, 0); \qquad P_2(x_2, y_2).$$

Since the figure is a parallelogram, the abscissa of the fourth vertex must be $x_1 + x_2$ and its ordinate must be $y_2$. This point is then

$$P_3(x_1 + x_2, y_2).$$

The mid-point of $P_0P_3$ is $\left(\dfrac{x_1 + x_2}{2}, \dfrac{y_2}{2}\right)$;

The mid-point of $P_1P_2$ is $\left(\dfrac{x_1 + x_2}{2}, \dfrac{y_2}{2}\right)$.

These mid-points therefore coincide, and the theorem is proved.

### Example 2

Prove that the mid-point of the hypotenuse of a right triangle is equidistant from the vertices.

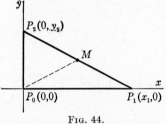

FIG. 44.

*Solution* (Fig. 44)

After drawing any right triangle we may again choose the coordinate system in the most convenient way as shown in the figure. Then if $M$ is the mid-point of $P_1P_2$, its coordinates are $(\frac{1}{2}x_1, \frac{1}{2}y_2)$. The distance of $M$ from $P_1$ or $P_2$ is of course $\frac{1}{2}P_1.P_2$ or $\frac{1}{2}\sqrt{x_1^2 + y_2^2}$. Its distance from $P_0$ is also $\frac{1}{2}\sqrt{x_1^2 + y_2^2}$. Hence the theorem is proved.

It should be evident to the student that our special choice of axes does not result in a loss in generality in the theorem. The theorems concern properties of the geometrical figures themselves and are independent of the coordinate system to which they are referred. In each case we have drawn the figure first and then added the coordinate system in a convenient position.

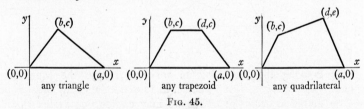

FIG. 45.

It must be emphasized that in using this analytical method we carry out the proof *algebraically*, using the *coordinates* of the points. We do not use the figure that we have drawn except as an aid in visualizing the problem. The coordinates then, rather than the figure, must express the given data. If in Example 1 we had used $(x_3, y_3)$ as the coordinates of $P_3$, we would not have been dealing with a parallelogram—*even though we had drawn a figure that looked like one.* It is the use of $(x_1 + x_2, y_2)$ as the coordinates of $P_3$ that makes the figure a parallelogram.

A suitable choice of axes and coordinates for proving theorems concerning any triangle, trapezoid, or general quadrilateral is shown in Fig. 45.

### PROBLEMS

**1.** Draw each of the following triangles and find its area:

(a) $A(1, 1)$     $B(8, 4)$     $C(2, 6)$.

(b) $A(-2, -3)$ $B(0, 4)$     $C(6, 0)$.

(c) $A(4, -1)$   $B(-2, -3)$ $C(1, 3)$.

(d) $A(-6, 2)$   $B(1, -3)$   $C(-1, -5)$.

**2.** Draw each of the following parallelograms and find its area:

(a) $A(2, -2)$     $B(8, 2)$     $C(9, 7)$ $D(3, 3)$.

(b) $A(-4, 0)$     $B(0, -3)$ $C(6, 0)$ $D(2, 3)$.

(c) $A(-4, -3)$ $B(3, -5)$ $C(6, 8)$ $D(-1, 10)$.

**3.** Find the area of each of the following polygons by breaking it up into triangles:

(a) $A(-2, -1)$ $B(4, 0)$     $C(6, 3)$ $D(-3, 6)$.

(b) $A(-4, -2)$ $B(0, -4)$ $C(6, 0)$ $D(2, 6)$ $E(-6, 4)$.

(c) $A(0, 0)$       $B(4, 0)$     $C(6, 3)$ $D(2, 8)$ $E(-3, 4)$.

**4.** The area of triangle $ABC$ in Fig. 46 is $\frac{1}{2}AB$ times $h$ or $\frac{1}{2}AB \cdot AC$ $\sin(\alpha - \beta)$. Starting with this, derive the expression for the area as a determinant. HINT: Note that $\sin(\alpha - \beta) = \sin\alpha\cos\beta - \cos\alpha\sin\beta$ and that $AB\cos\beta = x_2 - x_1$; $AC\sin\alpha = y_3 - y_1$; etc.

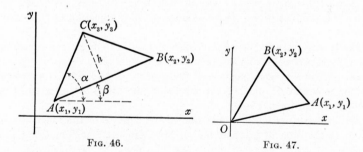

FIG. 46.                    FIG. 47.

**5.** The triangle $OAB$ in Fig. 47 has one vertex at the origin. Show that its area is $\frac{1}{2}\begin{vmatrix} x_1 & y_1 \\ x_2 & y_2 \end{vmatrix}$.

**6.** Show that the points $(-3, -4)$, $(0, -2)$, and $(9, 4)$ are collinear. HINT: Find the area of the triangle.

**7.** In the triangle $A(-2, -6)$ $B(10, -1)$ $C(2, 8)$, find the length of the altitude drawn from $C$.   HINT: Find the area and use the fact that area $= \frac{1}{2}$ base $\times$ altitude.

**8.** Find the shortest distance from $A(8, 4)$ to the line that passes through $(0, -4)$ and $(6, 2)$.   See hint in Prob. 7.

**9.** Find the shortest distance from the origin to the line that passes through $(1, 3)$ and $(4, 7)$.   See hint in Prob. 7.

**10.** What is the locus of points $(x, y)$ for which $\begin{vmatrix} x & y & 1 \\ 2 & 3 & 1 \\ 4 & 7 & 1 \end{vmatrix} = 0$?

Prove the following theorems analytically:

**11.** The line joining the mid-points of two sides of a triangle is parallel to the third side and equal to one-half of it.

**12.** The line joining the mid-points of the nonparallel sides of a trapezoid is equal to one-half the sum of the parallel sides.

**13.** The diagonals of a square are perpendicular to each other.

**14.** The diagonals of an isosceles trapezoid are equal.

**15.** The line segments that join the mid-points of the successive sides of any rectangle form a rhombus.

**16.** The line segments that join the mid-points of the successive sides of any quadrilateral form a parallelogram.

**17.** If two medians of a triangle are equal, the triangle is isosceles.

**18.** The sum of the squares of the four sides of any parallelogram equals the sum of the squares of the diagonals.

**19.** The line segments joining the mid-points of the opposite sides of any quadrilateral bisect each other.

**20.** In any triangle, the square of the side opposite an acute angle is equal to the sum of the squares of the other two sides decreased by twice the product of one of those sides by the projection of the other upon it.

**21.** In any triangle, the sum of the squares of the medians is equal to three-fourths the sum of the squares of the three sides.

**22.** In any triangle, the sum of the squares of two sides is equal to twice the square of one-half the third side plus twice the square of the median drawn to that side.

**23.** In any quadrilateral, the sum of the squares of the four sides is equal to the sum of the squares of the diagonals plus four times the square of the line segment joining the mid-points of the diagonals.

## 18. Equation of a locus.—In Chap. I we defined the graph or locus of a given equation as the totality of all points whose coordinates satisfy the equation. In each problem the equation was given and we plotted the locus.

We now consider the problem of finding the equation

of a graph or locus, all points of which satisfy some given geometrical condition. The procedure will be illustrated by two examples.

### Example 1

Find the equation of the locus or graph, all points of which are at a distance of 5 units from the point (3, 2).

*Solution* (Fig. 48)

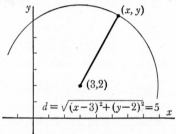

Let $(x, y)$ be the coordinates of *any* point on this curve. The condition to be imposed is that its distance from the point (3, 2) shall equal 5; *i.e.*

$$\sqrt{(x-3)^2 + (y-2)^2} = 5.$$

Squaring both sides and simplifying we have

Fig. 48.

$$(x-3)^2 + (y-2)^2 = 25$$

or

$$x^2 + y^2 - 6x - 4y - 12 = 0.$$

This is evidently the equation of the circle of radius 5 with center at (3, 2).

### Example 2

Find the equation of the curve all points of which are twice as far from the line $l$ drawn parallel to the $y$-axis and 3 units to the left of it, as from the origin.

*Solution* (Fig. 49)

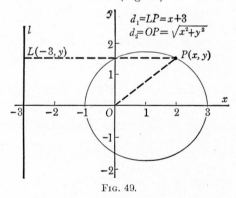

Fig. 49.

Let $(x, y)$ be the coordinates of *any* point on this curve, and let its distances from the line $l$ and from the origin be $d_1$ and $d_2$, respectively.

Then
$$d_1 = x - (-3) = x + 3;$$
$$d_2 = \sqrt{x^2 + y^2}.$$

The condition to be imposed is that $d_1 = 2d_2$, or

$$x + 3 = 2\sqrt{x^2 + y^2}.$$

Regarding the distances as undirected we may square both sides, obtaining the result

$$3x^2 + 4y^2 - 6x - 9 = 0.$$

The graph of this equation is a curve called an *ellipse*. A general definition of the ellipse will be given later.

These examples make it clear that the procedure for solving such problems is as follows:

*Step* 1. *Let* $(x, y)$ *be the coordinates of* **any** *point on the locus or graph whose equation is required.*

*Step* 2. *Express the given geometrical condition as an algebraic equation in the variable coordinates* $x$ *and* $y$.

*Step* 3. *Simplify the equation obtained in step* 2. *The result is the required equation.*

### PROBLEMS

**1.** Find the equation of the locus of all points at a distance of 4 units from $A(-1, 2)$.

**2.** Find the equation of the circle with center at $(-2, -4)$ and radius 3 units.

**3.** A point moves in the $xy$-plane in such a way as to be always equidistant from the origin and the point $(6, 4)$. Find the equation of its path and plot it.

**4.** A point moves in the $xy$-plane in such a way as to be always equidistant from the two given points $A$ and $B$. Find the equation of its path and plot it:

(*a*) $A(2, 6)$ $B(8, -2)$.        (*b*) $A(-2, 3)$ $B(4, 3)$.
(*c*) $A(5, 2)$ $B(-3, -4)$.      (*d*) $A(0, -1)$ $B(-6, 0)$.

**5.** Find the equation of the curve all points of which are equidistant from the $y$-axis and the point $(3, 2)$.

**6.** Find and plot the equation of the locus of points equidistant from the given line and the given point:

(*a*) the line $x = 2^*$ and the point $(6, 0)$.

* The line whose equation is $x = 2$ is parallel to the $y$-axis and 2 units to the right of it.

(b) the line $y = 4$ and the point $(2, 8)$.

**7.** Find the equation of the curve all points of which are twice as far from the point $(6, 0)$ as from the origin.

**8.** Find the equation of the curve all points of which are twice as far from $A(-6, 0)$ as from $B(3, 0)$.

**9.** A point moves in the $xy$-plane so that the sum of the slopes of the lines joining it to $(1, 4)$ and $(1, -2)$ is always equal to 2. Find the equation of its path and plot it.

**10.** A point moves in the $xy$-plane so that the slope of the line joining it to $(6, ?)$ is always equal to twice the slope of the line joining it to the origin. Find the equation of its path and plot it.

**11.** The slope of the line joining any point $P$ of a certain curve to the origin is equal to one-third the slope of the line joining $P$ to $(1, 1)$. What is the equation of this curve?

**12.** A point moves in the $xy$-plane in such a way that its distance from the $y$-axis is always equal to twice its distance from the point $(4, 0)$. Find the equation of its path.

**13.** A point moves in the $xy$-plane so that the sum of the squares of its distances from the points $A$ and $B$ is equal to the square of the distance from $A$ to $B$. Find the equation of its path. Why is the path a circle?

(a) $A(-5, 0)$ $B(5, 0)$.          (b) $A(0, 0)$     $B(6, 0)$.
(c) $A(1, 0)$   $B(4, 4)$.          (d) $A(-2, -3)$ $B(4, -8)$.

**14.** Find the equation of the locus of points that are 4 units farther from the point $(4, 1)$ than from the line $x = 2$.

**15.** From any point $P(x, y)$ on a certain curve the sum of the distances to $(-4, 0)$ and $(4, 0)$ is equal to 10. What is the equation of this curve?

**16.** A point moves in the $xy$-plane in such a way that the difference of its distances from $(-3, 0)$ and $(3, 0)$ is always equal to 5. Find the equation of its path.

# CHAPTER III

## THE LINE. LINEAR FUNCTIONS

**19. Introduction.**—A line $l$ is completely determined if the coordinates of two points on it are specified. It may also be determined by specifying one point and the slope, or by giving certain other information—such as the length and direction of the shortest segment that can be drawn from the origin to the line.

We proceed now to derive formulas for writing down the equation of a line in terms of the various data that may be given to determine it. We shall see that in each case we are led to an equation of first degree in $x$ and $y$, the particular form of the equation depending on the nature of the given data.

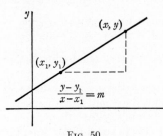

FIG. 50.

**20. The point-slope form.**— Let a line be determined by specifying its slope $m$ and the coordinates $(x_1, y_1)$ of one point on it. In order to find its equation we need merely to note that if $(x, y)$ are the coordinates of *any* other point on the line, then (Fig. 50)

$$\frac{y - y_1}{x - x_1} = m$$

or

$$y - y_1 = m(x - x_1).$$

This is called the *point-slope form* of the equation of a line. It may be used as a formula for writing down the equation of a line when its slope and one point on it are known.

*Example*

The equation of the line through $(-4, 2)$ with slope $\frac{3}{2}$ is

$$y - 2 = \tfrac{3}{2}[x - (-4)]$$

or

$$3x - 2y + 16 = 0.$$

**21. The slope-intercept form.**—If a line intersects the $y$-axis at $(0, b)$ as in Fig. 51, then $b$ is called the *y-intercept* of the line. The equation of the line in terms of its slope $m$ and its $y$-intercept $b$ is found by using $(0, b)$ in place of $(x_1, y_1)$ in the point-slope formula. The result is

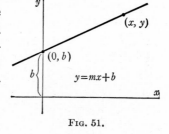

$$y - b = m(x - 0)$$

Fig. 51.

or

$$\boldsymbol{y = mx + b.}$$

This is called the *slope-intercept form* of the equation of a line. It may be used conveniently for writing down the equation when the slope and $y$-intercept are known.

*Example*

The equation of the line with slope $\frac{1}{2}$ and $y$-intercept $-3$ is

$$y = \tfrac{1}{2}x + (-3)$$

or

$$x - 2y - 6 = 0.$$

**22. Given two points.**—If a line is determined by specifying the coordinates $(x_1, y_1)$ and $(x_2, y_2)$ of two points on it, one may find its slope (if $x_1 \neq x_2$) from the formula

$$m = \frac{y_2 - y_1}{x_2 - x_1}.$$

The equation may then be written down by using one of the given points (either will do) and the slope.

*Example*

Find the equation of the line through $A(-4, 2)$ and $B(2, -1)$.

*Solution* (Fig. 52).

The slope of the line is

$$\frac{2 - (-1)}{-4 - 2} = -\frac{1}{2}.$$

The equation, obtained by using point $A$ and the slope, is

$$y - 2 = -\tfrac{1}{2}[x - (-4)]$$

or

$$x + 2y = 0.$$

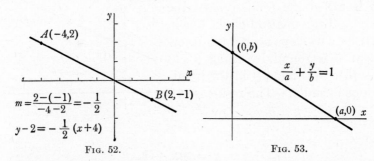

FIG. 52.            FIG. 53.

**23. The intercept form.**—Figure 53 shows a line intersecting the $x$-axis at $(a, 0)$ and the $y$-axis at $(0, b)$. The equation of the line in terms of these *intercepts* can be obtained by the method of the preceding section. Its slope is

$$m = \frac{b - 0}{0 - a} = -\frac{b}{a}.$$

Using the point $(a, 0)$ and the slope we find its equation to be

$$y - 0 = -\frac{b}{a}(x - a)$$

or

$$bx + ay = ab.$$

This can be put into a somewhat more convenient form by dividing both sides by $ab$. The result is

$$\frac{x}{a} + \frac{y}{b} = 1.$$

This is called the *intercept form* of the equation of a line.

It can be used conveniently for writing down the equation of a line when its intercepts are known. We of course assume here that neither $a$ nor $b$ is equal to zero.

### Example

The equation of the line that crosses the $x$-axis at $x = 4$ and the $y$-axis at $y = -1$ is

$$\frac{x}{4} + \frac{y}{-1} = 1$$

or

$$x - 4y - 4 = 0.$$

**24. Lines parallel to the coordinate axes.**—Figure 54 shows a line parallel to the $x$-axis and with $y$-intercept $b$. It is evident that every point on this line satisfies the equation $y = b$, and, conversely, every point with ordinate equal to $b$ is on the line. The equation of the line is therefore

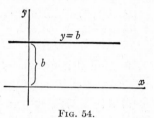

Fig. 54.

$$y = b.$$

Similarly, the equation of a line parallel to the $y$-axis, and crossing the $x$-axis at $x = a$, is

$$x = a.$$

### PROBLEMS

**1.** Find the equation of the line through the given point $A$ with the given slope $m$:

(a) $A(4, 2)$;    $m = -1$.       (b) $A(-3, 1)$; $m = \frac{3}{2}$.
(c) $A(-1, -\frac{3}{2})$; $m = \frac{1}{2}$.    (d) $A(2, -\frac{4}{3})$; $m = -\frac{1}{2}$.
(e) $A(-\frac{7}{2}, 0)$;   $m = -2$.       (f) $A(2, 0)$;    $m = -\frac{3}{4}$.

**2.** Find the equation of the line determined by the points $A$ and $B$:

(a) $A(1, 2)$;    $B(5, 7)$.       (b) $A(-2, -3)$; $B(4, \frac{1}{2})$.
(c) $A(-3, 4)$; $B(\frac{7}{3}, \frac{1}{3})$.    (d) $A(5, 1)$;    $B(0, -\frac{1}{2})$.
(e) $A(4, 2)$;    $B(4, 7)$.       (f) $A(-2, \frac{3}{2})$;    $B(0, \frac{3}{2})$.

**3.** Find the equation of the line with given $y$-intercept $b$ and slope $m$, or given intercepts $a$ and $b$:

(a) $b = \frac{5}{2}$,    $m = \frac{1}{2}$.    (b) $b = 6$,    $m = -2$.
(c) $b = 0$,    $m = \frac{2}{3}$.    (d) $a = 3$,    $b = -7$.
(e) $a = -\frac{5}{2}$, $b = \frac{2}{3}$.    (f) $a = -4$, $b = -\frac{4}{3}$.

**4.** Show that the equation of a line through the origin with slope $m$ is $y = mx$.

**5.** The vertices of a rectangle are the points $(0, 0)$, $(6, 0)$, $(0, 3)$, $(6, 3)$. Write the equations of its sides and diagonals.

**6.** Find the equation of the line that is the perpendicular bisector of the given segment $AB$:

(a) $A(2, 2)$    $B(8, 4)$.    (b) $A(-3, -1)$ $B(0, 2)$.
(c) $A(-6, 0)$ $C(0, -\frac{3}{2})$.    (d) $A(-4, 0)$    $B(-1, 3)$.

**7.** In the triangle $ABC$, find the equation of the altitude drawn from $A$ perpendicular to side $BC$:

(a) $A(0, 1)$    $B(6, 3)$    $C(3, 8)$.
(b) $A(-2, 3)$    $B(-4, -6)$ $C(6, 2)$.
(c) $A(-4, -5)$ $B(8, -1)$    $C(-2, 4)$.

**8.** Find the equation of the line through $A$ perpendicular to the line whose equation is given:

(a) $A(-2, 6)$; $y = 2x - 5$.
(b) $A(0, -1)$; $y = \frac{2}{3}x + 3$.

**9.** What is the equation of the line through $(-6, 4)$ parallel to the line $y = 2x - 5$?

**10.** What point on the line $2x - 3y = 30$ is equidistant from the points $A(1, 3)$ and $B(7, 9)$? HINT: Find the point where the perpendicular bisector of segment $AB$ intersects the given line.

**11.** What point on the line $7y - 6x = 49$ is equidistant from the points $A(-4, 0)$ and $B(6, -4)$? See hint in Prob. 10.

**12.** What are the coordinates of the center of the circle that passes through $A(8, 7)$ $B(6, -7)$ and $C(-8, -5)$? HINT: Find the point of intersection of the perpendicular bisectors of segments $AB$ and $BC$. Why?

**13.** What are the coordinates of the center of the circle that passes through $A(1, 5)$, $B(8, 4)$ and $C(7, -3)$? See hint in Prob. 12.

**14.** Show that the equation of the line determined by the points $(x_1, y_1)$ and $(x_2, y_2)$ may be written in the form

$$\begin{vmatrix} x & y & 1 \\ x_1 & y_1 & 1 \\ x_2 & y_2 & 1 \end{vmatrix} = 0.$$

**15.** Use the determinant of Prob. 14 to find the equations of the lines determined by the following points.  Check by using the slope-intercept or intercept form:

(a)  $A(2, 3)$   $B(6, -1)$.       (b)  $A(6, 0)$   $B(0, -3)$.
(c)  $A(-2, 4)$ $B(\frac{3}{2}, \frac{2}{3})$.       (d)  $A(-\frac{5}{2}, 0)$ $B(0, 1)$.

**16.** Find the area of the triangle $A(-3, 5)$ $B(-2, -2)$ $C(6, 2)$ by multiplying $\frac{1}{2}BC$ by the altitude drawn from $A$.  Check by using the determinant.

**25. The general equation of first degree.**—Any equation that is of the first degree in the variables $x$ and $y$ can be written in the form

$$Ax + By + C = 0$$

where $A$, $B$, and $C$ are constants and $A$ and $B$ are not both zero.

If $B = 0$, the graph of the equation is a line parallel to the $y$-axis.  If $B \neq 0$, the equation can be solved for $y$, the result being

$$y = -\frac{A}{B}x - \frac{C}{B}.$$

The graph in this case is a line with slope $-A/B$ and $y$-intercept $-C/B$.  Thus in all cases the graph of an equation of first degree in $x$ and $y$ is a line.  It can be shown, conversely, that every line in the $xy$-plane has an equation that is of the first degree in $x$ and $y$.  Because of these facts, such an equation is called a *linear equation*.

From the above discussion it is evident that a general linear equation can be changed into the slope-intercept form by simply solving it for $y$ in terms of $x$.  The coefficient of $x$ will be the slope, and the constant term will be the $y$-intercept.

*Example*

Solving the equation $3x - 4y = 8$ for $y$ we get

$$y = \tfrac{3}{4}x - 2.$$

The slope of the line is $\tfrac{3}{4}$ and its $y$-intercept is $-2$.

If it is desired to change a general linear equation into

the intercept form, one may first find the intercepts and then rewrite the equation in the desired form.

**26. Parallel and perpendicular lines.**—The condition for parallelism of two lines having slopes $m_1$ and $m_2$ is that $m_1 = m_2$. Let the equations of the lines be

$$A_1x + B_1y + C_1 = 0,$$
$$A_2x + B_2y + C_2 = 0.$$

The slope of the first is $m_1 = -A_1/B_1$ and that of the second is $m_2 = -A_2/B_2$. If the $A$'s and $B$'s are different from zero, the condition for parallelism becomes

$$\frac{A_1}{B_1} = \frac{A_2}{B_2} \qquad \text{or} \qquad \frac{A_1}{A_2} = \frac{B_1}{B_2}.$$

The corresponding condition for perpendicularity is that $m_1 = -1/m_2$; this means that

$$-\frac{A_1}{B_1} = \frac{B_2}{A_2} \qquad \text{or} \qquad \mathbf{A_1A_2 + B_1B_2 = 0.}$$

*Example*

The lines $\begin{cases} 2x + 3y - 6 = 0 \\ 4x + 6y - 10 = 0 \end{cases}$ are parallel since $\dfrac{A_1}{A_2} = \dfrac{B_1}{B_2} = \frac{1}{2}$. The lines $\begin{cases} 2x + 3y - 6 = 0 \\ 9x - 6y + 1 = 0 \end{cases}$ are mutually perpendicular since

$$A_1A_2 + B_1B_2 = 2(9) + 3(-6) = 0.$$

**27. Angle between two lines.**—Let $l_1$ and $l_2$ be two lines intersecting at $P$ and having slopes $m_1 = \tan \alpha_1$ and $m_2 = \tan \alpha_2$, respectively.

The smallest counterclockwise angle $\theta$ through which $l_1$ would have to be rotated about $P$ to make it coincide with $l_2$ is called the angle from $l_1$ to $l_2$. This is a particular one of the two supplementary angles of intersection of $l_1$ and $l_2$. We wish to find this angle (or its tangent) in terms of the slopes of the two lines. There are two cases:

Case i. $\alpha_1 < \alpha_2$ (Fig. 55a).

Since the exterior angle $\alpha_2$ is equal to $\alpha_1 + \theta$, we have

$$\theta = \alpha_2 - \alpha_1.$$

Then,

$$\tan \theta = \tan (\alpha_2 - \alpha_1)$$
$$= \frac{\tan \alpha_2 - \tan \alpha_1}{1 + \tan \alpha_2 \tan \alpha_1}$$
$$= \frac{m_2 - m_1}{1 + m_2 m_1}.$$

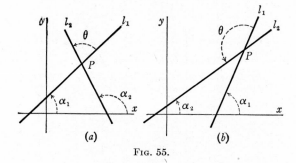

FIG. 55.

CASE II. $\alpha_1 > \alpha_2$ (Fig. 55b).
In this case,

$$180° - \theta = \alpha_1 - \alpha_2;$$
$$\tan (180° - \theta) = \frac{\tan \alpha_1 - \tan \alpha_2}{1 + \tan \alpha_1 \tan \alpha_2}$$
$$\tan \theta = \frac{\tan \alpha_2 - \tan \alpha_1}{1 + \tan \alpha_1 \tan \alpha_2}$$
$$= \frac{m_2 - m_1}{1 + m_1 m_2}.$$

The result is the same in both cases and we therefore state the following:

**Theorem:** *If two lines $l_1$ and $l_2$ have slopes $m_1$ and $m_2$, respectively, and if $\theta$ is the angle from $l_1$ to $l_2$, then*

$$\boldsymbol{\tan \theta = \frac{m_2 - m_1}{1 + m_1 m_2}.}$$

*Example*

Find the angle of intersection of the lines $2y - x = 2$ and $2x - y = 4$.

*Solution* (Fig. 56)

The slopes of the lines are $\frac{1}{2}$ and 2, respectively.   Calling the first line $l_1$ and the second $l_2$ we have

$$\tan \theta = \frac{2 - \frac{1}{2}}{1 + 2(\frac{1}{2})} = \frac{3}{4}.$$

Using tables we find that $\theta = 36°\ 52'$. This is the angle from $l_1$ to $l_2$. Interchanging the numbers 2 and $\frac{1}{2}$ in the numerator of the above fraction would give the tangent of the angle from $l_2$ to $l_1$. The result would of course be $-\frac{3}{4}$. Note that the two angles are supplementary and

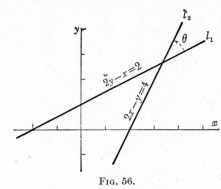

Fig. 56.

that their tangents therefore differ only in sign. The other angle would be $180° - 36°\ 52' = 143°\ 8'$.

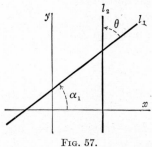

Fig. 57.

In deriving our formula for $\tan \theta$ we assumed that neither line is parallel to the $y$-axis. A case in which $l_2$ is parallel to the $y$-axis is shown in Fig. 57. It is left for the student to show that in this case $\tan \theta = \cot \alpha_1 = 1/m_1$.

**28. Linear functions.**—A function of the form $mx + b$ is called a *linear function of x*. If a quantity $Q$ depends on $x$ in such a way that the relation between them can be expressed in the form

$$Q = mx + b,$$

then $Q$ is said to be a linear function of $x$.

### Example 1

If a man starts at a point 260 miles from Chicago and drives toward that city at 40 m.p.h., his distance from Chicago varies with the time in accordance with the equation

$$D = 260 - 40t.$$

The distance is therefore a linear function of the elapsed time, and the graph of the relation is the line shown in Fig. 58. The slope of the line is $-40$,[*] and this means that the distance $D$ decreases 40 miles each hour.

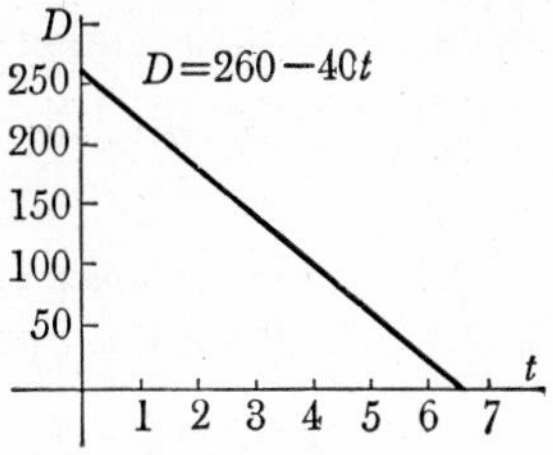

FIG. 58.

### Example 2

On the Fahrenheit thermometer, water freezes at 32° and boils at 212° under standard atmospheric pressure. The corresponding centigrade temperatures are 0° and 100°. Since the temperature difference between freezing and boiling is 180°F., or 100°C., it is evident that each degree on the centigrade scale is equivalent to $\frac{180}{100}$ or $\frac{9°}{5}$ Fahrenheit. It follows immediately that

$$T_F = 32° + \tfrac{9}{5}T_C.$$

The graph of this linear relation is the line shown in Fig. 59. The slope is $\frac{9}{5}$ and this means that the Fahrenheit temperature increases $\frac{9°}{5}$ for each degree increase in centigrade temperature.

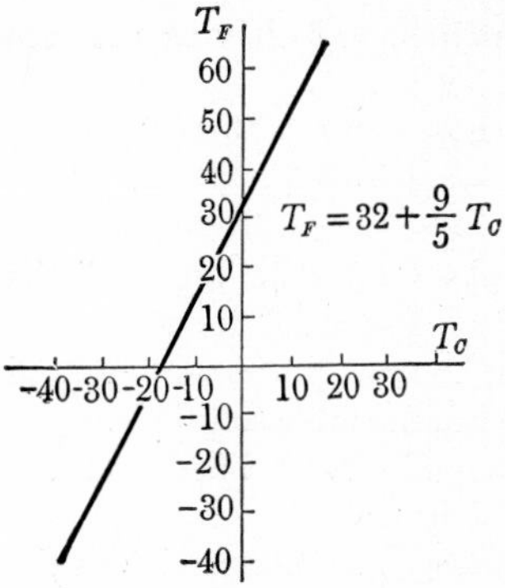

FIG. 59.

*It is evident from these examples that if a quantity Q varies* **linearly** *with x in accordance with a law of the form*

$$Q = mx + b,$$

*then* **m,** *which is the slope of the graph, is the rate at which Q changes relative to x; i.e., Q increases or decreases by m units for each unit of change in x.*

### PROBLEMS

**1.** Write each of the following equations in the slope-intercept form and thus find the slope and $y$-intercept:

* This slope is equal to the tangent of the angle of inclination that the graph would have if it were drawn using equal units on both axes. There is a distortion in Fig. 58 due to the use of different units. This is often the case in applied problems.

(a) $x + 4y - 6 = 0.$      (b) $2x - 3y + 10 = 0.$
(c) $3y - x - 2 = 0.$      (d) $2x + 1.6y - 0.4 = 0.$
(e) $0.2x + y = 0.$      (f) $3.6x - 0.9y = 8.$

**2.** Find the intercepts of the line through the two given points $A$ and $B$, and write the equation of the line in the intercept form:

(a) $A(-1, 2)$ $B(6, 10).$      (b) $A(10, 1)$   $B(-10, 3).$
(c) $A(-3, 4)$ $B(1, -6).$      (d) $A(2.6, 1.4)$ $B(3.8, 2).$

**3.** What value must be assigned to $A$ or $B$ if the given pair of lines is to be (1) parallel, (2) perpendicular?

(a) $Ax + 2y = 5$      (b) $x + 3y - 7 = 0$
      $3x - y = 7.$            $5x + By - 1 = 0.$
(c) $4x + 3y = 6$      (d) $6x + 1.8y = 5$
      $Ax - 7y = 2.$            $4x + By = 1.$

**4.** Find the equations of two lines through $A$, one parallel and the other perpendicular to the given line:
(a) $A(1, 6); x - 2y - 2 = 0.$
(b) $A(0, 0); 2x - 6y = 5.$
(c) $A(1, -1); 2y - 3x = 7.$

**5.** What is the equation of a line through $(6, -3)$ having the sum of its intercepts equal to 10?

**6.** Given the pair of linear equations $\begin{cases} A_1x + B_1y + C_1 = 0 \\ A_2x + B_2y + C_2 = 0. \end{cases}$
Show that:
(a) If $A_1/A_2 = B_1/B_2 \neq C_1/C_2$, the graphs are parallel lines and the equations are inconsistent, *i.e.*, they have no common solution.
(b) If $A_1/A_2 = B_1/B_2 = C_1/C_2$, the graphs are coincident lines and the equations are dependent, *i.e.*, they have innumerable solutions.
(c) If $A_1/A_2 \neq B_1/B_2$, the graphs are nonparallel lines and the equations have one and only one common solution.

**7.** Find the point of intersection and the angles of intersection of the following lines:
(a) $3y - 2x + 2 = 0; x + y = 6.$
(b) $4y - 3x + 11 = 0; 2y - x + 5 = 0.$
(c) $3x - 5y + 9 = 0; x + 4y + 3 = 0.$

**8.** Find the angle from the line $A(0, -6)$ $B(8, 0)$ to the line $C(-1, 1)$ $D(7, -3).$

**9.** Find the angles of the following triangles:
(a) $A(-2, -2)$ $B(4, 2)$     $C(0, 6).$
(b) $A(1, -1)$    $B(3, 0)$     $C(-2, 5).$
(c) $A(-3, 2)$   $B(5, 2)$     $C(0, -2).$
(d) $A(-2, 6)$   $B(-2, -4)$ $C(2, 1).$

**10.** Find the angles of the following parallelograms:

(a) $A(0, 0)$　　$B(6, 2)$　　$C(8, 6)$　　$D(2, 4)$.

(b) $A(-4, -3)$ $B(6, 2)$　　$C(10, 10)$ $D(0, 5)$.

(c) $A(-5, 2)$　$B(-3, -2)$ $C(6, 1)$　$D(4, 5)$.

**11.** What angle does the line $2x - 3y + 6 = 0$ make with the line $x = 4$?

**12.** Figure 60 shows a line through a given point $(x_1, y_1)$ and having direction angles $\alpha$ and $\beta$ with the coordinate axes. Show that the equation of the line can be written in the form

$$\frac{x - x_1}{\cos \alpha} = \frac{y - y_1}{\cos \beta}.$$

This is called the direction cosine form, or symmetrical form, of the equation of the line. HINT: First write the equation in the form

$$y - y_1 = m(x - x_1)$$

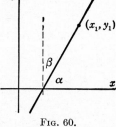

FIG. 60.

where $m = \tan \alpha = \sin \alpha / \cos \alpha = \cos \beta / \cos \alpha$.

**13.** Express the circumference of a circle as a function of its diameter and draw the graph. At what rate does the circumference increase, relative to the diameter? Assuming the earth to be a sphere, suppose that a band were placed around it at the equator; how long a piece would have to be inserted in this band in order to make it stand out at a distance of 1 in. from the earth all the way around?

**14.** A sum of $100 is placed at simple interest at a rate of 4 per cent per annum. Express the amount at the end of time $t$ (years) as a function of $t$ and make the graph.

**15.** Express the length of the diagonal of a cube as a function of the length $x$ of its edge. Make the graph. What is the rate at which the length of the diagonal changes relative to $x$?

**16.** The force $F$ required to stretch a spring an amount $x$ beyond its free length is (within certain limits) proportional to $x$. This force for a certain spring is 20 lb. when $x = 2\frac{1}{2}$ in. Express $F$ as a function of $x$ and draw the graph. What is the physical significance of its slope?

**17.** An automobile radiator holds 16 qt. and is filled with a solution that is 20 per cent alcohol. If $x$ quarts are drained out and replaced by an 80 per cent alcohol solution, what is the resulting concentration (in terms of $x$)? Make the graph. What is the significance of its slope?

**18.** The coefficient of expansion (change in length per unit length per degree change in temperature) for steel is 0.0000065, using the Fahrenheit scale. A steel rod is 30 ft. long at 50°F. Express its length at $t°$ as a function of $t$ and make the graph. What is the physical significance of its slope and $y$-intercept?

**19.** A car leaves point $A$ at noon and travels due north toward $B$ which is 300 miles away at a speed of 40 m.p.h. At the same time another car starts from $B$ and travels toward $A$ at 20 m.p.h. Express the distance of each car from $B$ in terms of the time $t$ (hours) after noon. By making the graphs on the same axes find when and where they will meet. Solve also by analytical methods.

**20.** A car leaves a certain point at noon and travels at 40 m.p.h. Two hours later another car leaves the same point and travels on the same highway at 52 m.p.h. Determine when the second car will overtake the first, using both analytical and graphical methods.

**29. The normal form.**—A line $l$ is completely determined if the length and direction of the shortest segment that

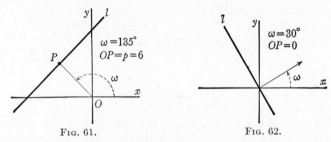

Fig. 61.                    Fig. 62.

can be drawn from the origin to $l$ is specified. Thus in Fig. 61 $l$ is determined by specifying that $OP = 6$ units and $\omega = 135°$. The segment $OP$ is called the *normal* to $l$; *it is a directed segment, the positive direction being by definition*

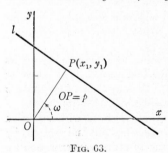

Fig. 63.

*from $O$ to $P$.* The directed distance $OP$, denoted by $p$, is therefore always positive (or zero if $l$ goes through the origin). *The direction of $OP$ is specified by giving the counterclockwise angle $\omega < 360°$ from $OX$ to $OP$.* In case $l$ goes through the origin so that $OP = 0$, we choose the direction of the normal such that $\omega < 180°$ as indicated in Fig. 62.

We wish now to find the equation of a line $l$ in terms of the length $p$ and direction angle $\omega$ of its normal. Assuming at first that $l$ is not parallel to either axis, we may do this by using the point-slope formula. The coordinates of $P$ are (Fig. 63)

$$x_1 = p \cos \omega; \qquad y_1 = p \sin \omega.$$

The slope of $OP$ is $\tan \omega$, so the slope of $l$ is

$$m = -\frac{1}{\tan \omega} = -\frac{\cos \omega}{\sin \omega}.$$

The equation of $l$ is then

$$y - p \sin \omega = -\frac{\cos \omega}{\sin \omega}(x - p \cos \omega).$$

Multiplying by $\sin \omega$ and simplifying, we get

$$\boldsymbol{x \cos \omega + y \sin \omega = p.}$$

This is called the *normal form* of the equation of a line. It can be used conveniently for writing down the equation when $p$ and $\omega$ are known.

### Example

The equation of the line for which $\omega = 240°$ and $p = 8$ is (Fig. 64)

$$x \cos 240° + y \sin 240° = 8.$$

Since $\cos 240° = -\frac{1}{2}$ and $\sin 240° = -\sqrt{3}/2$, this becomes

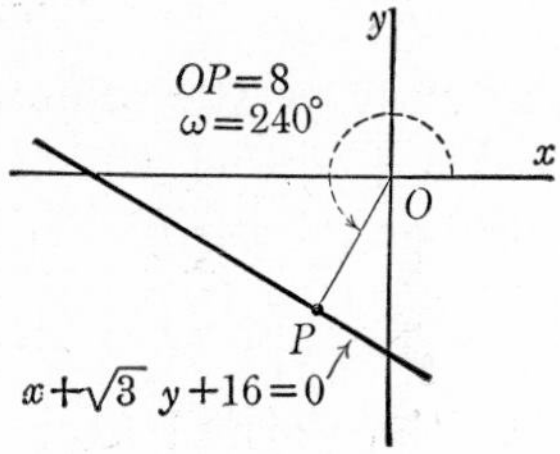

$$-\frac{1}{2}x - \frac{\sqrt{3}}{2}y = 8$$

or

$$x + \sqrt{3}\,y + 16 = 0.$$

FIG. 64.

In our derivation we assumed that $l$ is not parallel to either axis because we wanted to use the slopes of $OP$ and $l$. The student can easily show that the same equation applies if $l$ is parallel to either axis. In such a case, either $\sin \omega$ or $\cos \omega$ is zero and the other is $\pm 1$; the equation

$$x \cos \omega + y \sin \omega = p$$

reduces to $x = \pm p$ or $y = \pm p$. There is nothing special about the case in which $l$ goes through the origin except that $p = 0$.

### Example

The equation of the line for which $\omega = 135°$ and $p = 0$ is (Fig. 65)

$$x \cos 135° + y \sin 135° = 0.$$

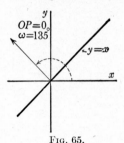

Since $\sin 135° = 1/\sqrt{2}$ and $\cos 135° = -1/\sqrt{2}$ this reduces to

$$-\frac{1}{\sqrt{2}} x + \frac{1}{\sqrt{2}} y = 0$$

or

$$y = x.$$

Fig. 65.

**30. Reduction of $Ax + By + C = 0$ to the normal form.** In order to change a general linear equation into the normal form we first note that in the equation

$$x \cos \omega + y \sin \omega = p$$

the sum of the squares of the coefficients of $x$ and $y$ is $\cos^2 \omega + \sin^2 \omega$, which is equal to 1 and that $p$ is a positive number (or zero). In order to put the equation

$$Ax + By + C = 0$$

into the normal form, we first multiply through by some number $N$, whose value is yet to be determined, obtaining

$$NAx + NBy + NC = 0.$$

We now try to determine $N$ so that the sum of the squares of the coefficients of $x$ and $y$ shall be equal to 1; thus

$$N^2A^2 + N^2B^2 = 1;$$

this condition is satisfied if

$$N = \pm \frac{1}{\sqrt{A^2 + B^2}}.$$

Finally, we choose the sign before the radical opposite to that of $C$ because $p$ must be positive. If $C = 0$, we choose this sign to agree with that of $B$ so that $\sin \omega$ will be positive; this is in accordance with our agreement that in this case $\omega <. 180°$.

The procedure is covered by the following:

**Rule :** *In order to change the equation $Ax + By + C = 0$ into the normal form, divide through by $\pm \sqrt{A^2 + B^2}$, choosing the sign before the radical opposite to that of $\cdot C$. If $C = 0$, choose the sign the same as that of $B$.*

### Example

Change the equation $3x - 4y + 16 = 0$ into the normal form and find $\cos \omega$, $\sin \omega$, and $p$.

*Solution* (Fig. 66)

$$\pm \sqrt{A^2 + B^2} = \pm \sqrt{3^2 + (-4)^2} = \pm 5.$$

Since $C(= 16)$ is positive, we choose the negative sign and divide through by $-5$. The result is

$$-\tfrac{3}{5}x + \tfrac{4}{5}y = \tfrac{16}{5}.$$

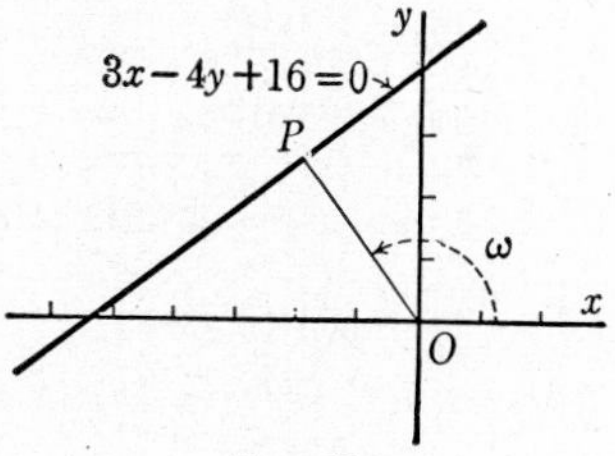

Fig. 66.

For this line, $\cos \omega = -\tfrac{3}{5}$, $\sin \omega = \tfrac{4}{5}$, and $p = \tfrac{16}{5}$. The value of $p$ is the perpendicular distance from the origin to the line.

**31. Distance from a line to a point.**—The directed distance from the $y$-axis to a point $Q(x_1, y_1)$ is of course equal to $x_1$; the distance from the $x$-axis to $Q$ is $y_1$. We consider now the problem of determining the directed

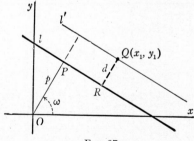

Fig. 67.

distance from any given line to a given point. The normal form of the equation of the line is particularly useful for this purpose.

The derivation of the required formula varies somewhat with the positions of the given line and point relative to the coordinate system. For the present we assume the data to be such that the situation is represented by Fig. 67.

Let the normal equation of the given line $l$ be

$$x \cos \omega + y \sin \omega = p$$

and let the given point be $Q(x_1, y_1)$. Through $Q$ draw a line $l'$ parallel to $l$. If the length and direction of the normal to $l'$ are $p'$ and $\omega'$, respectively, then $\omega' = \omega$ and $p' = OP + RQ = p + d$ where $d = RQ$ is the required *directed* distance. The normal equation of $l'$ is then

$$x \cos \omega + y \sin \omega = p + d.$$

Now the point $Q(x_1, y_1)$ is on this line, and hence *its coordinates must satisfy this equation. That is,*

$$x_1 \cos \omega + y_1 \sin \omega = p + d.$$

Solving for $d$ we have

$$d = x_1 \cos \omega + y_1 \sin \omega - p.$$

If the data is such that the lines $l$ and $l'$ are on opposite sides of the origin, the derivation is slightly different since in this case $\omega' = \omega \pm 180°$, but the final result is the same. Leaving the details of this case to the student we state the following:

**Rule :** *To find the directed distance from the line*

$$Ax + By + C = 0$$

*to the point $Q(x_1, y_1)$, proceed as follows:*

*Step 1. Change the equation of the line into the normal form and transpose $p$ to the left-hand side, thus obtaining an equation of the form*

$$x \cos \omega + y \sin \omega - p = 0.$$

*Step 2. In this equation, replace $x$ and $y$, respectively, by the coordinates $x_1$ and $y_1$ of the given point $Q$. The value* *of the left-hand side is now equal to d; i.e.,*

$$d = x_1 \cos \omega + y_1 \sin \omega - p.$$

It must be emphasized that $d = RQ$ is a *directed distance* measured *from the line to the point*. It is positive if the sense of $RQ$ agrees with that of $OP$ in Fig. 67; *i.e., it is positive if Q and the origin are on opposite sides of the line l. If Q and the origin are on the same side of l, the directed distance is negative.*

### Example

Find the distance from the line $x - 2y - 2 = 0$ to the point $A(-3, 2)$.

*Solution* (Fig. 68)

*Step 1.* Since $C$ is negative ($= -2$), we get the normal equation of the line by dividing through by $+\sqrt{5}$. This gives

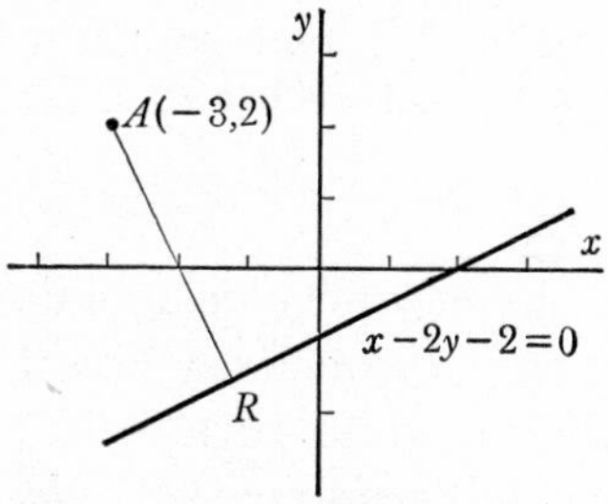

Fig. 68.

$$\frac{x}{\sqrt{5}} - \frac{2y}{\sqrt{5}} - \frac{2}{\sqrt{5}} = 0.$$

*Step 2.* Replacing $x$ and $y$ by $-3$ and $2$, respectively, we have

$$d = -\frac{3}{\sqrt{5}} - \frac{4}{\sqrt{5}} - \frac{2}{\sqrt{5}} = -\frac{9}{\sqrt{5}}.$$

*The directed distance comes out negative because A and the origin are on the same side of the line, making RA and OP opposite in sense.*

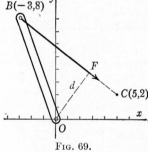

FIG. 69.

### 32. Moment of a force.—The

rod shown in Fig. 69 is pivoted at $O$ and can rotate about an axis through $O$ perpendicular to the plane of the figure. The arrow or *vector* represents a force applied at $B$ in the direction shown. The *moment* of this force with respect to the axis of rotation is defined as the product of the magnitude of the force and the perpendicular distance from its line of action to $O$. That is,

### Moment = $F \times d$.

This quantity, which is expressed in foot-pounds if $F$ is in pounds and $d$ in feet, is a measure of the tendency of the force $F$ to make the rod turn about $O$.

In the example given, the line of action of the force is determined by the points $B(-3, 8)$ and $C(5, 2)$. The distance $d$ can be found by the methods of the preceding section as follows: The slope of $BC$ is $-\frac{3}{4}$, and its equation is found to be $3x + 4y - 23 = 0$. The distance $d$ is of course $\frac{23}{5}$, and so the moment is $\frac{23}{5}F$. If the distances are in feet and if $F = 50$ lb., then the moment is

$$\tfrac{23}{5}(50) = 230 \text{ ft.-lb.}$$

A body may be acted upon by certain forces that tend to turn it in one way about a given axis, and by other forces that tend to turn it in the opposite direction. *A fundamental principle of physics states that the two opposite moments must be numerically equal if the body remains at rest.* One can often use this principle to solve simple problems of mechanics.

### Example

The rod $OA$ in Fig. 70 is fastened to the wall by a smooth pin at $O$, about which the rod may rotate. It is held in the horizontal position shown by a cord $BC$. Compute the tensile pull $T$ produced in the cord when a vertical load of 20 lb. is applied at $A$.

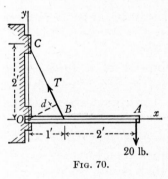

FIG. 70.

### Solution

The 20-lb. load produces a moment of $20 \times 3 = 60$ ft.-lb. tending to turn the rod downward (clockwise) about $O$. The pull in the cord must produce an equal moment in the opposite sense. That is (Fig. 70)

$$T \times d = 20 \times 3.$$

To find $d$ we note that since the intercepts of $BC$ are 1 and 2 its equation is

$$\frac{x}{1} + \frac{y}{2} = 1 \qquad \text{or} \qquad 2x + y - 2 = 0.$$

If this were put in the normal form by dividing by $\sqrt{5}$, the value of $p$ would be $2/\sqrt{5}$; this is the length $d$ in the figure. We have then

$$T\,\frac{2}{\sqrt{5}} = 20(3);$$

$$T = 30\,\sqrt{5} = 67.1 \text{ lb.}$$

## PROBLEMS

**1.** Draw each of the following lines and write its equation in the normal form:

(a) $p = 4;\ \omega = 30°$.　　　　(b) $p = 6;\ \omega = 135°$.
(c) $p = 0;\ \omega = 120°$.　　　　(d) $p = 4;\ \omega = 270°$.
(e) $p = 2;\ \omega = 200°$.　　　　(f) $p = 8;\ \omega = 180°$.

**2.** Change each of the following equations into the normal form and find the values of $\cos\omega$, $\sin\omega$, and $p$:

(a) $x + y + 1 = 0$.　　　　(b) $3x - 4y - 8 = 0$.
(c) $2x + 4y - 8\sqrt{5} = 0$.　　　　(d) $5x - 12y = 26$.
(e) $x + 5y = 0$.　　　　(f) $3x - y = 0$.

**3.** Draw the line determined by the following data and obtain the normal form of its equation:
(a) Through $(-3, 8)$ and $(3, 0)$.
(b) With intercepts $a = 2,\ b = -1$.
(c) Through $(4, 1)$ with slope 1.
(d) With $y$-intercept 8 and slope $-\frac{3}{4}$.

**4.** Draw the following pairs of parallel lines and find the distance between them:
(a) $3x - 4y + 20 = 0;\ 3x - 4y + 32 = 0$.
(b) $x - 2y - 9 = 0;\ 2x - 4y + 17 = 0$.

**5.** The radius of a circle with center at the origin is 10. What are the equations of the tangent lines to this circle that have a slope of $\frac{3}{4}$?

**6.** Find the values of $p$ and $\omega$ in terms of the intercepts $a$ and $b$.

**7.** Find the value of $p$ in terms of $m$ and the $y$-intercept.

**8.** Show that the formula for the directed distance from the line $Ax + By + C = 0$ to the point $(x_1, y_1)$ can be written in the form

$$d = \frac{Ax_1 + By_1 + C}{\pm\sqrt{A^2 + B^2}},$$

where the sign before the radical is opposite to that of $C$ if $C \neq 0$ and the same as that of $B$ if $C = 0$.

**9.** Find the directed distance from the given line to the given point and state the significance of the sign:

(a) $\frac{5}{13}x - \frac{12}{13}y - 2 = 0$; (2, 1).

(b) $x + y + 6 = 0$;       (−4, −3).

(c) $3x + y = 0$;          (2, 4).

(d) $3x + 4y - 24 = 0$; (4, 3).

**10.** In each of the following triangles find the length $h$ of the altitude drawn from $A$ to the side $BC$.   Check by using the formula:

$$\text{area} = \tfrac{1}{2}BC \times h,$$

the area being obtained from the determinant:

(a) $A(2, 7)$   $B(2, 1)$ $C(6, 5)$.

(b) $A(4, -2)$ $B(3, 5)$ $C(-3, -3)$.

(c) $A(6, 0)$   $B(3, 2)$ $C(-2, 1)$.

**11.** A line is drawn through $(-7, 0)$ and $(5, 5)$, and a circle of radius 2 is drawn with its center at $(2, 6)$.   Is the line tangent to the circle, does it intersect the circle at two points, or does it fail to touch the circle?

**12.** Show that the equations of the two bisectors of the angles between the lines $A_1x + B_1y + C_1 = 0$ and $A_2x + B_2y + C_2 = 0$ are given by the equations

$$\frac{A_1x + B_1y + C_1}{\sqrt{A_1{}^2 + B_1{}^2}} = \pm \frac{A_2x + B_2y + C_2}{\sqrt{A_2{}^2 + B_2{}^2}}.$$

HINT: Let $P(x, y)$ be any point on a bisector (Fig. 71); then $d_1 = d_2$ or $d_1 = -d_2$, according as these directed distances have like or unlike signs.

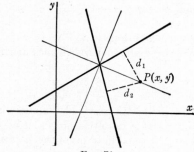

FIG. 71.

**13.** Draw the lines $3x - 4y + 12 = 0$ and $5x + 12y - 60 = 0$, and find the equations of the bisectors of the angles between them.

**14.** Find the point where the bisector of angle $A$ in triangle $A(-2, 1)$ $B(1, 4)$ $C(5, 0)$ cuts side $BC$.

**15.** Find the center and radius of the inscribed circle in triangle $ABC$ of Prob. 14.

**16.** Two vertices of a triangle are $A(2, -1)$ and $B(7, 11)$.   Find the equation of the path along which the third vertex may move if the area of the triangle remains equal to 65.   Use two methods.

In each of the following problems, member $OA$ is connected to the wall or foundation by means of a smooth pin and rotation of $OA$ about $O$ is prevented by the cable $AB$ or $BC$.

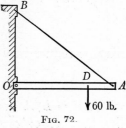

**17.** Find the tension in cable $AB$ due to the 60-lb. load applied at $D$ on member $OA$ (Fig. 72). $OB = OD = 6$ ft. $DA = 2$ ft.

**18.** Find the tension in $AB$ (Prob. 17) if the load is 80 lb. and the member $OA$ weighs 20 lb. This weight is equivalent to an additional vertical load of 20 lb. applied to the middle of $OA$.

FIG. 72.

**19.** Compute the tension produced in $CB$ (Fig. 73) when a horizontal pull of 10 lb. is applied at $A$. $OA = CB = 5$ in.; $OB = 3$ in.

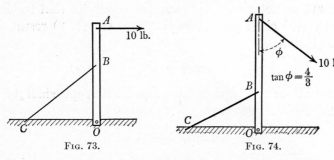

FIG. 73.                    FIG. 74.

**20.** Compute the tension produced in $CB$ (Fig. 74) when a pull of 10 lb. is applied at $A$ in the direction shown. $OA = 6$ in., $OB = 2$ in., $OC = 4$ in.

**33. Number of essential constants.**—Some of the forms in which the equation of a line can be written are

$$y = mx + b; \quad \frac{x}{a} + \frac{y}{b} = 1; \quad x \cos \omega + y \sin \omega = p.$$

Each of these equations contains two constants such that the line is completely determined when their values have been fixed. Thus if $m = 2$ and $b = 4$ in the first of the above forms, we have the line $y = 2x + 4$.

When the equation is written in the form

$$Ax + By + C = 0,$$

there are *three* constants. We can, however, divide through by any one of them whose value is not zero, thus reducing the number to two. Thus if $A \neq 0$, the equation

$$Ax + By + C = 0$$

may be reduced to

$$x + dy + e = 0$$

where $d = B/A$ and $e = C/A$. It is therefore clear that the number of *essential* constants is two. The student will readily connect this with the fact that two geometrical conditions suffice to determine a line; for each such condition yields, in general, an algebraic equation in the constants to be determined. Thus the condition that the line $y = mx + b$ shall pass through the point (6, 2) results in the equation

$$6m + b = 2;$$

the additional condition that its $x$-intercept shall be 5 means algebraically that

$$5m + b = 0.$$

These equations have the unique simultaneous solution $m = 2$, $b = -10$. The equation of the line satisfying the two conditions is then

$$y = 2x - 10.$$

**34. Systems of lines.**—In the equation $y = mx + b$, let us fix the value of $m$, say let $m = 2$, but leave the value of $b$ unspecified. We have then the equation

$$y = 2x + b.$$

It defines a line with slope 2 for each value assigned to $b$; furthermore, any line with slope 2 can be obtained from it by a proper choice of $b$. It is therefore said to define the *system of lines* or *family of lines* with slope 2. Several are shown in Fig. 75.

If one wishes to find the equation of the line with slope 2, which also satisfies one other condition, he may start with the above equation and determine the proper value of $b$.

## Example

Find the equation of the line with slope 2 which passes through (8, 3).

*Solution* (Fig. 75)

Since the slope is 2, the equation is

$$y = 2x + b$$

where $b$ is to be determined. Now, if the line goes through (8, 3), these coordinates must satisfy the equation, *i.e*,

$$3 = 2(8) + b \qquad \text{or} \qquad b = -13.$$

The required equation is then

$$y = 2x - 13.$$

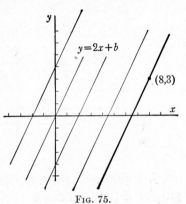

Fig. 75.

In general, one may wish to find the equation of the line satisfying two conditions. He may start by writing down the equation defining the system of lines all of which satisfy *one* of the conditions. This equation will contain one arbitrary constant called the *parameter* of the system. He may then proceed to determine the value of this parameter in order that the second condition may be satisfied.

## Example

Find the equation of the line having its $x$-intercept equal to twice its $y$-intercept, and passing through $(-2, 8)$.

*Solution* (Fig. 76)

The system of lines satisfying the first condition is

$$\frac{x}{2b} + \frac{y}{b} = 1.*$$

We want the member of this system for which $y = 8$ when $x = -2$; this means that

$$\frac{-2}{2b} + \frac{8}{b} = 1 \qquad \text{or} \qquad b = 7.$$

*We disregard the trivial solution of a line through the origin.

The desired equation is then

$$\frac{x}{14} + \frac{y}{7} = 1.$$

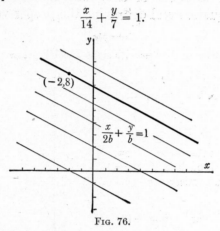

Fig. 76.

**35. Equations representing two or more lines.**—The graphs of the equations

$$x - y = 0,$$
$$x + 6y - 6 = 0$$

are, respectively, the lines $l_1$ and $l_2$ in **Fig. 77.** If we multiply the left-hand members of the equations and set the product equal to zero, we have the equation

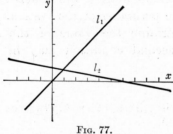

Fig. 77.

(1)  $(x - y)(x + 6y - 6) = 0$

or,

(2)  $x^2 + 5xy - 6y^2 - 6x + 6y = 0.$

The product in (1) is equal to zero for all pairs of values of $x$ and $y$ that make either factor zero, and for no other values. Consequently, the graph of (1), which is the same as (2), consists of the *two* lines $l_1$ and $l_2$.

More generally, if the graph of an equation $g(x, y) = 0$* is a curve $C_1$ and the graph of $h(x, y) = 0$ is a curve $C_2$,

---

* By an equation of the form $g(x, y) = 0$, we mean an equation in $x$ and $y$ in which all terms have been put on the left-hand side, leaving the right-hand side zero.

then the graph of the equation

$$g(x, y) \cdot h(x, y) = 0$$

consists of the curves $C_1$ and $C_2$. The extension to any number of factors is obvious. It follows that *if the left-hand member of an equation of the form*

$$f(x, y) = 0$$

*can be factored into real linear factors, the graph consists of the corresponding lines.*

### Example 1

The equation $x^3 - xy^2 = 0$ can be written in the form

$$x(x - y)(x + y) = 0.$$

The graph then consists of the lines $x = 0$, $x - y = 0$, and $x + y = 0$.

### Example 2

The equation $x^3 - 2x^2y + xy^2 - 2y^3 = 0$ can be written in the form $(x^2 + y^2)(x - 2y) = 0$. Its graph therefore is the line $x - 2y = 0$. Why?

### PROBLEMS

**1.** Draw several members of each of the following systems of lines and determine what common property is possessed by all members of each system:

(a) $2y = x + b$.          (b) $y = mx - 2$.

(c) $y = c$.               (d) $y + 1 = m(x - 2)$.

(e) $x \cos \omega + y \sin \omega = 4$.     (f) $\dfrac{x}{a} + \dfrac{y}{2} = 1$.

**2.** Write the equation of the system of lines perpendicular to the line $A(-3, 1)$ $B(5, 5)$. Find the member of the system having its $x$-intercept equal to 6.

**3.** Write the equation of the system of lines with $y$-intercept 4. Find the member of this system that

(a) Passes through $(-2, 3)$.

(b) Is perpendicular to the line $2y = 5x$.

**4.** Write the equation of the system of lines with $x$-intercept $-4$ and find the member of the system that is parallel to the line $A(2, 3)$ $B(-3, 4)$.

**5.** Write the equation of the system of lines through $(6, -5)$. Find the two members of the system that form with the coordinate axes a triangle of area 20 square units.

**6.** Write the equation of the system of lines through $(6, 4)$. Find the members having the sum of their intercepts equal to 20.

**7.** Write the equation of the system of lines tangent to the circle of radius 10 with center at the origin. Find the one that is tangent at $(8, -6)$.

**8.** Write the equation of the system of lines with $y$-intercept $-4$. Sketch the curve $y = x^2$ and find the members of this system that are tangent to the curve. HINT: Solving $y = mx - 4$ and $y = x^2$ simultaneously leads to the equation $x^2 - mx + 4 = 0$. The two roots must be equal for tangency.

**9.** Write the equation of the system of lines with slope $-2$. Sketch the curve $y = x^2 - 8x + 18$ and find the member of this system that is tangent to the curve. See hint in Prob. 8.

**10.** Show that if the lines $A_1x + B_1y + C_1 = 0$ and

$$A_2x + B_2y + C_2 = 0$$

intersect at a point $P$, then the equation

$$(A_1x + B_1y + C_1) + k(A_2x + B_2y + C_2) = 0,$$

where $k$ is any real number, represents a line through $P$. HINT: The equation is linear and is satisfied by the coordinates of $P$. Why?

**11.** A line goes through the point of intersection of the lines

$$2x + y - 10 = 0$$

and $3x - 2y - 1 = 0$. Its $y$-intercept is 1. Find its equation with and without the use of Prob. 10.

**12.** A line goes through the point of intersection of the lines

$$2x + 3y - 1 = 0$$

and $x + y - 3 = 0$, and is perpendicular to the line $y = 2x + 4$. Find its equation using Prob. 10.

Make the graphs of the following equations after factoring their left-hand members:

**13.** $x^2 - 4x = 0$.          **14.** $4x^2 - 9y^2 = 0$.

**15.** $3x^2 - 4xy - 12x = 0$.   **16.** $x^3y + 2xy^3 = 0$.

**17.** $xy - 2y - 3x + 6 = 0$.   **18.** $2x^2 - 3xy - 2y^2 = 0$.

**19.** $x^2 - y^2 + 2x - 2y = 0$.

**20.** $x^2y^2 - 2x^2y - 2xy^2 + 4xy = 0$.

**21.** $x^3 + x^2y - 2x^2 - 2xy = 0$.

**22.** $x^3 + x^2y + x^2 + y^2x + y^3 + y^2 = 0$.

# CHAPTER IV

## THE POLYNOMIAL CURVES

**36. Introduction.**—We define a *polynomial in x* to be a function that can be written in the form

$$a_0x^n + a_1x^{n-1} + a_2x^{n-2} + \cdots + a_{n-1}x + a_n$$

where the $a$'s are any constants and $n$ is a positive integer. The polynomial is said to be of *degree n* if $a_0 \neq 0$. This type of function is also called a *rational integral function* of $x$, but we shall use the name polynomial because it is shorter. In accordance with our definition, the functions

$$2x - 3, \qquad (x^2 - 2)^3, \qquad \text{and} \qquad x^5 - \sqrt{2}\,x^3 + x$$

are polynomials in $x$ of degree 1, 6, and 5, respectively. The functions

$$\sqrt{x - 6}, \qquad \frac{x^2 - 1}{x^2 + 1}, \qquad \text{and} \qquad x^3 + 2\sqrt{x} - 7$$

are *not* polynomials. By a *polynomial curve* we shall mean the graph of the equation

$$y = \text{a polynomial in } x.$$

The equations $y = c$ and $y = mx + b$ are the special cases of degree 0 and 1, respectively. Their graphs, which are straight lines, have already been studied. We consider now the graphs of polynomials of degree higher than 1.

**37. The equation $y = ax^2 + bx + c$.**—The general shape of the graph of this equation is illustrated by Fig. 78. The curve is called a *parabola*.* If $a$ is positive, the

---

\* In Prob. 16, page 36, the parabola was defined as the path of a point which moves in a plane so that its undirected distances from a fixed point and a fixed line in the plane remain equal. In Chap. VIII it will be proved that the graph of $y = ax^2 + bx + c$ is such a curve.

parabola opens upward and has a lowest or *minimum point* which is called its *vertex*. This is the case illustrated. If *a* is negative, the parabola opens downward and the vertex is its highest or *maximum point*.

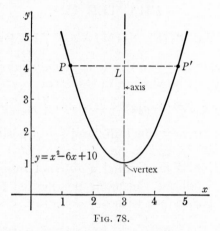

Fig. 78.

The line through the vertex parallel to the *y*-axis is called the *axis* of the parabola. *The curve is symmetrical with respect to this line;* by this we mean that if the paper were folded along this line the two "halves" of the parabola would coincide. This may be proved as follows:

Write the equation $y = ax^2 + bx + c$ in the form $ax^2 + bx + c - y = 0$ and then solve it for *x* in terms of *y*; the result is

$$x = -\frac{b}{2a} \pm \frac{\sqrt{b^2 - 4a(c - y)}}{2a}.$$

It follows that, corresponding to any value $y_1$ of *y* [such that $b^2 - 4a(c - y_1) > 0$], there are two values of *x*, one of which is less than $-b/2a$ by the same amount that the other exceeds $-b/2a$. The two corresponding points *P* and *P'* (Fig. 78) are then situated so that $PL = LP'$.

It is evident that the axis of the parabola is the line $x = -b/2a$. Substituting this value for *x* in the equation we find that $y = c - \frac{b^2}{4a}$. Consequently,

*Equation of axis is* $x = -\dfrac{b}{2a}$

*Coordinates of vertex are* $\left(-\dfrac{b}{2a},\ c - \dfrac{b^2}{4a}\right)$.

In making the graph it is usually desirable to draw the axis and locate the vertex. A few other points, such as the intercepts on the axes, may then be sufficient for drawing the curve.

### Example

Make the graph of the equation $y = x - 0.08x^2$.

#### Solution (Fig. 79)

In this case $a = -0.08$, $b = 1$, and $c = 0$. The axis of the parabola is easily found to be the line $x = 6\frac{1}{4}$, and the vertex is the point $(6\frac{1}{4}, 3\frac{1}{8})$. The intercepts on the $x$-axis, obtained by setting $y = 0$ and solving the resulting quadratic equation for $x$, are 0 and $12\frac{1}{2}$. Plotting a few additional points we have the graph shown.

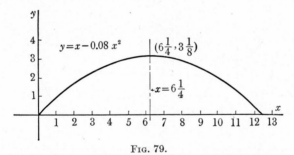

FIG. 79.

If the unit on each axis represents 1 ft., this curve is approximately the path traveled by a ball thrown from the origin with a velocity of 20 ft. per second at an angle of 45° with the horizontal $x$-axis. This can be proved by using the fundamental principles of physics.

The equation $y = ax^2$ is the special case in which $b = c = 0$. In this case the vertex is at the origin and the axis of the parabola is the $y$-axis.

It is evident that the graph of $y = ax^2 + c$ is simply the curve $y = ax^2$ shifted by an amount $c$ in the $y$-direction. The graph could be obtained by plotting the parabola $y = ax^2$ and the line $y = c$, and adding ordinates as indi-

cated in Fig. 80.   Here we have added 1 to each ordinate
of $y = x^2$ to obtain the graph of $y = x^2 + 1$.

*It can be shown that the graph of $y = ax^2 + bx + c$ is*
*precisely the same curve as the graph of $y = ax^2$.** The

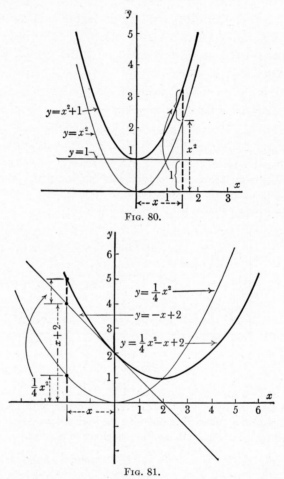

FIG. 80.

FIG. 81.

difference is merely in the location of the curve relative to
the axes.   The graph could be obtained by drawing the
parabola $y = ax^2$ and the line $y = bx + c$ and adding
ordinates as indicated in Fig. 81.   The result is the para-

* See Prob. 10, p. 106.

bola $y = ax^2$ translated in the $x$-direction by an amount $-b/2a$ and in the $y$-direction by an amount $c - \dfrac{b^2}{4a}$. In the case shown we have obtained the graph of

$$y = \tfrac{1}{4}x^2 - x + 2$$

by drawing the parabola $y = \tfrac{1}{4}x^2$ and the line $y = -x + 2$ and adding the two ordinates for each value of $x$. The resulting parabola is the curve $y = \tfrac{1}{4}x^2$ moved two units to the right and one unit upward. It thus appears that *the shape of the parabola $y = ax^2 + bx + c$ is completely determined by the numerical value of $a$.* The values of $b$ and $c$ affect only the *position* of the curve relative to the axes.

We shall not at present pursue further the idea of obtaining the graph of an equation of the form $y = f(x) + \varphi(x)$ by drawing the curves $y = f(x)$ and $y = \varphi(x)$ separately and adding the ordinates. We shall however use the method later on in connection with the graphs of equations such as $y = x + \dfrac{2}{x}$ and $y = 3 \sin x + \sin 2x$.

### PROBLEMS

**1.** State which of the following functions are polynomials in $x$ and in each case give the degree:

(a) $4x^2 + \sqrt{x} + 5$.  (b) $\sqrt{6}\,x$.

(c) $x^2(x - 2)$.  (d) $\dfrac{x}{x + 1}$.

Sketch each of the following parabolas after drawing the axis and locating the vertex and intercepts:

**2.** $y = x^2 - 7x + 10$.  **3.** $x^2 + y = 5x - 4$.
**4.** $y = 2x^2 + x - 6$.  **5.** $y = 10 - x - 2x^2$.
**6.** $4y + 6x = x^2 + 13$.  **7.** $y = 4x - 1.6x^2$.
**8.** $2x^2 + y + 4 = 0$.  **9.** $y = (x - 3)^2$.

**10.** What condition must be satisfied by the coefficients $a$, $b$, and $c$ in order that the parabola $y = ax^2 + bx + c$ may

(a) Cross the $x$-axis at two distinct points.
(b) Be tangent to the $x$-axis.
(c) Fail to touch the $x$-axis.

**11.** For what values of $b$ is the parabola $y = x^2 + bx + 25$ tangent to the $x$-axis?

**12.** Show that if the parabola $y = ax^2 + bx + c$ crosses $x$-axis at $x = x_1$ and $x = x_2$, the abscissa of the vertex is $\frac{1}{2}(x_1 + x_2)$.

**13.** In general, one and only one curve whose equation is of the form $y = ax^2 + bx + c$ can be passed through three given points. Find the equation and sketch the curve in the following cases:

    (a) $A(0, 4)$        $B(1, 3)$    $C(4, 24)$.

    (b) $A(-2, -16)$ $B(1, 11)$   $C(2, 8)$.

    (c) $A(-2, -4)$   $B(0, -6)$ $C(4, 2)$.

**14.** Draw on the same axes the graphs of $y = x^2$ and $y = 2x - 3$; obtain the graph of $y = x^2 + 2x - 3$ by adding ordinates.

**15.** Obtain the graph of $y = x^2 + x$ by plotting $y = x^2$ and $y = x$ and adding the ordinates.

**16.** Draw the graphs of $y = x^2$ and $y = x^2 - 6x + 5$; verify that they are congruent by showing that they have equal widths at equal distances from their respective vertices.

**17.** Draw the graphs of $y = -x^2$ and $y = 4x - x^2$; verify that they are congruent by showing that they have equal widths at equal distances from their respective vertices.

**18.** Express the surface area $S$ of a cube as a function of the length $x$ of its edge and make the graph. What length on the graph represents $S$ if $x = 2$ in.? $2\frac{1}{2}$ in.? What length represents the amount of increase in the surface area when the edge increases from 2 to $2\frac{1}{2}$ in.?

**19.** Make a graph showing how the area of a circle varies with its radius.

**20.** A farmer has 600 ft. of fence and wishes to enclose a rectangular plot and divide it into two equal parts by a cross fence joining the midpoints of two sides. Express the area enclosed as a function of the width $x$. Make the graph. What dimensions give the largest area and what is this area?

**21.** With 400 yd. of fence it is desired to enclose a rectangular field along the straight bank of a stream. No fence is needed along the stream. Express the area enclosed as a function of the width $x$ of the field. Make the graph and find the dimensions of the field which make the area largest.

**22.** A man operates a rooming house having 30 rooms. He estimates that he could keep all these rooms rented at \$18 per month each but would have one vacancy for each dollar per month added to this price. Express his gross revenue in terms of the number $x$ of dollars charged in excess of 18. Make the graph and determine the rental for maximum gross revenue.

**23.** A projectile is fired with velocity $v_0$ ft. per second at an angle $\alpha$ with the horizontal. If air resistance is neglected, the equation of its path can be shown to be

$$y = (\tan \alpha)x - \frac{g}{2v_0{}^2 \cos^2 \alpha} x^2,$$

where $g$ is the gravitational constant ($= 32$ ft./sec.$^2$, approximately) and the axes are taken as shown in Fig. 79. Sketch the path if $\alpha = 45°$ and $v_0 = 80$ ft. per second. Find the maximum height reached by the projectile.

**24.** If air resistance is neglected, the equation of the path traveled by a baseball that is thrown horizontally can be obtained by putting $\alpha = 0$ in the equation of Prob. 23. What is the minimum initial speed if the ball is to drop not more than $4\frac{1}{2}$ ft. in a horizontal distance of 60 ft.?

**25.** If a stone is thrown vertically upward from the ground with an initial velocity of $v_0$ ft. per second, its distance $S$ above the ground at the end of $t$ sec. is given by the formula

$$S = v_0 t - \tfrac{1}{2}gt^2$$

where $g$ is the gravitational constant ($= 32$ ft./sec.$^2$, approximately). Draw this "distance-time" curve if $v_0 = 128$, and from the graph discuss the way in which $S$ varies with $t$. What is the maximum height reached by the stone?

**38. Synthetic substitution.**—In order to find the value of the polynomial $ax^2 + bx + c$ when $x = x_1$ we may substitute $x_1$ for $x$, obtaining $ax_1{}^2 + bx_1 + c$. Another procedure, which we shall call *synthetic substitution*, is illustrated below:

$$
\begin{array}{lll}
a \quad b & c & \quad |x_1 \\
\hline
\quad ax_1 & ax_1{}^2 + bx_1 & \\
\hline
a \quad ax_1 + b & \mathbf{\textit{ax}_1{}^2 + \textit{bx}_1 + \textit{c}} &
\end{array}
$$

The steps are as follows:

1. *Write down the coefficients $a$, $b$, and $c$, and place the number $x_1$ to the right as shown.*

2. *Multiply $a$ by $x_1$, place the product under $b$, and add.*

3. *Multiply this result ($ax_1 + b$) by $x_1$, place the product under $c$, and add. This last result ($ax_1{}^2 + bx_1 + c$) is the value of $ax^2 + bx + c$ when $x = x_1$.*

The method can obviously be extended to a polynomial of higher degree. One must be careful to attach the proper sign to each coefficient and to use 0 for the coefficient of any missing power of $x$ in the polynomial; thus $3x^2 - 6$ is equivalent to $3x^2 + 0x - 6$.

### Example 1

Find the value of $x^4 - 3x^2 - 8x + 6$ when $x = 3$.

*Solution*

$$
\begin{array}{rrrrr|r}
1 & +0 & -3 & -8 & +6 & \underline{\;3} \\
  & 3 & +9 & +18 & +30 & \\
\hline
1 & +3 & +6 & +10 & +36 &
\end{array}
$$

The answer is $+36$; the student may check it by direct substitution.

### Example 2

Find the value of $4x^3 + 6x^2 + 8$ when $x = -2$.

*Solution*

$$
\begin{array}{rrrr|r}
4 & +6 & +0 & +8 & \underline{-2} \\
  & -8 & +4 & -8 & \\
\hline
4 & -2 & +4 & +0 &
\end{array}
$$

The answer in this case is 0; this means that the graph of

$$y = 4x^3 + 6x^2 + 8$$

crosses (or touches) the $x$-axis at $x = -2$.

**39. The equation $y = ax^3 + bx^2 + cx + d$.**—An example of this type of equation is the one whose graph is shown

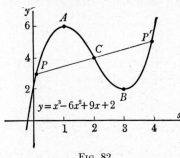

FIG. 82.

in Fig. 82. In this particular case the curve has a *maximum point A* and a *minimum point B*. (A point $A$ on a curve is said to be a maximum point if the value of $y$ is larger at this point than it is immediately to the right or left. A minimum point is similarly defined.)

On the curve shown there is another important point $C$ such that the part of the curve to the left of $C$ is *concave downward**\** while the part to the right is *concave upward; $C$ is called an *inflection point.*

\* An arc is said to be concave downward over an interval if a tangent line traversing the arc from left to right rotates in the clockwise sense.

The graph of $y = ax^3 + bx^2 + cx + d$ may have either of the forms shown in Fig. 83 instead of that of Fig. 82. It therefore may or may not have a maximum and a minimum point. *It can be shown by methods of calculus that*

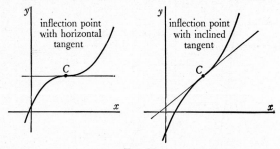

inflection point with horizontal tangent

$C$

inflection point with inclined tangent

$C$

FIG. 83.

*the curve always has an inflection point and that the abscissa of this point is* $-b/3a$. The curve is concave upward to the right of this point and downward to the left if $a > 0$, and in the reverse sense if $a < 0$. Furthermore, it can be shown that *the curve is always symmetrical with respect to its inflection point.** By this we mean that any line through $C$ that cuts the curve elsewhere, cuts it in two points $P$ and $P'$ such that $CP = CP'$ (Fig. 82).

In making the graph one may locate the inflection point if this is convenient and then plot several points on each side of this making use of the symmetry of the curve. Synthetic substitution may be used in computing the ordinates. The $y$-intercept is of course $y = d$. The $x$-intercepts are the real roots of the equation

$$ax^3 + bx^2 + cx + d = 0.$$

The curve may therefore cross the $x$-axis at three points or at only one point; it may cross at one point and be tangent to the axis at another point.

**40. Polynomials of higher degree.**—An example of the graph of a polynomial of fourth degree is shown in Fig. 84. In general, such a curve has no property of symmetry like

* In this connection, see Prob. 21, p. 106.

those of second or third degree.* Its maximum, minimum, and inflection points can be found conveniently by

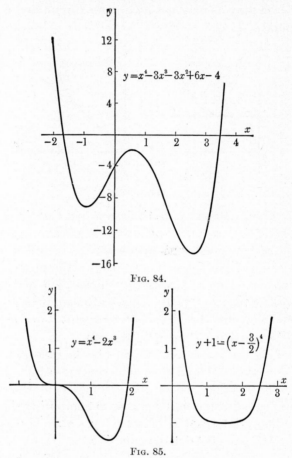

$$y = x^4 - 3x^3 - 3x^2 + 6x - 4$$

Fig. 84.

$$y = x^4 - 2x^3$$

$$y + 1 = \left(x - \frac{3}{2}\right)^4$$

Fig. 85.

methods of calculus, but for the present the graph must be obtained by the rather laborious procedure of plotting points. Synthetic substitution may of course be used in computing the ordinates. Other possible shapes are indicated in Fig. 85. The intercepts on the $x$-axis are the

* It does, however, have a property that might be called *oblique symmetry* with respect to a line. See the article entitled "Tangent Triangles to a Biquadratic Curve" by J. S. Frame in the *American Mathematical Monthly*, October, 1944.

real roots of the equation $ax^4 + bx^3 + cx^2 + dx + e = 0$; the curve can therefore cross this axis at not more than four points. Similar considerations apply to polynomials of degree higher than the fourth.

In connection with the graphs of polynomials the student should note the following important fact: *For values of x that are sufficiently large numerically, the term of highest degree in the polynomial is larger than all other terms combined; consequently, the sign of the polynomial is the same as that of the highest degree term for such values of x.*

### Example

The graph of $y = -2x^3 + 4x + 45$ lies below the $x$-axis for large positive values of $x$ because as $x$ increases $y$ must eventually become and remain negative. Similarly, $y$ is certainly positive for large negative values of $x$.

**41. Graph of a factored polynomial.**—If the right-hand side of the equation

(1) $$y = (x - 1)^2(x - 3)(x - 6)$$

is multiplied out, the result is

$$y = x^4 - 11x^3 + 37x^2 - 45x + 18.$$

For the purpose of sketching the graph it is much more convenient to leave the equation in the form (1). From this form we can easily obtain the intercepts and visualize the general shape of the curve. Thus we see immediately that

$$y = 0 \quad when \quad x = 1, 1, 3, \ and\ 6.$$

These are the $x$-intercepts. By examining the signs of the various factors in the right-hand member of (1), we further observe that (Fig. 86)

*For $x > 6$, all factors are positive so $y$ is positive.*

*For $3 < x < 6$, the factor $(x - 6)$ alone is negative so $y$ is negative.*

*For $x < 3$, the factors $(x - 3)$ and $(x - 6)$ are negative so $y$ is again positive except at $x = 1$ where $y = 0$.*

It should be noted particularly that the curve crosses the
$x$-axis at $x = 3$ and $x = 6$ but *touches it without crossing at
the double root* $x = 1$.   The reason is obvious: The factor

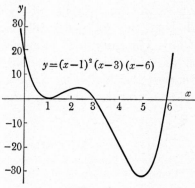

$$y=(x-1)^2(x-3)(x-6)$$

Fig. 86.

$x - 6$, for example, is negative for $x < 6$ and positive for
$x > 6$; the sign of this factor, and consequently the sign
of $y$, changes therefore when $x$ goes through the value 6.

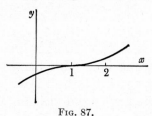

Fig. 87.

On the other hand, the factor $(x -
1)^2$ is positive both for $x < 1$ and
$x > 1$, and the sign of $y$ does not
change when $x$ goes through the
value 1.   If this factor had been
$(x - 1)^3$, it is clear that the curve
would have crossed the axis at
$x = 1$.   It can be shown that in this case there would
have been an inflection point with horizontal tangent line
at $x = 1$.   In the neighborhood of $x = 1$ the curve would
have had roughly the shape shown in Fig. 87.

Polynomial curves occur rather often in various kinds of
physical and geometrical problems.

### Example

A right circular cylinder of radius $x$ is inscribed in a right circular
cone of radius 12 in. and height 9 in.   Express the volume $V$ of the
cylinder in terms of $x$ and make the graph showing how $V$ varies with $x$.

*Solution*

The volume is $\pi x^2 h$ where, from the similar triangles in Fig. 88,

$$\frac{h}{12 - x} = \frac{9}{12}, \quad \text{or} \quad h = \tfrac{3}{4}(12 - x).$$

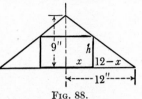

Hence, for any value of $x$ between 0 and 12 in.,

$$V = \frac{3\pi}{4} x^2(12 - x) \text{ cu. in.}$$

FIG. 88.

The graph of this relation is shown in Fig. 89. It is a polynominal curve of third degree with a double root at $x = 0$ and a single root at $x = 12$. The inflection point on the curve is at $x = -b/3a = 4$. The value of $x$ for which $V$ is largest appears to be about 8.

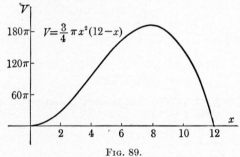

FIG. 89.

**42. Graph of $y^2 = $ a polynomial in $x$.**—In Fig. 90 the cubic curve drawn lightly is the graph of $y = x(x^2 - 4)$. The equation

$$y^2 = x(x^2 - 4)$$

is of course equivalent to $y = \pm \sqrt{x(x^2 - 4)}$. The ordinates to this curve are therefore numerically equal to the square roots of the corresponding ordinates to the cubic. The graph is the heavy curve consisting of two parts; it is of course symmetrical with respect to the $x$-axis.

If $p_n(x)$ represents a polynomial in $x$ of degree $n$, the general shape of the graph of $y^2 = p_n(x)$, at least if $n \lessgtr 3$, can usually be most easily visualized by sketching the graph of $y = p_n(x)$ and then taking the square roots of the ordinates as we have done in Fig. 90. We shall not here discuss the various cases that may arise, but the student may wish to study them independently.

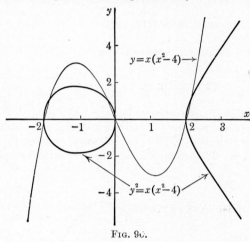

Fig. 90.

## PROBLEMS

Sketch the following curves. Use synthetic substitution in computing the ordinates in Probs. 1 to 10:

**1.** $y = x^3 - 3x^2 - 6x + 10$.

**2.** $y = x^3 - 5x^2 + 3x + 9$.

**3.** $y = x^3 - 7x^2 + 10x$.

**4.** $y = 3x - x^3 - 3$.

**5.** $y = x^3 - 9x^2 + 24x - 20$.

**6.** $y = x^3 - 6x^2 + 12x + 4$.

**7.** $y = 6x^2 - x^3 - 6$.

**8.** $y = x^4 - 16x^2$.

**9.** $y = 8x^2 + 2x^3 - x^4$.

**10.** $y = 3x^4 - 8x^3 + 2$.

**11.** $y = x(x + 2)^2(8 - x)$

**12.** $y = 4x^2(x^2 - 4)$.

**13.** $y = 4x^3 - 3x^4$.

**14.** $y = (x - 1)^2(x^2 - 4)$.

**15.** From a 12- by 18-in. sheet of tin a box is made by cutting a square from each corner and turning up the sides. Express the volume $V$ of the box as a function of the edge $x$ of the square cut out. Make the graph and estimate the value of $x$ for which $V$ is largest.

**16.** The base of a right pyramid 15 in. in height is a square 9 in. on each side. A rectangular box whose base is a square $x$ in. on a side is inscribed in the pyramid. Express the volume $V$ of this box as a function of $x$. Make the graph and estimate the value of $x$ for which $V$ is largest (see Fig. 91).

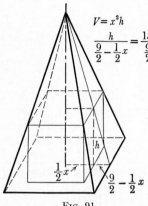

$$V = x^2 h$$

$$\frac{h}{\frac{9}{2} - \frac{1}{2}x} = \frac{15}{\frac{9}{2}}$$

$$\frac{1}{2}x$$

$$\frac{9}{2} - \frac{1}{2}x$$

Fig. 91.

**17.** A right circular cylinder of height $y$ is inscribed in a sphere of diameter 6 in. Express the volume $V$ of the cylinder in terms of $y$ and from the graph discuss the way in which $V$ varies with $y$.

**18.** The number 8 is to be divided into two positive parts, $x$ and $8 - x$, so that the product $x^3(8 - x)$ shall be as large as possible. Make a graph showing how this quantity varies with $x$ and estimate the value of $x$ for which it is largest.

In each of the following, sketch the two curves on the same axes; obtain the second curve from the first by the method of Art. **42:**

**19.** $y = x^3;\ y^2 = x^3$.

**20.** $y = 4 - x^2;\ y^2 = 4 - x^2$.

**21.** $y = x(x + 2)(x - 3);\ y^2 = x(x + 2)(x - 3)$.

**22.** $y = 9x^2 - x^4;\ y^2 = 9x^2 - x^4$.

# CHAPTER V

## RATIONAL FRACTIONAL FUNCTIONS

**43. Introduction.**—The quotient of two polynomials in $x$ is called a *rational fractional function of $x$*. Examples are

$$\frac{x+1}{x^2-4}, \quad \frac{4}{x}, \quad \text{and} \quad \frac{x^2+2x-7}{x-3}.$$

In connection with the second example it should be observed

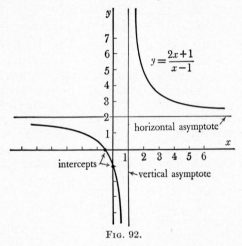

Fig. 92.

that our definition of a polynomial allows us to regard a constant as a polynomial of degree zero. Equations of the form

$$y = \frac{N(x)}{D(x)},$$

where $N$ and $D$ are polynomials, give rise to a wide variety of curves. In many applications one does not need an accurately plotted graph—all that is necessary is a reasonably accurate sketch. This can often be obtained by plotting only a few points and making use of properties

94

of the graph that can be discovered by studying the equation. We proceed now to the consideration of such properties. Most of the methods and results are applicable to any equation, but some of them are particularly useful in connection with the type now under consideration. As an illustrative example we shall use the equation

$$y = \frac{2x + 1}{x - 1}$$

whose graph is shown in Fig. 92.

**44. Intercepts.**—The intercepts can be found, just as in the case of the straight line, by setting $y = 0$ and solving for $x$, and setting $x = 0$ and solving for $y$. In this way we find easily that the graph of $y = (2x + 1)/(x - 1)$ crosses the $x$-axis at $x = -\frac{1}{2}$ and the $y$-axis at $y = -1$.

**45. Symmetry.**—We have already defined symmetry of a curve with respect to a line (page 80) and with respect to a point (page 87). In general it would be difficult to determine, by studying a given equation, whether or not there exists some line or point with respect to which the graph is symmetrical. It is easy, however, to determine whether or not the graph is symmetrical with respect to one of the coordinate axes or the origin—and this information is often useful. The tests are as follows:

SYMMETRY TO $x$-AXIS: *The graph of an equation in $x$ and $y$ is symmetrical with respect to the $x$-axis if and only if the equation obtained by replacing $y$ by $-y$ is identical with the original equation.* Thus the graph of $y^2 = 4x$ is symmetrical with respect to the $x$-axis. Here $(-y)^2 = 4x$ is identical with $y^2 = 4x$.

SYMMETRY TO $y$-AXIS: *The graph is symmetrical with respect to the $y$-axis if and only if the equation obtained by replacing $x$ by $-x$ is identical with the original equation.*

SYMMETRY TO ORIGIN: *The graph is symmetrical with respect to the origin if and only if the equation obtained by replacing $x$ by $-x$ and $y$ by $-y$ is identical with the original equation.* Thus the graph of $y = x^3$ is symmetrical with respect to the origin. Here, $-y = (-x)^3$ is identical with $y = x^3$.

We shall not give detailed proofs of these tests. The student will easily see that if replacing $x$ by $-x$ does not 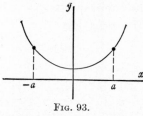 alter the given equation, then the same value is obtained for $y$ when $x = -a$ as when $x = +a$. The corresponding two points, when plotted, are symmetrically placed with respect to the $y$-axis (Fig. 93).

FIG. 93.

It can be shown, conversely, that if the graph is symmetrical to the $y$-axis, the equation is unaltered by replacing $x$ by $-x$. Similar considerations apply in the other cases.

**46. Horizontal and vertical asymptotes.**—Consider again the equation

$$y = \frac{2x + 1}{x - 1}$$

and let $x$ take the sequence of values

$$2, 1\tfrac{1}{2}, 1\tfrac{1}{4}, 1\tfrac{1}{8}, 1\tfrac{1}{16}, \cdots ,$$

getting closer and closer to 1. The corresponding values of $y$ are

$$5, 8, 14, 26, 50, \cdots .$$

It is obvious that as $x$ approaches nearer and nearer to 1 the corresponding values of $y$ become larger and larger beyond bound. This situation results from the fact that *the denominator of the fraction is approaching zero while the numerator is approaching a number different from zero,* namely, 3. It is easy to show that if $x$ approaches 1 from the other side ($x = \tfrac{1}{2}, \tfrac{3}{4}, \tfrac{7}{8}$, etc.) the values of $y$ again become numerically large, but in this case they are negative.

The behavior of the graph in the neighborhood of $x = 1$ is that indicated in Fig. 92. It should be observed that there is no value of $y$, and consequently no point on the graph, at the place where $x$ *equals* 1. Excluding this one point however, there are values of $y$ for $x$ as *near* 1 as we please.

Furthermore, for $x$ *sufficiently* near 1 the value of $y$ is *arbitrarily large* numerically. The situation is described by saying that the curve approaches the line $x = 1$ "asymptotically," and the line is called an *asymptote* to the curve.

It should be reasonably clear that the graph of

$$y = \frac{N(x)}{D(x)}$$

will have one of these vertical asymptotes at each value of $x$ for which the denominator is zero and the numerator different from zero. Assuming the fraction to be in lowest terms we may state the following:

**Rule:** *To find the vertical asymptotes to the graph of* $y = N(x)/D(x)$, *set* $D(x) = 0$ *and solve the resulting equation for* $x$.

### Example

The graph of $y = \dfrac{2x}{x^2 - 4}$ will have vertical asymptotes at $x = 2$ and $x = -2$.

**Horizontal asymptotes.**—Returning to the equation $y = (2x + 1)/(x - 1)$, let us think of $x$ taking on the values 10, 100, 1,000, $\cdots$ becoming indefinitely large. The corresponding values of $y$ are $2\frac{1}{3}$, $2\frac{1}{33}$, $2\frac{1}{333}$ $\cdots$. It is evident that as $x$ gets larger and larger the value $y$ gets closer and closer to 2, the difference between $y$ and 2 approaching zero. The behavior of the curve is therefore that indicated in Fig. 92. Similarly, if $x$ is negative and becomes larger and larger numerically, the value of $y$ again approaches 2. The line $y = 2$ is a *horizontal asymptote* to the curve.

In order to find the horizontal asymptote (if there is one) to the graph of $y = N(x)/D(x)$ one must evidently find out what happens to the value of the fraction when $x$ becomes indefinitely large. There are three cases:

CASE I. *Degree of $N$ lower than that of $D$.* In this case the value of the fraction approaches zero as $x$ becomes larger and larger, and the graph is asymptotic to the $x$-axis.

### Example

The graph of $y = (x + 1)/(x^2 + 4)$ is asymptotic to the $x$-axis since $y$ approaches zero as $x$ becomes larger and larger. The student should compute $y$ for $x = 10, 100,$ and $1,000$. See also Prob. 23 in the next set.

Case II. *Degree of N same as that of D.* In this case, as $x$ becomes larger and larger, the fraction approaches a value that is the quotient of the coefficients of the highest power of $x$. If $N(x) = a_0 x^n + a_1 x^{n-1} + \cdots + a_n$ and $D(x) = b_0 x^n + b_1 x^{n-1} + \cdots + b_n$, the horizontal asymptote is the line $y = a_0/b_0$.

### Example

The graph of $y = (6x^2 + x + 4)/(2x^2 - 1)$ is asymptotic to the line $y = 3$. Note that for very large values of $x$ the fraction is nearly the same as $6x^2/2x^2$ which is of course equal to 3. Observe also that by long division

$$\frac{6x^2 + x + 4}{2x^2 - 1} = 3 + \frac{x + 7}{2x^2 - 1}.$$

As $x$ becomes larger and larger, the second term on the right approaches zero (by Case I) and the right-hand side must then approach 3. This indicates the way in which the proof for Case II may be carried out. See also Prob. 24 in the next set.

Case III. *Degree of N higher than that of D.* In this case, as $x$ becomes larger and larger, the numerical value of $y$ also increases indefinitely; there is no horizontal asymptote.

### Example

The graph of $y = (x^2 + 1)/(x - 1)$ has no horizontal asymptote. In this case, by long division,

$$\frac{x^2 + 1}{x - 1} = x + 1 + \frac{2}{x - 1}.$$

As $x$ becomes larger and larger, the third term on the right approaches zero. This means that for very large values of $x$ the fraction $(x^2 + 1)/(x - 1)$ is almost equal to $x + 1$. The line $y = x + 1$ is, in fact, an *inclined asymptote* to the curve. There are general methods of finding inclined asymptotes, but these will not be discussed here.

**47. Curve discussion.**—By "discussing" the graph of an equation of the form $y = N(x)/D(x)$ we shall mean finding the intercepts, testing for symmetry, and locating the vertical and horizontal asymptotes. Any other information that can be easily obtained from the equation, and that will be of value in sketching the graph, should be included in the discussion. In the problems of the next set, the student should first write out the discussion in the brief form given in the following example. He should then use the discussion and plot only a few necessary points in sketching the graph.

### Example

Discuss and sketch the graph of $y = \dfrac{8}{x^2 + 4}$.

### Solution

1. *Intercepts:* $\begin{cases} \text{on } x\text{-axis—none.} \\ \text{on } y\text{-axis—at } y = 2. \end{cases}$

2. *Symmetry:* $\begin{cases} \text{to } x\text{-axis—no.} \\ \text{to } y\text{-axis—yes.} \\ \text{to origin—no.} \end{cases}$

3. *Asymptotes:* $\begin{cases} \text{vertical—none.} \\ \text{horizontal—the } x\text{-axis } (y = 0). \end{cases}$

4. *Other information:* It is evident from the equation that $y$ is positive for all values of $x$; furthermore, $y$ has its largest value 2 at $x = 0$, and decreases from this value toward 0 as $x$ increases.

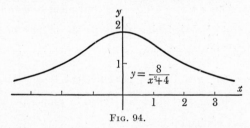

Fig. 94.

The graph is shown in Fig. 94. It is necessary to plot a few points near the $y$-intercept in order to get the proper shape of the curve in this region. The curve is obviously concave downward in the middle part but concave upward where it approaches the $x$-axis asymptotically. It therefore must have two symmetrically placed inflection points. These can be located by methods of calculus.

### PROBLEMS

Discuss and sketch the graphs of the following equations:

**1.** $y = \dfrac{1}{x}$.

**2.** $y = \dfrac{1}{x^2}$.

**3.** $y = \dfrac{12}{x - 2}$.

**4.** $y = \dfrac{6}{2x + 3}$.

**5.** $y = \dfrac{4 - x}{x}$.

**6.** $y = \dfrac{x}{(x - 2)^2}$.

**7.** $y = \dfrac{8}{x^2 + 1}$.     **8.** $y = \dfrac{4x}{x^2 + 4}$.     **9.** $y = \dfrac{4x}{x^2 - 4}$.

**10.** $y = \dfrac{8}{x^2 - 4}$.     **11.** $y = \dfrac{9 - x^2}{x^2 - 4}$.     **12.** $y = \dfrac{x^2}{x^2 - 16}$.

**13.** $y = \dfrac{x^2 - 4}{x^2 + 4}$.     **14.** $y = \dfrac{x^2}{(x - 2)(x - 4)}$.

**15.** If the graph of a given equation is symmetrical with respect to both the $x$- and $y$-axes, is it necessarily symmetrical with respect to the origin? Is the converse true?

**16.** The equation $y = \dfrac{x^2 + 1}{x}$ is equivalent to $y = x + \dfrac{1}{x}$. Obtain its graph by sketching the separate graphs of $y = x$ and $y = 1/x$ and adding ordinates.

**17.** The equation $y = \dfrac{x^3 + 1}{x}$ is equivalent to $y = x^2 + \dfrac{1}{x}$. Obtain its graph by sketching the separate graphs of $y = x^2$ and $y = 1/x$ and adding ordinates.

**18.** The equation $y = \dfrac{x^2 + 3}{x - 1}$ is equivalent to $y = x + 1 + \dfrac{4}{x - 1}$. Obtain its graph by sketching the separate graphs of $y = x + 1$ and $y = \dfrac{4}{x - 1}$ and adding ordinates.

**19.** The equation $y = \dfrac{x^2 + 4x + 1}{x^2 + 1}$ is equivalent to $y = 1 + \dfrac{4x}{x^2 + 1}$. Obtain its graph by sketching the separate graphs of $y = 1$ and $y = \dfrac{4x}{x^2 + 1}$ and adding ordinates.

**20.** The equation $y = \dfrac{x^3 + 3x}{2x^2 + 4}$ is equivalent to $y = \tfrac{1}{2}x + \dfrac{x}{2x^2 + 4}$. Obtain its graph by sketching the separate graphs of $y = \tfrac{1}{2}x$ and $y = \dfrac{x}{2x^2 + 4}$ and adding ordinates.

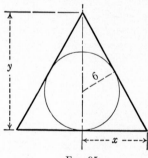

FIG. 95.

**21.** A right circular cone of height $y$ is circumscribed about a sphere whose radius is 6 in. (Fig. 95). Express its volume $V$ in terms of $y$ and sketch the graph showing how $V$ varies with $y$. HINT: $V = \tfrac{1}{3}\pi x^2 y$ and from similar triangles $x/y = 6/\sqrt{(y - 6)^2 - 6^2}$.

**22.** A rectangular box to contain 108 cu. ft. is to be made with a square base. The cost per square foot of material for bottom, top, and sides is 1, 5, and 6 cents,

respectively.    Express the cost $C$ of material in dollars as a function of the
length $x$ of the edge of the square base.    Draw the graph showing how
the cost varies with $x$.

**23.**  Consider the fraction $(3x^2 + x + 4)/(5x^3 + 7x^2 - 6)$.   By dividing each term of both numerator and denominator by $x^3$, which is the
highest power of $x$ that occurs in the fraction, we have the identity

$$\frac{3x^2 + x + 4}{5x^3 + 7x^2 - 6} = \frac{\dfrac{3}{x} + \dfrac{1}{x^2} + \dfrac{4}{x^3}}{5 + \dfrac{7}{x} - \dfrac{6}{x^3}} \qquad (x \neq 0).$$

Now as $x$ becomes larger and larger, each term in the numerator on the
right side approaches zero; the second and third terms in the denominator also approach zero.    The numerator therefore approaches zero
while the denominator approaches 5 and the fraction consequently
approaches zero.    By extending this idea to the general case, write out
a proof for Case I, Art. 46.

**24.**  Using the method suggested in Prob. 23 write out a proof for
Case II, Art. 46.

Discuss and sketch the graphs of the following equations after solving
for $y$ in terms of $x$.    Wherever convenient, use the method of composi-
tion of ordinates as suggested in Probs. 16 to 19:

**25.**  $2xy + 6y - 3x + 4 = 0$.

**26.**  $xy - 3x + y - 2 = 0$.

**27.**  $xy + x + y = 0$.

**28.**  $y - x^2y - 2x = 0$.

**29.**  $2xy + 4y = x^2 - 3$.

**30.**  $2x^2y + 2y = (x + 1)^2$.

**31.**  $x^2(y + 2) + 4(y + 1) = x(x^2 + 4)$.

**32.**  $x^2y + y + x^2 = x^3 + 5x - 1$.

Discuss and sketch the graphs of the following equations:

**33.**  $xy + 2y + 2x = 3$.          **34.**  $xy - 2y + 3x = 5$.

**35.**  $xy = x^2 - 4$.              **36.**  $x^2y + 2x^2 = 8$.

**37.**  $x^2y + 4y = 2x^2 + 9$.      **38.**  $x^2y = 4x - y + 2$.

**39.**  $x^2(y - 2) = 8x - 4y + 8$.  **40.**  $4x^2y = x^4 - 16x^2 + 4$.

**41.**  $2xy - x^2 = 4y + 2x + 8$.   **42.**  $x^2y - 4y = x^2 + 4x$.

**43.**  $(x^2 - 1)^2y - x = 0$.      **44.**  $x^2y + xy = 3x - y + 6$.

**45.**  $(x + 1)^2y - 8x = 0$.       **46.**  $(x^2 - 9)^2y = 4x(x^2 - 4)$.

# CHAPTER VI

## TRANSFORMATION OF COORDINATES

**48. Introduction.** — The equation of a curve is an analytical statement of the relation that exists between the two coordinates of every point on it. The equation thus depends on the location of the coordinate axes relative to the curve. Figure 96 shows a line and two sets of axes,

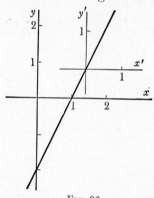

the first being designated by $x$ and $y$ and the second by $x'$ and $y'$. The equation of the line with respect to the first set of axes is $2x - y = 2$. With respect to the second set it is $y' = 2x'$ since the line goes through the origin with slope 2. If a set of axes were drawn with the $x$-axis parallel to the line, its equation with respect to this set would be of the form $y = c$.

Fig. 96.

It is often necessary to solve the following problem: Given the equation of a curve with respect to an initial set of axes, find the equation of the *same curve* with respect to another specified set of axes. If the new axes are parallel to the original ones, and have the same positive directions, the transformation is called a *translation* of axes. If the origin remains fixed and the new axes are obtained by revolving the original ones about this point through a specified angle, the transformation is called a *rotation* of axes.

**49. Translation of axes.** — Let $P(x, y)$ be any point on a curve whose equation is assumed known with respect to an initial set of axes (Fig. 97). Now let the axes be translated so that the new origin has coordinates $(h, k)$ relative to the

102

original axes. This means of course a translation of $h$ units in the $x$-direction and $k$ units in the $y$-direction. Let the coordinates of $P$ relative to the new coordinate system

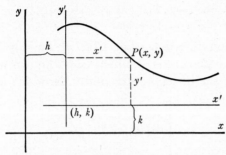

FIG. 97.

be $(x', y')$. From the figure it is evident that we have the following relation:

$$x = x' + h,$$
$$y = y' + k.$$

This relation holds for every point in the plane, and consequently, in order to find the equation of the curve relative to the new axes, we must take the original equation and

*Replace x by x' + h;*
*Replace y by y' + k.*

All the distances involved are directed distances and may of course be either positive or negative.

### Example

What does the equation of the parabola $y = x^2 - 6x + 5$ become if the axes are translated so as to place the origin at the vertex?

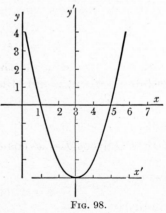

FIG. 98.

*Solution* (Fig. 98)

The coordinates of the vertex are $(3, -4)$. We therefore let $h = 3$ and $k = -4$. Substituting $x' + 3$ for $x$ and $y' - 4$ for $y$, in the equation $y = x^2 - 6x + 5$, and simplifying, we have

$$y' - 4 = (x' + 3)^2 - 6(x' + 3) + 5$$
$$= x'^2 + 6x' + 9 - 6x' - 18 + 5$$

or, finally,

$$y' = x'^2.$$

This is of course the result that one would expect in view of previously discussed properties of the parabola.

**50. Rotation of axes.**—Let $P(x, y)$ be any point on a curve whose equation is assumed to be known with respect to an initial set of axes (Fig. 99). Now let the axes be

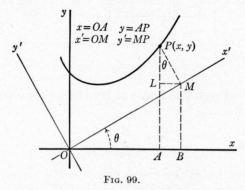

$$
\begin{array}{ll}
x = OA & y = AP \\
x' = OM & y' = MP
\end{array}
$$

Fig. 99.

rotated through an angle $\theta$ and let the coordinates of $P$ relative to the new axes be $(x', y')$. Then

$$x = OA, \qquad y = AP;$$
$$x' = OM, \qquad y' = MP.$$

The relations between the new and old coordinates are obtained, with the aid of a little trigonometry, as follows:

$$x = OA = OB - AB = OB - LM;$$

but

$$OB = OM \cos \theta = x' \cos \theta, \qquad \text{and} \qquad LM = MP \sin \theta$$
$$= y' \sin \theta;$$

hence

$$x = x' \cos \theta - y' \sin \theta.$$

Similarly,

$$y = AP = AL + LP = BM + LP;$$

but

$$BM = OM \sin \theta = x' \sin \theta, \qquad \text{and} \qquad LP = MP \cos \theta$$
$$= y' \cos \theta;$$

hence
$$y = x' \sin \theta + y' \cos \theta.$$

It follows that, in order to find the equation of the curve relative to the new axes, we must take the original equation and

*Replace x by x' cos θ − y' sin θ;*
*Replace y by x' sin θ + y' cos θ.*

### Example

Find the new equation of the line $4y - 3x = 10$ when the axes are rotated through the angle $\theta$ shown in Fig. 100 whose tangent is $\frac{3}{4}$.

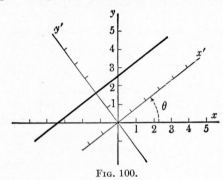

FIG. 100.

### Solution

In this case $\cos \theta = \frac{4}{5}$ and $\sin \theta = \frac{3}{5}$. We must therefore let

$$\begin{cases} x = \frac{4}{5}x' - \frac{3}{5}y'; \\ y = \frac{3}{5}x' + \frac{4}{5}y'. \end{cases}$$

Substituting these for $x$ and $y$ in the equation $4y - 3x = 10$, we have

$$4(\tfrac{3}{5}x' + \tfrac{4}{5}y') - 3(\tfrac{4}{5}x' - \tfrac{3}{5}y') = 10;$$

this easily reduces to
$$y' = 2.$$

This result was to be expected; for the slope of the given line is $\frac{3}{4}$ and its distance from the origin is 2. After the rotation, the line is parallel to the new $x'$-axis and two units above it.

### PROBLEMS

In each of the following, find the equation of the given line or curve when the axes are translated so that the given point becomes the origin; draw the graph and show both sets of axes:

1. $y = \frac{1}{2}x - 3$        (0, −3).
2. $x + y = 4$        (2, 2).

**3.** $y = x^2 - 7x + 10$ $\qquad$ (2, 0).

**4.** $y = 4x - x^2$ $\qquad$ (2, 4).

**5.** $y = x^3 - 3x^2 - x + 3$ $\qquad$ (1, 0).

**6.** $y = x^3 - 8x^2 + 20x - 15$ $\quad$ (2, 1).

**7.** $y = \dfrac{2x + 1}{x - 1}$ $\qquad$ (1, 2).

**8.** $y = \dfrac{-2x^2}{x^2 + 4}$ $\qquad$ (0, -2).

**9.** $y = \dfrac{3x^2 + x + 3}{x^2 + 1}$ $\qquad$ (0, 3).

**10.** Show that the equation $y = Ax^2 + Bx + C$ becomes $y' = Ax'^2$ when the axes are translated so that the origin is at the vertex of the parabola.

**11.** Find the new coordinates of the following points when the axes are rotated through 30°:

$\qquad$ (a) (8, 6) $\qquad$ (b) (-6, -6) $\qquad$ (c) (0, 10).

**12.** Solve Prob. 11 if the angle of rotation is 45°.

**13.** Solve Prob. 11 if the angle of rotation is 90°.

**14.** Draw the line $2x + y = 2$ and find its new equation when the axes are rotated through the positive acute angle whose tangent is $\frac{1}{2}$.

**15.** Draw the line $5x - 12y = 52$ and find its new equation when the axes are rotated through the positive acute angle whose tangent is $\frac{5}{12}$.

**16.** Show that the equation $x^2 + y^2 = a^2$ remains unchanged when the axes are rotated through any angle $\theta$.

**17.** Sketch the parabola $y = x^2$. Find its new equation when the axes are rotated through 45°.

**18.** Sketch the curve $y = 1/x$. Find its new equation when the axes are rotated through 45°.

**19.** Solve the transformation equations $x = x' \cos\theta - y' \sin\theta$, $y = x' \sin\theta + y' \cos\theta$ for $x'$ and $y'$ in terms of $x$ and $y$.

**20.** Show that the degree of an equation in $x$ and $y$ is unchanged by either translation or rotation of the axes. HINT: In each case $x$ and $y$ are replaced by *linear* expressions in $x'$ and $y'$.

**21.** It has been stated (page 87) that the cubic curve

$$y = ax^3 + bx^2 + cx + d$$

always has an inflection point and that the abscissa of this point is $x = -b/3a$. Show that the equation becomes $y' = ax'^3 + \left(c - \dfrac{b^2}{3a}\right)x'$ when the axes are translated so as to move the origin to the inflection point. Discuss the special case in which $b^2 = 3ac$.

# CHAPTER VII

## THE CIRCLE

**51. The standard form.**—*A circle is defined as the path of a point that moves in a plane at a constant distance from a fixed point in the plane.* The fixed point is the *center* and the constant distance is the *radius* of the circle. We may derive the equation directly from this definition as follows:

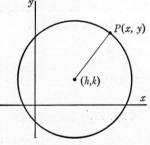

Fig. 101.

Let the coordinates of the center be $(h, k)$ and let the radius be $r$. Then if $P(x, y)$ is any point on the circle, we must have (Fig. 101)

$$\sqrt{(x - h)^2 + (y - k)^2} = r,$$

or

$$(1) \qquad (x - h)^2 + (y - k)^2 = r^2.$$

Conversely, any point whose coordinates satisfy this relation is on the circle. This is, therefore, the equation of the circle with center at $(h, k)$ and radius $r$. It is called the *standard form* of the equation of a circle. If $h = k = 0$, the equation reduces to

$$x^2 + y^2 = r^2,$$

which is the equation of a circle with center at the *origin* and radius $r$.

### Example

The equation of the circle with center at $(2, -1)$ and radius 3 is $(x - 2)^2 + (y + 1)^2 = 9$. By performing the indicated operations, the equation may be reduced to the form $x^2 + y^2 - 4x + 2y - 4 = 0$.

107

**52. The general form.**—If equation (1) above is multiplied out, the result obtained is

$$x^2 + y^2 - 2hx - 2ky + h^2 + k^2 - r^2 = 0.$$

This is an equation of the form

(2) $$x^2 + y^2 + Dx + Ey + F = 0,$$

and it is evident that any equation of the form (1) can be changed into this form. Conversely, an equation of the form (2) can be changed into form (1) by completing the squares in $x$ and $y$.

### Example

Transform the equation $x^2 + y^2 - 6x + 2y + 4 = 0$ into the standard form.

### Solution

First write the equation in the following way:

$$x^2 - 6x + y^2 + 2y = -4.$$

In order to complete the square in $x$ we must add 9, and in order to complete the square in $y$ we must add 1; we thus get

$$(x^2 - 6x + 9) + (y^2 + 2y + 1) = -4 + 10,$$

or

$$(x - 3)^2 + (y + 1)^2 = 6.$$

The equation is evidently that of a circle with center at $(3, -1)$ and radius $\sqrt{6}$. Observe that if the constant term in the given equation had been 10 instead of 4, the result would have been

$$(x - 3)^2 + (y + 1)^2 = 0.$$

The graph in this case is a circle of radius 0, or a *point circle*. Finally, if the constant had been greater than 10, say 12, the result would have been

$$(x - 3)^2 + (y + 1)^2 = -2.$$

In this case there is no graph; *i.e.*, the equation is not satisfied by *any* pair of real values of $x$ and $y$.

By similarly completing the square in the general case one can prove the following:

**Theorem:** *The equation $x^2 + y^2 + Dx + Ey + F = 0$ represents a circle, a point circle, or no locus, according as*

$\dfrac{D^2}{4} + \dfrac{E^2}{4} - F$ *is positive, zero, or negative; the coordinates*

*of the center of the circle are* $\left( -\dfrac{D}{2}, -\dfrac{E}{2} \right)$ *and its radius is*

$r = \sqrt{\dfrac{D^2}{4} + \dfrac{E^2}{4} - F}.$

The equation $x^2 + y^2 + Dx + Ey + F = 0$ is called the *general form* of the equation of a circle.

**53. Circle satisfying three conditions.**—The equation of a circle contains three arbitrary constants, these constants being $D$, $E$, and $F$ in the general form and $h$, $k$, and $r$ in the standard form. In general one can find the equation of the circle determined by three specified conditions by setting up three equations in $D$, $E$, and $F$, or $h$,

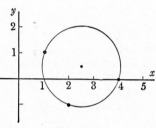

Fig. 102.

$k$, and $r$, and solving for these constants. Either form may be used, but in some cases one may be more convenient than the other.

### Example 1

Find the equation of the circle through the points (1, 1), (4, 0), and (2, −1).

*Solution* (Fig. 102)

The equation can be written in the form

$$x^2 + y^2 + Dx + Ey + F = 0$$

where $D$, $E$, and $F$ are to be determined from the fact that, since the circle passes through the given points, their coordinates must satisfy the equation; *i.e.*,

$$1 + 1 + D + E + F = 0$$
$$16 + 0 + 4D + 0 + F = 0$$
$$4 + 1 + 2D - E + F = 0.$$

Solving these equations we find $D = -5$, $E = -1$, $F = 4$; the required equation is then

$$x^2 + y^2 - 5x - y + 4 = 0.$$

The center of the circle is the point $(\frac{5}{2}, \frac{1}{2})$, and its radius is

$$r = \sqrt{\tfrac{25}{4} + \tfrac{1}{4} - 4} = \tfrac{1}{2}\sqrt{10}.$$

The student may devise other ways of solving the problem.

### *Example 2*

Find the equation of a circle tangent to the $x$-axis, having its center on the line $y = 2x + 1$, and passing through the point $(-2, 8)$.

#### *Solution* (Fig. 103)

We may write the equation in the form

$$(x - h)^2 + (y - k)^2 = r^2$$

where $h$, $k$, and $r$ are to be determined from the given conditions as follows:

The fact that the center is on the line $y = 2x + 1$ means that its coordinates $(h, k)$ satisfy this equation; *i.e.*,

$$k = 2h + 1.$$

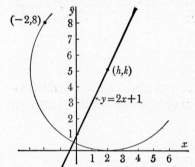

FIG. 103.

The condition that the circle is tangent to the $x$-axis means that

$$k = r.$$

Finally, the condition that the circle passes through the point $(-2, 8)$ requires that

$$(-2 - h)^2 + (8 - k)^2 = r^2.$$

Solving these equations we find that

$$h = 2, \qquad k = 5, \qquad r = 5$$

or

$$h = 26, \qquad k = 53, \qquad r = 53.$$

There are then *two* circles satisfying the given conditions; their equations are

$$(x - 2)^2 + (y - 5)^2 = 25,$$
$$(x - 26)^2 + (y - 53)^2 = 2{,}809.$$

The first of these is shown in the figure.

### PROBLEMS

**1.** In each of the following, write the equation of the circle with center at $C$ and radius $r$ in both the standard and general forms:

(a) $C(3, 2)$; $\quad r = 1$. $\qquad\qquad$ (b) $C(-1, -4)$; $r = 5$.

(c) $C(4, 0)$;   $r = 2$.          (d) $C(0, -6)$;   $r = 6$.
(e) $C(-8, 1)$; $r = 3$.          (f) $C(-3, 4)$;   $r = 5$.

**2.** Find the center and radius of each of the following circles and draw the graph when it exists:

(a) $x^2 + y^2 + 8x - 6y + 25 = 0$.
(b) $x^2 + y^2 + 2x + y - 1 = 0$.
(c) $x^2 + y^2 - 5x + 6y + 9 = 0$.
(d) $2x^2 + 2y^2 + 4x - 5y + 2 = 0$.
(e) $3x^2 + 3y^2 - 24x + 10y = 0$.
(f) $x^2 + y^2 + 6x + 6y + 20 = 0$.

**3.** Show that the equation of the circle with center at $(r, 0)$ and radius $r$ (Fig. 104) is $x^2 + y^2 = 2rx$. What is the corresponding equation for the circle of radius $r$ with center at $(0, r)$?

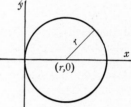

Fig. 104.

**4.** Find the equation of the circle satisfying the following conditions:

(a) Has the line segment $A(-2, 1) B(6, 5)$ as a diameter.

(b) Passes through $(6, 0)$ and $(24, 0)$ and is tangent to the $y$-axis.

(c) Has its center on the line $2x - y = 4$ and is tangent to both axes.

(d) Passes through $(-1, 4)$ and $(3, -8)$ and has its center on the $x$-axis.

**5.** A point moves so that it is always twice as far from the origin as from the point $(6, 0)$. Find the equation of its path and draw the graph.

**6.** Draw a square with center at the origin and with each side 4 units long. A point moves so that the sum of the squares of its distances from the lines forming the sides of this square is equal to 34. Find the equation of its path and draw the graph.

**7.** Does the circle $4x^2 + 4y^2 - 32x - 48y + 127 = 0$ intersect the line $x - 2y = 2$ at two points, at one point, or not at all? Hint: Compare the radius of the circle with the distance from its center to the line.

**8.** Find the equation of the circle that passes through the points:

(a) $(-2, 0)$, $(8, 0)$, $(-6, 4)$.
(b) $(2, 0)$, $(4, 2)$, $(5, 1)$.
(c) $(0, -2)$, $(4, -2)$, $(3, -1)$.
(d) $(1, 3)$, $(0, 4)$, $(-2, 3)$.

**9.** Find the equation of the circle with center at $(5, -3)$ and tangent to the line $3x - 4y = 12$. Draw the graph.

**10.** Find the equation of the circle with center at $(-2, 1)$ and tangent to the line $x + y = 2$.

**11.** Find the equation of the circle that is tangent to the line

$$4x - 3y = 2$$

at $(-1, -2)$ and passes through the point $(6, -1)$.

**12.** Find the equation of the circle that is tangent to the line

$$x + 2y = 4$$

at $(6, -1)$ and passes through the point $(5, 2)$.

**13.** Find the equation of the circle that passes through the origin and the point $(-1, -3)$ and is tangent to the line $2x + y + 10 = 0$. Two solutions.

**14.** Find the equation of the line that is tangent to the circle

$$x^2 + y^2 - 10x - 6y + 29 = 0$$

at the point $(3, 4)$. HINT: The tangent line is perpendicular to the radius.

**15.** Show that the equation of the line drawn tangent to the circle $x^2 + y^2 = r^2$ at any point $P(x_1, y_1)$ on its circumference is $x_1x + y_1y = r^2$.

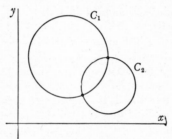

FIG. 105.

**16.** Let the equations of two intersecting circles $C_1$ and $C_2$ (Fig. 105) be, respectively, $x^2 + y^2 + D_1x + E_1y + F_1 = 0$ and

$$x^2 + y^2 + D_2x + E_2y + F_2 = 0.$$

Show that for every value of $k$ except $-1$ the equation

$$(x^2 + y^2 + D_1x + E_1y + F_1) + k(x^2 + y^2 + D_2x + E_2y + F_2) = 0$$

represents a circle through the points of intersection of $C_1$ and $C_2$. What does it represent for $k = -1$? HINT: If $k \neq -1$, the equation represents a circle. Furthermore, the equation is satisfied by the coordinates of the points of intersection of $C_1$ and $C_2$. Why?

# CHAPTER VIII

## THE PARABOLA, ELLIPSE, AND HYPERBOLA

**54. Introduction.**—In the chapter on polynomial curves we stated that the graph of the equation $y = ax^2 + bx + c$ is called a *parabola*. We shall now give geometrical definitions for this and two closely related curves called, respectively, the *ellipse* and *hyperbola*. Using these definitions we shall derive standard equations for these curves and discuss briefly their most important properties. We shall find that the equations encountered are all of second degree in $x$ and $y$; *i.e.*, they are special cases of the general equation

$$Ax^2 + Bxy + Cy^2 + Dx + Ey + F = 0$$

in which some of the coefficients are zero. Finally, we shall show that every equation of second degree in $x$ and $y$ has for its graph (if it has a graph) one of these curves or a limiting case thereof; and it will be pointed out that these loci are the various sections that may be cut from a right circular cone by passing a plane through it.

**55. The parabola.**—*The parabola is defined as the locus of a point that moves in such a way that its undirected distances from a fixed point and a fixed line are equal.* Thus if the point $P$ (Fig. 106) moves so that $FP = LP$, it will trace out a parabola. The fixed point $F$ is called the *focus* and the fixed line $l$ the *directrix* of the parabola.

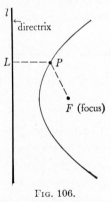

Fig. 106.

Naturally, the equation that one obtains for the curve

113

depends on his choice of coordinate axes relative to the focus and directrix. If we choose the axes as indicated in

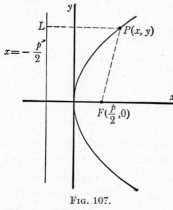

Fig. 107, and if the *directed* distance from the directrix to the focus is $p$, then the coordinates of $F$ are $(p/2, 0)$ and the equation of the directrix is $x = -p/2$. The equation of the curve is then easily obtained as follows:

The condition that any point $P(x, y)$ lie on the curve is that

Fig. 107.           $FP = LP$,

but

$$FP = \sqrt{\left(x - \frac{p}{2}\right)^2 + y^2} \text{ and } LP = x + \frac{p}{2}; \text{ we therefore}$$

require that

$$\sqrt{\left(x - \frac{p}{2}\right)^2 + y^2} = x + \frac{p}{2},$$

where the distances are to be regarded as undirected. Squaring both sides we have

$$x^2 - px + \frac{p^2}{4} + y^2 = x^2 + px + \frac{p^2}{4}$$

which reduces to

(1)                $$y^2 = 2px.$$

Conversely, it is easy to show that, for any point $P$ whose coordinates satisfy this equation, $FP = LP$ and the point is on the parabola.

Equation (1) is the equation of the parabola if the $x$-axis is the axis of the curve and its vertex is at the origin. In the case shown, $p$ is positive and the parabola opens to the right. If $p$ is negative, the focus is to the left of the directrix and the parabola opens to the left.

### Example

In the equation $y^2 = -8x$, $p = -4$; the focus is at $(-2, 0)$, and the directrix is the line $x = 2$ (see Fig. 108).

If the axes are chosen so that the focus is on the $y$-axis and the vertex at the origin, we find in a similar way that the equation is

(2) $$x^2 = 2py$$

where the focus is above the directrix if $p$ is positive, and below if $p$ is negative. This latter equation is of course

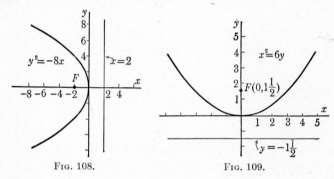

FIG. 108.  FIG. 109.

equivalent to the equation $y = ax^2$ which we met in the chapter on polynomial curves.

### Example

In the equation $x^2 = 6y$, or $y = \frac{1}{6}x^2$, $p = 3$; the focus is at $F(0, 1\frac{1}{2})$, and the directrix is the line $y = -1\frac{1}{2}$ (see Fig. 109).

**56. Parabola with vertex at $(h, k)$.**—Let a parabola have its vertex at $(h, k)$ and its axis parallel to the $x$-axis as indicated in Fig. 110. We may insert new axes $x'$ and $y'$ through the vertex as shown, and the equation of the curve relative to these axes is

$$y'^2 = 2px'.$$

In order to find the equation relative to the $x$- and $y$-axes we may use the transformation for translation of axes, in the inverse sense:

$$x = x' + h, \qquad \therefore \; x' = x - h;$$
$$y = y' + k, \qquad \therefore \; y' = y - k.$$

Making these substitutions we have

**(3)** $$(y - k)^2 = 2p(x - h).$$

This is the standard form of the equation of a parabola with vertex at $(h, k)$ and axis parallel to the $x$-axis. The

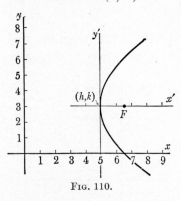

FIG. 110.

parabola opens to the right if $p$ is positive and to the left if $p$ is negative. Equation (1) is of course the special case of (3) in which $h = k = 0$.

If (3) is multiplied out, the result is an equation of the form

**(4)** $y^2 + Dx + Ey + F = 0.$

Conversely, any equation of the form (4) can be transformed into form (3) by completing the square in $y$ if $D \neq 0$. It is therefore evident that *any equation of the form* (4) *represents a parabola with its axis parallel to the x-axis unless $D = 0$.*

### Example

Transform the equation $y^2 - 6y - 6x + 39 = 0$ into standard form and draw the graph.

### Solution

First write the equation in the form

$$y^2 - 6y = 6x - 39.$$

Now to complete the square in $y$, add 9 to both sides:

$$y^2 - 6y + 9 = 6x - 30.$$

This equation may be written in the standard form (3) as follows:

$$(y - 3)^2 = 6(x - 5).$$

* In this exceptional case the equation contains only one variable and represents a pair of parallel or coincident lines, or has no locus. Thus the graph of $y^2 - 7y + 10 = 0$ is two parallel lines, $y = 2$ and $y = 5$; the equation $y^2 + 2y + 3 = 0$ has no graph.

The graph is a parabola with vertex at (5, 3). The value of $p$ is 3, so the focus is $1\frac{1}{2}$ units to the right of the vertex. We have then

*Coordinates of focus;* $(6\frac{1}{2}, 3)$;
*Equation of directrix;* $x = 3\frac{1}{2}$.

The graph is shown in Fig. 110.

By similarly completing the square in $x$, any equation of the form $x^2 + Dx + Ey + F = 0$ can be put into the form

**(5)**        $$(x - h)^2 = 2p(y - k)$$

if $E \neq 0$. This is the standard form of the equation of a parabola with vertex at $(h, k)$ and axis parallel to the $y$-axis. It opens upward if $p$ is positive and downward if $p$ is negative. *It should be observed that the equation*

$$y = ax^2 + bx + c$$

*which we met in the discussion of polynomial curves is of this form.*

### Example

The equation $y = x^2 + 4x + 1$ may be put into standard form (5) by completing the square in $x$:

$$y + 3 = x^2 + 4x + 4,$$
$$(x + 2)^2 = y + 3.$$

The graph is a parabola with vertex at $(-2, -3)$ and axis parallel to the $y$-axis. In this case $2p = 1$ so the parabola opens upward and the focus is $\frac{1}{4}$ unit above the vertex.

**57. Applications.**—The parabola has a multitude of scientific applications, only a few of which can be mentioned here.

It has already been stated (page 81) that when a projectile such as a ball or stone is thrown into the air its path is a parabola except for a slight deviation due to air resistance. This deviation is appreciable in the case of a projectile fired at high velocity from a gun.

Certain types of bridge construction employ parabolic arches; the curve in which a suspension-bridge cable hangs is approximately a parabola if the load is distributed uniformly along the horizontal roadbed.

If a parabola be rotated about its axis, a surface called a *paraboloid* is generated. This surface is used as a reflector in automobile headlights and other searchlights because of the following property of the parabola: From any point $P$ on the curve, draw a line $PF$ to the focus and a line $PL$ parallel to the axis (Fig. 111). It can be proved that *these lines make equal angles with the tangent to the curve at $P$.* This means that if a source of light is placed at $F$ the light rays upon striking the reflecting surface will be reflected in rays parallel to the axis, thus throwing a cylindrical beam of light in this direction. This same principle is used in the reverse sense in the reflecting telescope; if the axis of a parabolic mirror is pointed toward a star, the rays from the star, upon striking the mirror, will all be reflected to the focus.

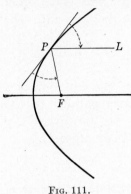

Fig. 111.

### PROBLEMS

**1.** In each of the following, find the coordinates of the focus and the equation of the directrix; draw the graph:

(a) $y^2 = 4x$.      (b) $y^2 = -6x$.      (c) $x^2 = -2y$.

(d) $y = 4x^2$.      (e) $x = 0.5y^2$.      (f) $x^2 = 0.4y$.

**2.** Find the equation of the parabola satisfying the following conditions:

(a) Vertex at origin, axis along $y$-axis; passes through (4, 2). HINT: The equation can be written in the form $y = ax^2$ or $x^2 = 2py$, and $a$ or $p$ can be found from the condition that $y = 2$ when $x = 4$.

(b) Vertex at (5, 3), axis parallel to $y$-axis; passes through (7, 2).

(c) Vertex at $(-4, -2)$, axis parallel to $x$-axis; passes through (0, 2).

**3.** The chord drawn through the focus of a parabola perpendicular to its axis is called the *latus rectum* of the parabola. Show that its length is $2p$.

**4.** Find the equation of the parabola whose axis is parallel to the $y$-axis, and which passes through the three given points:

(a)  $(-3, -6)$, $(1, 2)$, $(2, 9)$.

(b)  $(0, 0)$, $(2, -2)$, $(4, 20)$.

(c)  $(-2, -7)$, $(1, 2)$, $(3, -2)$.

**5.** The diameter of a parabolic reflector is 8 in., and its depth is 6 in. Locate the focus.

**6.** A parabolic arch has the dimensions shown in Fig. 112.  Find the equation of the parabola with respect to the axes shown.  Compute the values of $y$ at the points where $x = 5, 10,$ and 15 ft.

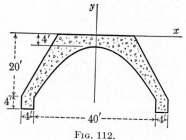

FIG. 112.

**7.** Draw a graph showing how $\cos 2\theta$ varies with $\cos \theta$.  HINT: $\cos 2\theta = 2 \cos^2 \theta - 1$; let $\cos 2\theta = y$ and $\cos \theta = x$.

**8.** If a ball is thrown vertically upward with initial velocity $v_0$ ft. per second, its distance above the ground after $t$ sec. is given approximately by the formula

$$y = v_0 t - 16t^2.$$

Draw this "distance—time curve" taking $v_0 = 40$ ft. per second.

**9.** In each of the following, transform the given equation into standard form (3) or (5), and sketch the curve.  In making the sketch use the fact that the width of the parabola at its focus is $2p$ (see Prob. 3):

(a)  $y^2 - 2y - x + 4 = 0$.  (b)  $x^2 + 6x - 4y + 13 = 0$.

(c)  $y^2 + 4y + 4x = 0$.  (d)  $y = 9x - x^2$.

**10.** By completing the square, transform the equation

$$y = ax^2 + bx + c$$

into standard form (5); find the coordinates of the vertex and the value of $p$ in terms of $a$, $b$, and $c$, and show that the distance from the vertex to the focus is $1/4a$.

**11.** A rectangular lot is to be enclosed by 80 yd. of fencing.  Express the area as a function of the length $x$ of one side and draw the graph. For what value of $x$ is the area largest?

**12.** A rectangular lot is to be fenced off along the straight bank of a river.  No fence is needed along the river, and 120 yd. of fencing are available.  Express the area enclosed as a function of the length $x$ of the side perpendicular to the river bank.  Make the graph and find the value of $x$ for which the area is largest.

**13.** A rectangular field is to be enclosed and divided into four lots by fences parallel to one of the sides.  A total of 800 yd. of fencing are available.  Find the dimensions of the largest field that can be enclosed.

**14.** When a ball is thrown with initial velocity $v_0$ ft. per second at an angle of 45° with the horizontal, it travels on a path whose equation is approximately

$$y = x - \frac{32x^2}{v_0{}^2}.$$

If $v_0 = 80$ ft. per second, find the horizontal distance traveled and the maximum height reached by the ball.

**58. The ellipse.**—*The ellipse is defined as the locus of a point which moves so that the sum of its undirected distances from two fixed points is a constant.* In Fig. 113 the points $F$ and $F'$ are 8 units apart; if $P$ moves so that $FP + F'P = 10$, it will trace out the ellipse shown. $F$ and $F'$ are called the *foci* of the ellipse, and the point midway between them is called its *center*.

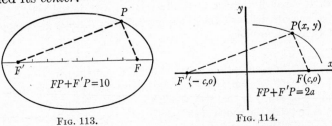

FIG. 113.                    FIG. 114.

In order to derive a simple equation for this curve we choose the axes as shown in Fig. 114 with the $x$-axis through the foci and the origin at the center. If the distance $F'F$ is denoted by $2c$, the coordinates of $F$ and $F'$ are $(c, 0)$ and $(-c, 0)$, respectively. Now let $P(x, y)$ move in such a way that $FP + F'P$ is always equal to some constant, which must of course be greater than $2c$, say

$$FP + F'P = 2a \qquad \text{where} \qquad a > c.$$

This requires that

$$\sqrt{(x - c)^2 + y^2} + \sqrt{(x + c)^2 + y^2} = 2a.$$

In order to simplify this equation we transpose the first radical to the right-hand side and square both sides:

$$\sqrt{(x + c)^2 + y^2} = 2a - \sqrt{(x - c)^2 + y^2};$$
$$x^2 + 2cx + c^2 + y^2 = 4a^2 - 4a\sqrt{(x - c)^2 + y^2} + x^2$$
$$- 2cx + c^2 + y^2;$$

this reduces to

$$a \sqrt{(x - c)^2 + y^2} = a^2 - cx.$$

Squaring again we have

$$a^2(x^2 - 2cx + c^2 + y^2) = a^4 - 2a^2cx + c^2x^2$$

or

$$(a^2 - c^2)x^2 + a^2y^2 = a^2(a^2 - c^2).$$

If we divide through by $a^2(a^2 - c^2)$, this becomes

$$\frac{x^2}{a^2} + \frac{y^2}{a^2 - c^2} = 1.$$

Now, the quantity $a^2 - c^2$ is positive since $a > c$; let us denote it by $b^2$. The equation then takes the form

(6)
$$\frac{x^2}{a^2} + \frac{y^2}{b^2} = 1$$

where $a$, $b$, and $c$ are related by the equation

$$a^2 = b^2 + c^2.$$

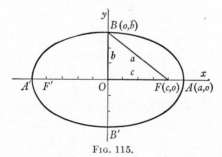

FIG. 115.

It can be proved, conversely, that if the coordinates of any point $P(x, y)$ satisfy (6) then $F'P + FP = 2a$ and the point is on the ellipse; (6) is then the equation of the ellipse with the axes as chosen.

The intercepts of the curve on the axes are easily found to be $(\pm a, 0)$ and $(0, \pm b)$. The points $A$ and $A'$ (Fig. 115) are called the *vertices* of the ellipse; the line $A'A$ whose length is $2a$ is its *major axis* and the line $B'B$ whose length is $2b$ is its *minor axis*. We thus have a graphical interpretation of the constants $a$ and $b$:

$c$ = *distance from center to focus* = $OF$;
$a$ = *distance from center to end of major axis* = $OA$;
$b$ = *distance from center to end of minor axis* = $OB$.

The relation between $a$, $b$, and $c$ appears in the triangle in Fig. 115; note that $BF = OA = a$.

### Example

In the equation $\dfrac{x^2}{25} + \dfrac{y^2}{9} = 1$, $a = 5$ and $b = 3$; $c = \sqrt{a^2 - b^2} = 4$, and the foci are at $(\pm 4, 0)$. This is the case shown in Fig. 115.

If we choose the $y$-axis through the foci, making their coordinates $(0, \pm c)$, the equation becomes

$$(7) \qquad\qquad \frac{x^2}{b^2} + \frac{y^2}{a^2} = 1.$$

### Example

In the equation $\dfrac{x^2}{9} + \dfrac{y^2}{16} = 1$, $a = 4$ and $b = 3$; $c = \sqrt{a^2 - b^2} = \sqrt{7}$, and the foci are at $(0, \pm \sqrt{7})$.

Observe that since $a^2 = b^2 + c^2$, *the larger of the two denominators is always $a^2$.* The foci are on the $x$-axis if this larger number is under $x^2$ and on the $y$-axis if it is under $y^2$.

**59. Eccentricity.**—The shape of the ellipse is determined by the ratio of $c$ to $a$. This ratio, which is a number between 0 and 1 since $a > c > 0$, is called the *eccentricity* of the ellipse and is denoted by the letter $e$:

$$e = \frac{c}{a}.$$

### Example

The equation $\dfrac{x^2}{64} + \dfrac{y^2}{16} = 1$ represents an ellipse in which $a = 8$ and $b = 4$; $c = \sqrt{64 - 16} = 4\sqrt{3}$, and its eccentricity is

$$4\sqrt{3}/8 = \sqrt{3}/2 = 0.866.$$

The student may show that if $c/a = \sqrt{a^2 - b^2}/a$ is near 1, then $b$ is small compared with $a$ and the ellipse is long and narrow. On the other hand, if $c/a$ is near zero then $b$ is nearly equal to $a$ and the ellipse is nearly a circle. In fact as $c$ approaches zero, and the foci consequently approach the center of the ellipse, the value of $b$ approaches that of $a$. If $b = a$, the equation $x^2/a^2 + y^2/b^2 = 1$ becomes $x^2 + y^2 = a^2$. *The circle may therefore be regarded as an ellipse with eccentricity 0.*

**60. Ellipse with center at $(h, k)$.**—Let an ellipse have its center at $(h, k)$ and its major and minor axes parallel to the coordinate axes as shown in Fig. 116. We may insert new

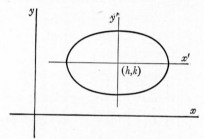

FIG. 116.

axes $x'$ and $y'$ through the center as shown, and the equation of the curve relative to these axes is

$$\frac{x'^2}{a^2} + \frac{y'^2}{b^2} = 1.$$

In order to find the equation relative to the $x$- and $y$-axes we let $x' = x - h$ and $y' = y - k$ as we did in the case of the parabola. The result is

(8)
$$\frac{(x - h)^2}{a^2} + \frac{(y - k)^2}{b^2} = 1.$$

This is the standard equation of the ellipse with center at $(h, k)$ and major axis parallel to the $x$-axis. If the major axis is parallel to the $y$-axis, the equation is

(9)
$$\frac{(x - h)^2}{b^2} + \frac{(y - k)^2}{a^2} = 1.$$

If either of these equations is multiplied out, the result is an equation of the form

$$(10) \qquad Ax^2 + Cy^2 + Dx + Ey + F = 0$$

in which $A$ and $C$ have the same sign. Conversely, any equation of the form (10) can be put into form (8) or (9) by completing the squares in $x$ and $y$ provided that $A$ and $C$ have the same sign and provided also that the constant appearing on the right side when the left side is expressed as a sum of squares is positive.

### *Example*

Transform the equation $x^2 + 4y^2 - 16x + 16y + 76 = 0$ into standard form.

### *Solution*

First write the equation in the form

$$(x^2 - 16x) + 4(y^2 + 4y) = -76.$$

Now add the numbers necessary to complete the squares:

$$(x^2 - 16x + 64) + 4(y^2 + 4y + 4) = -76 + 64 + 16.$$

Note that the value of the right-hand member is now positive. The equation may be written as

$$(x - 8)^2 + 4(y + 2)^2 = 4$$

or, in standard form, as

$$\frac{(x - 8)^2}{4} + \frac{(y + 2)^2}{1} = 1.$$

The graph is an ellipse with center at $(8, -2)$ and with $a = 2$ and $b = 1$; the major axis is parallel to the $x$-axis and $c = \sqrt{3}$. The coordinates of the foci can of course be found easily.

If in the above example the number on the right after the squares were completed had been zero, the graph would have been a "point ellipse"; *i.e.*, the point $(h, k)$. If the number had been negative, there would have been no locus. It is evident then that *every equation of the form* (10) *in which A and C have the same sign represents an ellipse, a single point or no locus.*

*Example*

Upon completing the squares, the equation

$$x^2 + 2y^2 - 2x + 16y + 45 = 0$$

becomes $(x - 1)^2 + 2(y + 4)^2 = -12$. There is no locus. If the constant 45 is replaced by 33, the locus is the point $(1, -4)$.

**61. Applications.**—The ellipse, like the parabola, has many scientific applications. Elliptic gears are used in certain kinds of machinery; arches in the form of semi-ellipses are often employed in the construction of stone and concrete bridges. The orbits in which the planets revolve about the sun are ellipses, the sun being at one focus. In the case of the earth the eccentricity of the ellipse is about $\frac{1}{60}$. In engineering drawing one must frequently draw ellipses because the orthographic projection of a circle on a plane not parallel to the plane of the circle is an ellipse.

### PROBLEMS

**1.** Draw each of the following ellipses; find the coordinates of the foci and compute its eccentricity:

(a) $\dfrac{x^2}{4} + \dfrac{y^2}{9} = 1.$      (b) $x^2 + 4y^2 = 25.$

(c) $4x^2 + 3y^2 = 12.$      (d) $50x^2 + 25y^2 = 1{,}250.$

(e) $\dfrac{3x^2}{4} + 2y^2 = 24.$      (f) $64x^2 + 81y^2 = 144.$

**2.** Find the equation of the ellipse with center at the origin and satisfying the following conditions:

(a) Focus at $(4, 0)$; $e = \frac{1}{2}$.

(b) One vertex at $(0, 6)$; $e = \frac{2}{3}$.

(c) One end of minor axis at $(4, 0)$; $e = 0.6$.

**3.** Find the equation of the ellipse satisfying the following conditions:

(a) Center at $(8, 4)$; one vertex at $(0, 4)$; $e = \frac{1}{2}$.

(b) Vertices at $(-3, -2)$, $(7, -2)$; one focus at $(5, -2)$.

(c) Center at $(4, -4)$; one end of minor axis at $(0, -4)$; one focus at $(4, 0)$.

**4.** What is the eccentricity of an ellipse whose major axis is twice as long as its minor axis? Ten times as long?

**5.** Show that an ellipse is symmetrical with respect to its major and minor axes and center.

**6.** The chord drawn through either focus of an ellipse perpendicular to its major axis is called the *latus rectum* of the ellipse. Show that its length is $2b^2/a$.

**7.** A point moves so tnat the sum of its distances from $(1, 0)$ and $(9, 0)$ is equal to 10. Find the equation of its path and sketch it.

**8.** A point moves so that its distance from the origin is equal to one-half its distance from the line $x + 9 = 0$. Find the equation of its path and sketch it.

**9.** A semielliptic arch in a stone bridge has a span of 20 ft. and a height of 6 ft. as shown in Fig. 117. In constructing the arch it is necessary to know its height at distances of 2, 4, 6, 8, and 9 ft. from its center as indicated by the dotted lines. Compute these heights to the nearest tenth of a foot.

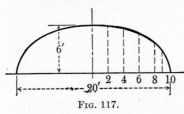

Fig. 117.

**10.** A rod $PQ$ of length 24 units moves so that $P$ is always on the $y$-axis and $Q$ on the $x$-axis. A point $M$ is on $PQ$ two-thirds of the way from $P$ to $Q$. Find the equation of the path traveled by $M$.

**11.** Transform each of the following equations into standard form and draw the ellipse if it exists:

(a) $9x^2 + 4y^2 - 24y = 0$.

(b) $9x^2 + y^2 - 36x - 8y + 43 = 0$.

(c) $4x^2 + 9y^2 + 24x - 36y + 36 = 0$.

(d) $x^2 + 4y^2 - 32y + 48 = 0$.

**12.** Find the points of intersection of the line $3x - 5y + 3 = 0$ and the ellipse $9x^2 + 25y^2 = 225$. Draw the graph.

**13.** The orbit in which the earth travels about the sun is an ellipse with the sun at one focus. The semimajor axis of the ellipse is 92.9 million miles, and its eccentricity is 0.0168. Compute the greatest and least distances of the earth from the sun.

**14.** Find the points of intersection of the line $9x - 5y = 60$ and the ellipse $9x^2 + 25y^2 = 90x$. Draw the graphs.

**62. The hyperbola.**—*The hyperbola is defined as the locus of a point which moves so that the difference of its undirected distances from two fixed points is a constant.*

The fixed points are called the *foci* of the hyperbola, and the point midway between them is called its *center*. The derivation of the standard equation for this curve parallels that for the ellipse, and for this reason the details will be left to the student.

Choosing the axes as shown in Fig. 118, and denoting by $2a$ the absolute value of the difference between $F'P$ and $FP$, we have

$$\sqrt{(x+c)^2 + y^2} - \sqrt{(x-c)^2 + y^2} = \pm 2a$$

where the positive sign applies to the points on the right-hand "branch" and the negative sign to those on the left. After the radicals have been removed by squaring, this equation can be put into the form

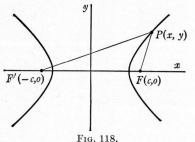

$$\frac{x^2}{a^2} - \frac{y^2}{c^2 - a^2} = 1.$$

FIG. 118.

Observe now that $a < c$ since the difference between two sides of a triangle is less than the third side. The quantity $c^2 - a^2$ is therefore positive and may be denoted by $b^2$; the equation then becomes

(**11**) $$\frac{x^2}{a^2} - \frac{y^2}{b^2} = 1$$

where $a$, $b$, and $c$ are connected by the equation

$$c^2 = b^2 + a^2.$$

The graph has the shape shown in Fig. 118. It is easy to show that it is symmetrical with respect to both axes and the origin, that its intercepts on the $x$-axis are $(\pm a, 0)$, and that it does not touch the $y$-axis. In fact, solving (11) for $y$ in terms of $x$ gives

$$y = \pm \frac{b}{a} \sqrt{x^2 - a^2}$$

from which it is evident that *there is no value of $y$ for any value of $x$ between $-a$ and $+a$.* It is also evident that $y$ increases indefinitely in absolute value as $x$ increases. Writing the above equation in the form

$$y = \pm \frac{bx}{a} \sqrt{1 - \frac{a^2}{x^2}}$$

and noting that the expression $\sqrt{1 - \dfrac{a^2}{x^2}}$ approaches 1 as $x$ becomes larger and larger, it becomes evident that for large values of $x$ the graph of the hyperbola nearly coincides with that of the lines

$$y = \pm \frac{b}{a} x.$$

*It can be proved that these lines are asymptotes to the curve.* (see Prob. 11, page 132).

The segment $A'A$ (Fig. 119) is called the *transverse axis* of the hyperbola, and the segment $B'B$ is called its *con-*

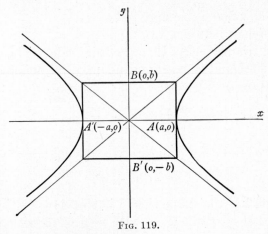

Fig. 119.

*jugate axis.* The diagonals of the rectangle drawn as shown in the figure obviously have the equations $y = \pm \dfrac{b}{a} x$; they are therefore the asymptotes.

The ratio of $c$ to $a$ is called the *eccentricity* of the hyperbola and is denoted by the letter $e$:

$$e = \frac{c}{a}.$$

*Since $a < c$, the eccentricity is greater than 1.*

If we had chosen the $y$-axis through the foci, making their coordinates $(0, \pm c)$, the equation would have been

$$(12) \qquad \frac{y^2}{a^2} - \frac{x^2}{b^2} = 1.$$

In the equation of the hypberola $a$ may be less than, equal to, or greater than $b$. One determines whether the foci are on the $x$- or $y$-axis by putting the equation in the standard form (11) or (12) with $+1$ on the right-hand side; if the coefficient of $x^2$ is then positive the foci are on the $x$-axis, while if that of $y^2$ is positive they are on the $y$-axis.

The standard form of the equation of a hyperbola with center at $(h, k)$ and transverse axis parallel to the $x$-axis is

$$(13) \qquad \frac{(x - h)^2}{a^2} - \frac{(y - k)^2}{b^2} = 1;$$

if the transverse axis is parallel to the $y$-axis, the corresponding equation is

$$(14) \qquad \frac{(y - k)^2}{a^2} - \frac{(x - h)^2}{b^2} = 1.$$

If either (13) or (14) is multiplied out, the result is an equation of the form

$$(15) \qquad Ax^2 + Cy^2 + Dx + Ey + F = 0$$

in which $A$ and $C$ have *opposite signs*. Conversely, an equation of the form (15) can be transformed into form (13) or (14) by completing the squares, provided $A$ and $C$ have opposite signs. The only exceptional case is that in which, when the left-hand side has been expressed as the difference of two squares, the right-hand side is zero. In this exceptional case the equation can be factored into real linear factors and represents two intersecting lines. Otherwise it of course represents a hyperbola.

**63. Equilateral hyperbola.**—If $b = a$, the equation

$$\frac{x^2}{a^2} - \frac{y^2}{b^2} = 1$$

takes the form

$$x^2 - y^2 = a^2.$$

The asymptotes in this special case are the lines $y = \pm x$ which are *mutually perpendicular*. This hyperbola is called an *equilateral* or *rectangular hyperbola*. It will be left to the student to show that if the axes are rotated through $-45°$ the equation becomes

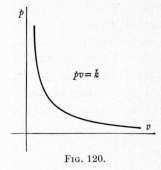

FIG. 120.

$$2xy = a^2.$$

In applications the equation of the equilateral hyperbola is often encountered in the form $xy = k$. Thus, the law connecting the pressure and volume of a perfect gas under constant temperature is $pv = k$. The graph (Fig. 120) shows pictorially the way in which the pressure of a given quantity of gas decreases as its volume increases.

A more general form of the equation of the equilateral hyperbola is

$$axy + by + cx + d = 0.$$

Upon solving for $y$, the equation becomes

$$y = -\frac{cx + d}{ax + b}.$$

This equation was studied in Chap. V on Rational Fractional Functions. The student can easily show, using the methods of that chapter, that the line $x = -b/a$ is the vertical asymptote and the line $y = -c/a$ is the horizontal asymptote. Figure 92, page 94, is an example.

It should be fairly obvious that the equation

$$axy + by + cx + d = 0$$

can be changed into the form $x'y' = k$ by making a translation of axes so as to move the origin to the center of the hyperbola. The required substitution is of course

$$x = x' - \frac{b}{a}; \qquad y = y' - \frac{c}{a}.$$

**64. Application.**—One of the applications of the hyperbola is in range finding. If the precise time at which the sound of a gun reaches two listening posts $F$ and $F'$ is recorded, this difference multiplied by the velocity of sound gives the difference of the distances of the gun from $F$ and $F'$. In our notation this difference is $2a$, and the gun is somewhere on the hyperbola having foci at $F$ and $F'$ and transverse axis $2a$. The "branch" of the hyperbola on which it is located is known since this depends only on which of the two stations received the sound first. By using a third station $F''$ with either $F$ or $F'$, the gun can similarly be located on a known branch of another hyperbola. Finally, a point of intersection of these curves gives the position of the gun.

### PROBLEMS

**1.** Sketch each of the following hyperbolas, draw its asymptotes, and give the coordinates of its vertices and foci:

(a) $25x^2 - 9y^2 + 225 = 0$.      (b) $4x^2 - y^2 = 100$.

(c) $9x^2 - 16y^2 - 144 = 0$.      (d) $9y^2 - x^2 - 36 = 0$.

**2.** What is the eccentricity of an equilateral hyperbola?

**3.** The two hyperbolas $x^2/a^2 - y^2/b^2 = 1$ and $y^2/b^2 - x^2/a^2 = 1$ are called *conjugate hyperbolas*. Show that the transverse axis of either is the conjugate axis of the other and that they have the same asymptotes. Draw both on the same axes taking $a = 5$ and $b = 3$.

**4.** Sketch the graph of $x^2 - y^2 = 4$. Find the new equation when the axes are rotated through 45°.

**5.** Show that when the axes are rotated through $-45°$ the equation $x^2 - y^2 = a^2$ becomes $2xy = a^2$.

**6.** The chord drawn through either focus of a hyperbola perpendicular to its transverse axis is called its *latus rectum*. Show that its length is $2b^2/a$.

**7.** Find the equation of the hyperbola satisfying the following conditions:

(a) Vertices at $(\pm 6, 0); e = \frac{3}{2}$.

(b) Vertices at $(0, \pm 4)$; foci at $(0, \pm 5)$.

(c) Foci at $(\pm 8, 0); e = 2$.

**8.** Find the equation of the hyperbola satisfying the following conditions:

(a) Center at $(4, 1)$; one focus at $(4, 6)$; $e = \frac{5}{3}$.

(b) Vertices at $(-3, 3)$, $(5, 3)$; one focus at $(-5, 3)$.

(c) Center at $(-2, -3)$; one vertex at $(-2, 0)$; $e = 2$.

**9.** A point moves so that its distance from $(8, 0)$ is 6 units more than its distance from $(-2, 0)$. Find the equation of its path and sketch it.

**10.** A point moves so that its distance from the origin is equal to twice its distance from the line $x = -6$. Find the equation of its path and sketch it.

**11.** Show that the difference between the ordinate to the line $y = \dfrac{bx}{a}$ and the positive ordinate to the hyperbola $\dfrac{x^2}{a^2} - \dfrac{y^2}{b^2} = 1$ approaches zero as $x$ increases indefinitely. HINT: The difference is

$$(b/a)(x - \sqrt{x^2 - a^2});$$

multiply and divide by $x + \sqrt{x^2 - a^2}$.

**12.** Transform each of the following equations into standard form and draw the locus:

(a) $x^2 - 4y^2 - 4x - 8y - 4 = 0$.

(b) $4x^2 - y^2 - 8x + 4y = 0$.

(c) $5x^2 - 4y^2 - 40x = 0$.

(d) $4x^2 - 3y^2 - 8x + 12y - 8 = 0$.

(e) $16y^2 - 9x^2 - 128y - 36x + 76 = 0$.

Draw the graphs of the following equations using the methods of Chap. V:

**13.** $xy + y + x = 0$.      **14.** $2xy - 4y - 6x = 5$.

**15.** $xy - 3y = 6$.      **16.** $3xy + 4y - 6x = 6$.

**17.** $xy + 2x = 5$.      **18.** $xy = y + 2x + 4$.

In each of the following, translate the axes so as to remove the first-degree terms from the equation. Draw the hyperbola and show both sets of axes:

**19.** $xy + 3y - x = 0$.      **20.** $xy - 4y = 6$.

**21.** $3xy + 6y - 8x + 4 = 0$.      **22.** $2xy - 2y + 6x = 9$.

**23.** Show that the equation $axy + by + cx + d = 0$ becomes

$$a^2x'y' = cb - ad$$

when the axes are translated so as to move the origin to the center of the hyperbola.

**24.** Show that the equation $xy - 2y - 2x - 3 = 0$ can be written in the form $y = 2 + \dfrac{7}{x - 2}$. Make the graph by drawing the separate graphs of $y = 2$ and $y = \dfrac{7}{x - 2}$ and adding ordinates.

**25.** Draw the graph of the equation $2xy + 6y - 3x = 11$ using the method suggested in Prob. 24.

**65. Sections of a cone.**—It can be proved that when a right circular cone (including both its upper and lower nappes) is cut by a plane, the section is a parabola, ellipse, or hyperbola if the plane does not pass through the vertex of the cone. If the plane does pass through the vertex, the section may be a single point, or two intersecting or coincident lines. All these loci are called *conic sections*, or simply *conics*. We may use the term *regular conic* to designate sections cut by planes that do not pass through the vertex and *degenerate conic* to denote those cut by planes through the vertex.*

**66. The general equation of second degree.**—The most general equation of second degree in $x$ and $y$ is

**(16)**     $Ax^2 + Bxy + Cy^2 + Dx + Ey + F = 0$

where $A$, $B$, and $C$ are not all zero. The special case in which $B = 0$ is

**(17)**         $Ax^2 + Cy^2 + Dx + Ey + F = 0.$

We have found that when (17) has a locus it is always a conic section. If the conic is not degenerate, it is

> *A parabola if $A$ or $C = 0$;*
> *An ellipse (or circle) if $A$ and $C$ have the same sign;*
> *A hyperbola if $A$ and $C$ have opposite signs.*

Furthermore, in each case the axis or axes of the conic are parallel to the coordinate axes.

We shall now show that if the $xy$ term is present it can

---

* We shall include also in this last designation a pair of parallel lines. They could not be cut from a cone but could be cut from a cylinder, which is a limiting case.

be removed by rotating the axes through a proper angle. This means that the most general equation of second degree (16) also represents a conic section (or no locus). When the $xy$ term is present, the axis or axes of the conic are

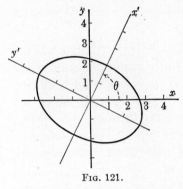

inclined to the coordinate axes.

### Example

The equation $5x^2 + 4xy + 8y^2 - 36 = 0$ represents an ellipse whose minor axis makes an angle $\theta$ whose tangent is 2 with the $x$-axis (Fig. 121). If the axes are rotated through this angle, the $xy$ term disappears and the equation, with respect to the new axes, becomes $(x'^2/4) + (y'^2/9) = 1$.

Fig. 121.

In order to show that the $xy$ term can be removed by rotating the axes through a proper angle, and to determine this angle, we take the equation

$$Ax^2 + Bxy + Cy^2 + Dx + Ey + F = 0$$

and let $x = x' \cos \theta - y' \sin \theta$, $y = x' \sin \theta + y' \cos \theta$; the result is a new equation of the form

(18) $\quad A'x'^2 + B'x'y' + C'y'^2 + D'x' + E'y' + F' = 0$

where

(19) $\quad \begin{cases} A' = A \cos^2 \theta + B \sin \theta \cos \theta + C \sin^2 \theta \\ B' = B \cos 2\theta - (A - C) \sin 2\theta \\ C' = A \sin^2 \theta - B \sin \theta \cos \theta + C \cos^2 \theta \\ D' = D \cos \theta + E \sin \theta \\ E' = E \cos \theta - D \sin \theta \\ F' = F. \end{cases}$

To eliminate the $x'y'$ term we must make $B' = 0$; *i.e.*, we must choose $\theta$ so that

$$B \cos 2\theta - (A - C) \sin 2\theta = 0.$$

The solution of this equation is

$$\tan 2\theta = \frac{B}{A - C} \qquad \text{if} \qquad A \neq C.$$

If $A = C$ (and $B \neq 0$), the required value of $\theta$ is given by $\cos 2\theta = 0$; *i.e.*, $\theta = \pm 45°$.

### *Example*

The angle through which the axes must be rotated to remove the $xy$ term from the equation

$$5x^2 + 4xy + 8y^2 - 36 = 0$$

is given by

$$\tan 2\theta = \frac{4}{5 - 8} = -\frac{4}{3}.$$

Since $\tan 2\theta = \dfrac{2 \tan \theta}{1 - \tan^2 \theta}$, this means that

$$\frac{2 \tan \theta}{1 - \tan^2 \theta} = -\frac{4}{3}$$

or

$$2 \tan^2 \theta - 3 \tan \theta - 2 = 0.$$

Solving this equation we find that

$$\tan \theta = 2 \text{ or } -\tfrac{1}{2}.$$

The $xy$ term will disappear if the axes are rotated through either of these angles (see Fig. 121).

**67. Identification of a conic.**—After the $xy$ term has been removed from a general equation of second degree by rotating the axes, the conic can be easily identified: If there is a graph, then

(a) *If $A'$ or $C' = 0$, it is a parabola;*
    (Degenerate case a pair of parallel or coincident lines)
(b) *If $A'$ and $C'$ have the same sign, it is an ellipse;*
    (Degenerate case a single point)
(c) *If $A'$ and $C'$ have opposite signs, it is a hyperbola.*
    (Degenerate case a pair of intersecting lines)

It is possible to give rules by which the conic can be identified without first removing the $xy$ term. For this purpose we state the following:

**Theorem:** *The graph (if it has a graph) of the equation*

$$Ax^2 + Bxy + Cy^2 + Dx + Ey + F = 0$$

*is*

(1) *A parabola (or its degenerate case) if* $B^2 - 4AC = 0$;
(2) *An ellipse (or its degenerate case) if* $B^2 - 4AC < 0$;
(3) *A hyperbola (or its degenerate case) if* $B^2 - 4AC > 0$.

The proof of this theorem depends upon the fact (proof of which is left to the student) that the value of the quantity $B^2 - 4AC$ is unchanged when the axes are rotated through any angle; *i.e.*, no matter what the angle $\theta$ of rotation may be,

$$B^2 - 4AC = B'^2 - 4A'C'.$$

Now if $\theta$ is chosen so that $B' = 0$, we have

$$B^2 - 4AC = -4A'C'.$$

It is immediately evident that

(1)  $B^2 - 4AC = 0$ if and only if $A'$ or $C' = 0$;
(2)  $B^2 - 4AC < 0$ if and only if $A'$ and $C'$ have the same sign;
(3)  $B^2 - 4AC > 0$ if and only if $A'$ and $C'$ have opposite signs.

The theorem follows immediately in view of statements (*a*), (*b*), and (*c*).

Finally we state as a matter of interest, but without giving the proof, that the graph will be the regular conic if $\Delta \neq 0$ and the degenerate conic if $\Delta = 0$ where

$$\Delta = \begin{vmatrix} 2A & B & D \\ B & 2C & E \\ D & E & 2F \end{vmatrix}$$

**68. Second definition of a conic.**—An alternate definition of a regular conic is as follows:

*A regular conic is the locus of a point which moves so that the ratio of its undirected distance from a fixed point F to that from a fixed line l is a constant e.* This positive constant is the eccentricity of the conic, and if

$e < 1$, *the conic is an ellipse;*
$e = 1$, *the conic is a parabola;*
$e > 1$, *the conic is a hyperbola.*

To derive the equation from this definition we let the fixed line, which is called a *directrix* of the conic, be the $y$-axis; we let the fixed point, which is called a *focus*, be the point $F(p, 0)$ (Fig. 122). The definition requires that if $P(x, y)$ is any point on the conic then

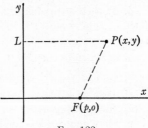

$$FP = e \cdot LP;$$

Fig. 122.

in terms of coordinates this means that

$$\sqrt{(x - p)^2 + y^2} = ex.$$

Squaring both sides, and simplifying, we have

$$x^2 - 2px + p^2 + y^2 = e^2 x^2,$$

or

$$(1 - e^2)x^2 + y^2 - 2px + p^2 = 0.$$

The student can easily see that if $e < 1$ the coefficients of $x^2$ and $y^2$ have the same sign and the conic is an ellipse; if $e = 1$, the coefficient of $x^2$ is zero and the conic is a parabola; if $e > 1$, the coefficients of $x^2$ and $y^2$ have opposite signs and the conic is a hyperbola.

### PROBLEMS

**1.** Draw a right circular cone (both nappes) and show how a plane must be passed in order that the section may be (*a*) a circle, (*b*) an ellipse, (*c*) a parabola, (*d*) a hyperbola.*

**2.** Determine the nature of each of the following conics assuming that it is not degenerate:

(*a*) $y^2 - 4x + 2 = 0$.          (*b*) $x^2 - 2x + 2y^2 = 4$.
(*c*) $4y^2 = 3x^2 - 6$.          (*d*) $x + y = x^2 + y^2$.
(*e*) $4 - x = x^2 - y^2$.          (*f*) $y^2 - 3y = 8 - x$.

**3.** Identify each of the following conics and find the sine and cosine

* No proof is intended.  In order to prove, for example, that a certain section is an ellipse, one must show that the sum of the distances from any point on the section to two fixed points (foci) is a constant.

of the positive acute angle through which the axes should be rotated in
order to eliminate the $xy$ term:

(a) $4x^2 + 4xy + 7y^2 = 8.$          (b) $5x^2 + 6xy - 3y^2 = 6.$
(c) $5x^2 + 24xy - 2y^2 = 48.$          (d) $3x^2 + 4xy + 3y^2 = 10.$
(e) $8x^2 + 8xy - 7y^2 = 35.$          (f) $34x^2 - 24xy + 41y^2 = 50.$

**4.** In each of the following, rotate the axes through a positive acute
angle so as to remove the $xy$ term; draw the curve and show both sets of
axes:

(a) $3x^2 + 4xy = 4.$          (b) $5x^2 + 4xy + 8y^2 = 36.$

(c) $16x^2 - 24xy + 9y^2 - 90x - 120y = 0.$

(d) $481x^2 - 216xy + 544y^2 = 10,000.$

(e) $16x^2 + 24xy + 9y^2 + 20x - 110y + 125 = 0.$

**5.** Show that for any angle $\theta$ through which the axes may be rotated
$B'^2 - 4A'C' = B^2 - 4AC$. This quantity is said to be an *invariant*
under the transformation of rotation because its value is not changed.

**6.** Show that $A' + C' = A + C$ and thus prove that this quantity
is an *invariant* under the transformation of rotation.

**7.** For each of the following equations evaluate $\Delta$ and $B^2 - 4AC$;
identify the locus with the aid of this information:

(a) $x^2 - xy - 6y^2 + x - 3y = 0.$

(b) $x^2 - 2xy + y^2 + x + 2y + 1 = 0.$

(c) $x^2 + xy + y^2 + 4y = 0.$

(d) $x^2 + xy + 4x + 3y + 4 = 0.$

**8.** A point moves so that its distance from the point $(3, 0)$ is equal to
one-half its distance from the $y$-axis. Find the equation of its path and
draw the graph.

**9.** A point moves so that its distance from the origin is equal to its
distance from the line $x + y + 1 = 0$. Find the equation of its path
and sketch it.

**10.** A point moves so that its distance from the point $(0, 6)$ is equal
to twice its distance from the $x$-axis. Find the equation of its path and
sketch it.

**11.** Show, by solving for $y$ in terms of $x$, that the equation

$$y^2 - 2xy + 2x^2 = 16$$

can be written in the form $y = x \pm \sqrt{16 - x^2}$. Obtain its graph by
drawing the separate graphs of $y = x$ and $y = \pm \sqrt{16 - x^2}$ and adding
ordinates.

**12.** Show, by solving for $y$ in terms of $x$, that the equation

$$x^2 - 2xy + y^2 + 2y - 3x - 3 = 0$$

can be written in the form $y = (x - 1) \pm \sqrt{x + 4}$. Obtain its graph
by the method suggested in Prob. 11.

# CHAPTER IX

## OTHER ALGEBRAIC CURVES

**69. Definitions.**—A plane curve is said to be an *algebraic curve* if it is the locus of an equation $f(x, y) = 0$ where $f(x, y)$ is a *polynomial* in $x$ and $y$. The general equations of this type of first and second degree are $Ax + By + C = 0$ and $Ax^2 + Bxy + Cy^2 + Dx + Ey + F = 0$. That of third degree can be written in the form

$$A_0x^3 + A_1x^2y + A_2xy^2 + A_3y^3 + B_0x^2 + B_1xy + B_2y^2 + C_0x + C_1y + D_0 = 0.$$

It is obvious that all the graphs studied so far—the line, the polynomial curves, the graph of $y^2$ = a polynomial in $x$, the graph of $y$ = a rational fractional function of $x$, and all the conics—are algebraic curves.

Any curve that cannot be defined by one or more equations of the type indicated above is called a *transcendental curve*. Examples are the graphs of $y = x + \sin x$ and $y = x \log x$. Transcendental curves and algebraic curves whose equations are of degree higher than the second are called *higher plane curves*.

In this chapter we shall study a few algebraic curves of higher degree.

**70. Discussion of algebraic curves.**—The graphing of an algebraic curve is often facilitated by first writing out a "discussion" similar to that employed in the chapter on rational fractional functions. More general methods of finding vertical and horizontal asymptotes are needed, and certain features included below should be added to the discussion.

1. INTERCEPTS: These are found as before by setting $y = 0$ and solving for $x$ and then setting $x = 0$ and solving

139

for $y$. Of course one may encounter difficulties in solving these equations.

2. Symmetry: The tests previously used for symmetry with respect to the axes and origin apply to any equation. In addition, it is worth while to note that *if the equation is unaltered by interchanging $x$ and $y$ the graph is symmetrical with respect to the line $y = x$.* A simple example is the equation $xy = k$.

3. Asymptotes: Vertical asymptotes may be found by the method used previously, provided the equation can be solved for $y$ in terms of $x$; similarly, if it can be solved for $x$ in terms of $y$ the horizontal asymptotes can be located by setting the denominator equal to zero (if the result is a fraction in lowest terms) and solving for $y$.

### Example

Solving the equation $x^2y^2 - 4y^2 - x^2 = 0$ for $y$ and for $x$ we get, respectively,

$$y = \pm \sqrt{\frac{x^2}{x^2 - 4}}; \qquad x = \pm \sqrt{\frac{4y^2}{y^2 - 1}}.$$

The lines $x = \pm 2$ are vertical asymptotes; the lines $y = \pm 1$ are horizontal asymptotes.

Observe now that the coefficient of the highest power of $y$ in the equation $x^2y^2 - 4y^2 - x^2 = 0$ is $x^2 - 4$, and that the vertical asymptotes are the lines whose equations are obtained by equating to zero its real linear factors; *i.e.*, $x - 2 = 0$, $x + 2 = 0$. Similarly, the coefficient of the highest power of $x$ is $y^2 - 1$, and the equations of the horizontal asymptotes result from equating to zero its real linear factors. It can be shown that the following rule applies to any algebraic curve:

*Obtain the equations of its vertical asymptotes by equating to zero the real linear factors of the coefficient of the highest power of $y$; obtain the equations of the horizontal asymptotes by equating to zero the real linear factors of the coefficient of the highest power of $x$.* If the coefficient of the highest power of $y$ (or $x$) is a constant, or if it has no real linear factors, then there are no vertical (or no horizontal) asymptotes.

### Example

The graph of $x^3 + xy^2 + 2x^2 - 2y^2 = 0$ has no horizontal asymptote since the coefficient of the highest power of $x$ is a constant.   The coefficient of the highest power of $y$ is $x$ − 2, and the line $x - 2 = 0$ is the only vertical asymptote (see Fig. 123).

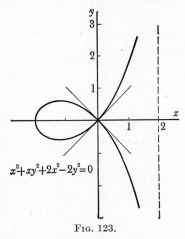

The proof of this rule will not be given.   It has obvious advantages in cases where it is difficult to solve the given equation for each variable in terms of the other.

$x^3 + xy^2 + 2x^2 - 2y^2 = 0$

Fig. 123.

4. EXCLUDED INTERVALS: If the equation is solved for $y$ in terms of $x$, square roots may occur in the right-hand member.   It may then be seen that certain ranges of values of $x$ will make the expression under the radical negative and will, therefore, yield no real value of $y$.   Such *excluded intervals* should be noted in the discussion.   Similarly, if the equation can be solved for $x$ in terms of $y$, certain excluded intervals on the $y$-axis may be noted.

### Example

Solving the equation $x^3 + xy^2 + 2x^2 - 2y^2 = 0$ for $y$ we get

$$y = \pm\, x \sqrt{\frac{x+2}{2-x}}.$$

If $x > 2$, the fraction under the radical is negative because the denominator is negative and the numerator is positive.   If $x < -2$, the fraction is again negative because the numerator is negative and the denominator is positive.   There is then no value of $y$ for $x > 2$ or for $x < -2$.   It would be difficult to solve for $x$ in terms of $y$, but we conclude that there is no excluded interval along the $y$-axis from the following consideration: If we substitute any value $y_1$ for $y$, the resulting equation is a cubic in $x$. A cubic must have one or three real roots, so there must be one or three real values of $x$ corresponding to each value of $y$ (see Fig. 123).

5. Tangent lines at the origin: If the curve goes through the origin, its behavior near that point can be studied by considering only the terms of *lowest* degree in $x$ and $y$ (since for very small values of $x$ and $y$ the terms of higher degree are comparatively negligible). In particular,

*To find the equation of the tangent line or lines at the origin, equate to zero the terms in the equation for which the sum of the exponents of $x$ and $y$ is smallest.*

### Example

The graph of $x^3 + xy^2 + 2x^2 - 2y^2 = 0$ goes through the origin. The equations of its tangent lines at that point are obtained by neglecting the terms $x^3$ and $xy^2$ and setting $2x^2 - 2y^2 = 0$. The curve is thus found to be tangent to the lines $y = x$ and $y = -x$ at the origin (see Fig. 123).

In working out the problems of the next set, the student should arrange the results of his discussion in an orderly fashion as indicated in the following examples.

### Example 1

Discuss and sketch the graph of $x^3 + xy^2 + 2x^2 - 2y^2 = 0$.

*Solution*

1. *Intercepts:* $\begin{cases} \text{on } x\text{-axis—at } (0, 0) \text{ and } (-2, 0). \\ \text{on } y\text{-axis—at } (0, 0). \end{cases}$
2. *Symmetry:* symmetrical to $x$-axis.
3. *Asymptotes:* $\begin{cases} \text{vertical—}x = 2. \\ \text{horizontal—none.} \end{cases}$
4. *Excluded intervals:* $\begin{cases} \text{on } x\text{-axis—}x \text{ cannot be } > 2 \text{ or } < -2. \\ \text{on } y\text{-axis—no excluded interval.} \end{cases}$
5. *Tangents at origin:* $y = x$ and $y = -x$.

The graph, which is shown in Fig. 123, is a curve called a *strophoid*. The general equation of this curve is $x^3 + xy^2 + kx^2 - ky^2 = 0$ where $k$ is a constant.

### Example 2

Discuss and sketch the graph of $x^2y + y - 4x = 0$.

*Solution*

1. *Intercepts:* $\begin{cases} \text{on } x\text{-axis—}(0, 0). \\ \text{on } y\text{-axis—}(0, 0). \end{cases}$
2. *Symmetry:* symmetrical to origin.

3. *Asymptotes:* $\begin{cases} \text{vertical—none.} \\ \text{horizontal—}y = 0 \ (x\text{-axis}). \end{cases}$

4. *Excluded intervals:* $\begin{cases} \text{on } x\text{-axis—no excluded interval.} \\ \text{on } y\text{-axis—}y \text{ cannot be} > 2 \text{ or} < -2. \end{cases}$

(Upon solving for $x$ in terms of $y$ we get $x = \dfrac{2 \pm \sqrt{4 - y^2}}{y}$ from which the last result above follows.)

5. *Tangents at origin:* $y - 4x = 0$ or $y = 4x$.

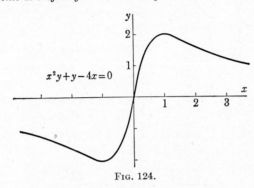

$x^2y + y - 4x = 0$

Fig. 124.

The graph is shown in Fig. 124.  Since the equation can be written in the form $y = \dfrac{4x}{x^2 + 1}$, it is of the type discussed in Chap. V.  The general equation of this curve, which is called the *serpentine*, is

$$x^2y + b^2y - a^2x = 0$$

where $a$ and $b$ are constants.

### Example 3

Discuss and sketch the graph of $x^3 + y^3 = 3xy$.

#### Solution

1. *Intercepts:* $\begin{cases} \text{on } x\text{-axis—}(0, 0). \\ \text{on } y\text{-axis—}(0, 0). \end{cases}$

2. *Symmetry:* $\begin{cases} \text{symmetrical to the line } y = x \text{ (since interchanging } x \\ \text{and } y \text{ leaves the equation unaltered).} \end{cases}$

3. *Asymptotes:* $\begin{cases} \text{vertical—none.} \\ \text{horizontal—none.} \end{cases}$

4. *Excluded intervals:* $\begin{cases} \text{none (since substituting a value for } x \text{ or } y \\ \text{leaves a cubic in the other variable).} \end{cases}$

5. *Tangents at origin:* $xy = 0$ or $x = 0$ and $y = 0$.

The curve is shown in Fig. 125.  It is called the *Folium of Descartes* and its general equation is $x^3 + y^3 = 3axy$.

This last example illustrates the fact that in some cases the discussion does not yield enough information to enable one to sketch the curve without plotting a fairly large

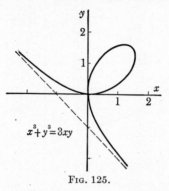

FIG. 125.

number of points. Observe also that each time one substitutes a value for $x$ he must solve a cubic equation in order to get the corresponding values of $y$. This is of course a laborious process, and it is partly for this reason that algebraic curves of higher degree are often studied by means of *parametric equations* which are discussed in Chap.

XII. It will be shown there that the above folium can be defined by means of the *two* equations

$$x = \frac{3t}{1 + t^3}, \qquad y = \frac{3t^2}{1 + t^3},$$

where $t$ is a third variable called a *parameter*.* The equation $x^3 + y^3 = 3xy$ results from the operation of eliminating $t$ between these two equations. The graph (Fig. 125) was actually plotted from these equations. Any value substituted for $t$ yields a pair of corresponding values of $x$ and $y$. Thus if we put $t = 2$, we get $x = \frac{2}{3}$ from the first equation and $y = \frac{4}{3}$ from the second. The point $(\frac{2}{3}, \frac{4}{3})$ is then a point on the curve.

### PROBLEMS

Discuss and sketch the graphs of the following equations: (Some of these equations are of previously considered types and are intended for review.)

**1.** $y = x^3$.          **2.** $y^2 = 4x^3$.          **3.** $x^2y = 9$.

**4.** $xy = x + 1$.          **5.** $9x^2 + 16y^2 = 72x$.

**6.** $y^2 = x^2(x - 1)$.          **7.** $y^2 = x(x - 4)(x - 6)$.

**8.** $x^2y - 4y - x^2 = 0$.          **9.** $x^2y + 4y = 8$.

**10.** $x^2y - 4y - 4x = 0$.          **11.** $x^2y + 4y = 8x$.

* See Prob. 10, p. 182.

**12.** $x^2y^2 - 4x^2 - 4y^2 = 0.$       **13.** $y^3 + x^2y + y^2 - x^2 = 0.$
**14.** $x^2y^2 + 4x^2 - 4y^2 = 0.$       **15.** $xy^2 - 4y - x = 0.$
**16.** $x^4 + y^4 = 16.$               **17.** $x^3 + xy^2 + 2y^2 = 6x^2.$

**18.** $x^3 + xy^2 = 4y^2.$             **19.** $y^2 = \dfrac{a^2x^2}{a^2 - x^2}$ (arclight curve).

**20.** $xy^2 - a^2y - b^2x = 0$ (the pilaster).

**21.** $y = \dfrac{8a^3}{x^2 + 4a^2}$ (the witch).       **22.** $y^2 = \dfrac{a^2x^2}{x^2 - a^2}.$

**23.** $y^2 = \dfrac{3ax^2 - x^3}{x + a}$ (the trisectrix).

**24.** $y^2 = \dfrac{x^3}{2a - x}$ (the cissoid).

**25.** $x^2 - 2y^3 - 8y^2 = 0$ (see Fig. 158, page 179).
**26.** $x^4 - 3xy^2 + 2y^3 = 0$ (see Fig. 157, page 178).
**27.** $(x^2 + y^2)^2 = 16x^2y$ (see Prob. 17, page 182).

Solve each of the following equations for $y^2$, obtaining $y^2 = f(x)$; then make a rough graph by first sketching the graph of $y = f(x)$ and then taking the square roots of the ordinates:

**28.** $x^2y^2 - 4y^2 = 2x^2 + 9.$       **29.** $x^2y^2 + y^2 = 4x + 2.$
**30.** $xy^2 + 2y^2 = 4x - 6.$         **31.** $9y^2 - x^2y^2 - x^2 = 0.$
**32.** $y^2(x^2 - 1)^2 = x.$           **33.** $y^2(x + 1)^2 = 8x.$
**34.** $(x^2 - 9)y^2 = 4x(x^2 - 4).$

# CHAPTER X

## THE TRIGONOMETRIC CURVES

**71. The sine and cosine curves.**—The graphs of $y = \sin x$ and $y = \cos x$ can of course be constructed by assigning values to $x$, finding the corresponding values of $y$ (from a table), and plotting the points. The curves are shown in

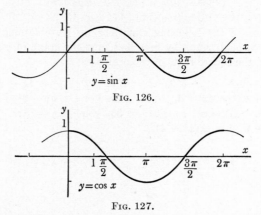

FIG. 126.

FIG. 127.

Figs. 126 and 127. The values of $x$ may be in either radians or degrees, but radian measure is often preferable.* It should be observed that since $\sin (x + \frac{1}{2}\pi) = \cos x$, the graph of $y = \cos x$ is identical with that of

$$y = \sin (x + \tfrac{1}{2}\pi);$$

this, in turn, is simply the graph of $y = \sin x$ with the origin translated $\frac{1}{2}\pi$ units in the positive $x$-direction.

**72. Periodic functions.**—*A function $f(x)$ is said to be periodic with period $k$ if, for all values of $x$,*

* Any student who is not thoroughly familiar with radian measure and with the general definitions of and relations between the trigonometric functions should study pages 7 to 12 of the introduction before proceeding with this chapter.

$$f(x + k) = f(x).$$

Since sin $(x + 2\pi) \equiv$ sin $x$, this function is periodic with period $2\pi$. If the graph were constructed for $x = 0$ to $2\pi$, that for $x = 2\pi$ to $4\pi$ could be obtained by simply repeating this part, and so on. Any piece of length $2\pi$ along the $x$-axis is called a *complete cycle* of the curve.

It follows from the above definition that sin $x$ also has periods $4\pi$, $6\pi$, etc. Ordinarily, when we speak of the period of a periodic function $f(x)$ we shall mean the *smallest* positive number $k$ for which $f(x + k) \equiv f(x)$.

From the definitions of the trigonometric functions (page 9) it is evident that they are all periodic with period $2\pi$; tan $x$ and cot $x$ also have the period $\pi$.

**73. Even and odd functions.**—A function $f(x)$ is said to be an *even* function if $f(-x) \equiv f(x)$; it is an *odd* function if $f(-x) \equiv -f(x)$. The graph of an even function is symmetrical with respect to the $y$-axis; that of an odd function is symmetrical with respect to the origin.

### Examples

cos $x$ and $x^2$ are even functions since cos $(-x) \equiv$ cos $x$ and $(-x)^2 \equiv x^2$; their graphs have symmetry with respect to the $y$-axis. Similarly, sin $x$, tan $x$, and $x^3$ are odd functions.

In general, a function $f(x)$ is neither even nor odd. However, any function can be expressed as the sum of an even and an odd function. Thus $e^x$ is neither even nor odd, but

$$e^x \equiv \frac{e^x + e^{-x}}{2} + \frac{e^x - e^{-x}}{2};$$

the first fraction on the right is an even function and the second is odd. More generally, $f(x)$ is expressed as the sum of an even and an odd function by writing

$$f(x) \equiv \frac{f(x) + f(-x)}{2} + \frac{f(x) - f(-x)}{2}.$$

**74. $y = a$ sin $nx$ or $a$ cos $nx$.**—The largest and smallest values of sin $\theta$ or cos $\theta$ are $+1$ and $-1$, respectively; the

corresponding largest and smallest values of the function
**a sin nx** or **a cos nx** are $\pm a$.  The constant **a** is called the
*amplitude* of the function.

It is easy to see that

$$a \sin n\left(x + \frac{2\pi}{n}\right) \equiv a \sin nx;$$

it follows that the function $a \sin nx$ is periodic with period
$2\pi/n$.  The same is true of $a \cos nx$.  Consequently,

*The graphs of $y = a \sin nx$ and $y = a \cos nx$ are sine and
cosine curves, respectively, having amplitude $a$ and period
$2\pi/n$.*

### Examples

The graph of $y = 4 \sin \pi x$ is a sine curve having amplitude 4 and
period $2\pi/\pi = 2$ radians.  That of $y = 2 \cos \frac{2}{3}x$ is a cosine curve with
amplitude 2 and period $2\pi/(\frac{2}{3}) = 3\pi$ (see Fig. 128).

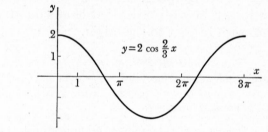

Fig. 128.

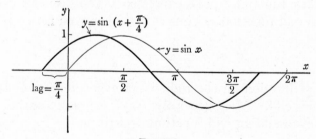

Fig. 129.

**75. $y = a \sin (nx + \alpha)$ or $a \cos (nx + \alpha)$.**—The graphs
of $y = \sin x$ and $y = \sin\left(x + \frac{\pi}{4}\right)$ are shown in Fig. 129.
They are of course identical except that the wave whose

equation is $y = \sin\left(x + \dfrac{\pi}{4}\right)$ "lags" behind by an amount

$\dfrac{\pi}{4}$. Similarly, the graph of $y = \sin\left(x - \dfrac{\pi}{4}\right)$ would "lead" that of $y = \sin x$ by the same amount.*

Considering now the more general case, we may easily show that the graph of $y = a \sin(nx + \alpha)$ is simply the curve $y = a \sin nx$ with an *angle of lag* whose amount is $\alpha/n$. The proof is as follows: Take the equation

$$y = a \sin(nx + \alpha)$$

and let $x = x' - \dfrac{\alpha}{n}$. This translates the origin to the left (if $\alpha$ is positive) by an amount $\alpha/n$, and the equation obtained is

$$y = a \sin nx'.$$

If $\alpha$ is negative, the translation is to the right and the negative angle of lag is called a *lead*.

Similar considerations of course apply to the equation $y = a \cos(nx + \alpha)$. Consequently,

*The graphs of $y = a$ sin $(nx + \alpha)$ and $y = a$ cos $(nx + \alpha)$ are sine and cosine curves, respectively, having amplitude a, period $2\pi/n$, and a lag (if $\alpha > 0$) or lead (if $\alpha < 0$) of $\alpha/n$.*

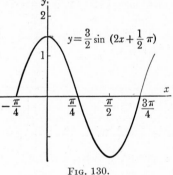

$y = \dfrac{3}{2} \sin\left(2x + \dfrac{1}{2}\pi\right)$

FIG. 130.

### Examples

The graph of $y = 3 \cos(4x - \frac{1}{2}\pi)$ has amplitude 3, period $2\pi/4 = \pi/2$, and a lead of $\frac{1}{2}\pi/4 = \pi/8$ radians. That of $y = \frac{3}{2} \sin(2x + \frac{1}{2}\pi)$ has amplitude $\frac{3}{2}$, period $2\pi/2 = \pi$, and a lag of $\frac{1}{2}\pi/2 = \pi/4$. This equation is of course equivalent to $y = \frac{3}{2} \cos 2x$ (see Fig. 130).

**76. The function $a$ sin $nx + b$ cos $nx$.**—The graphs of $y = \sin x$ and $y = \cos x$ are drawn lightly in Fig. 131.

* If $x$ denotes *time* the curve that we call lagging is *earlier*. Hence these terms are also used in the reverse sense.

By adding ordinates we have constructed the graph (heavy curve) of

$$y = \sin x + \cos x.$$

This appears to be also a sine or cosine curve with larger

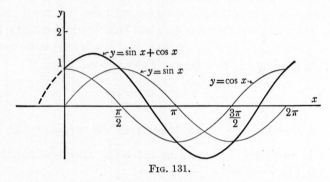

Fig. 131.

amplitude.    To show that this is actually the case we note that

$$\sin x + \cos x \equiv \sqrt{2}\left(\frac{1}{\sqrt{2}} \sin x + \frac{1}{\sqrt{2}} \cos x\right);$$

now since $\sin (\pi/4) = \cos (\pi/4) = 1/\sqrt{2}$, we have

$$\sin x + \cos x \equiv \sqrt{2}\left(\sin x \cos \frac{\pi}{4} + \cos x \sin \frac{\pi}{4}\right)$$

$$\equiv \sqrt{2} \sin \left(x + \frac{\pi}{4}\right).$$

It is thus shown that the graph of $y = \sin x + \cos x$ is identical with that of $y = \sqrt{2} \sin \left(x + \frac{\pi}{4}\right)$. *It is a sine curve with amplitude* $\sqrt{2}$, *period* $2\pi$, *and lag* $\pi/4$.

More generally, the equation

$$y = a \sin nx + b \cos nx$$

can be written in the equivalent form

$$y = \sqrt{a^2 + b^2}\left(\frac{a}{\sqrt{a^2 + b^2}} \sin nx + \frac{b}{\sqrt{a^2 + b^2}} \cos nx\right).$$

If we let $\alpha$ be an angle such that $\cos \alpha = a/\sqrt{a^2 + b^2}$ and $\sin \alpha = b/\sqrt{a^2 + b^2}$, as indicated in Fig. 132, the above equation becomes

$$y = \sqrt{a^2 + b^2} \, (\sin \, nx$$
$$\cos \alpha + \cos \, nx \, \sin \, \alpha)$$
$$= \sqrt{a^2 + b^2} \, \sin \, (nx + \alpha).$$

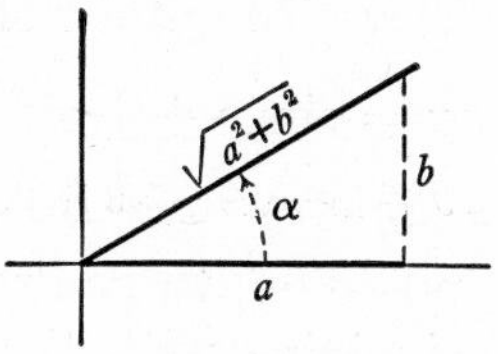

FIG. 132.

Consequently, *the graph of $y = a \, \sin$ $nx + b \, \cos \, nx$ is a sine curve with amplitude $\sqrt{a^2 + b^2}$, period $2\pi/n$, and a lag (or lead) of $\alpha/n$ where $\alpha$ depends upon $a$ and $b$ as indicated above.*

**77. Graphical addition of sine and cosine waves.**—In Fig. 133 we have drawn the graphs of $y = \sin x$ and

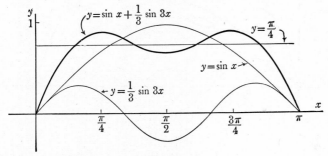

FIG. 133.

$y = \frac{1}{3} \sin 3x$. By adding the ordinates to these curves for each value of $x$, we have obtained the graph of the equation

$$y = \sin x + \tfrac{1}{3} \sin 3x.$$

We have also drawn the line $y = \pi/4$, and we may observe that the last curve lies rather close to this line throughout most of the interval from $x = 0$ to $\pi$.

In Fig. 134 we have drawn the graphs of $y = \sin x$, $y = \frac{1}{3} \sin 3x$, and $y = \frac{1}{5} \sin 5x$. By adding the three ordinates for each value of $x$ we have constructed the graph of the equation

$$y = \sin x + \tfrac{1}{3} \sin 3x + \tfrac{1}{5} \sin 5x.$$

It may again be observed that this curve lies near the line

$y = \pi/4$ throughout most of the interval. It is shown in higher mathematics that if one should construct the successive graphs of the equations

$$y = \sin x + \tfrac{1}{3} \sin 3x + \tfrac{1}{5} \sin 5x + \tfrac{1}{7} \sin 7x,$$
$$y = \sin x + \tfrac{1}{3} \sin 3x + \tfrac{1}{5} \sin 5x + \tfrac{1}{7} \sin 7x + \tfrac{1}{9} \sin 9x,$$

and so on, these graphs would come successively nearer to coinciding with the line $y = \pi/4$ throughout any interval that lies inside the interval $x = 0$ to $\pi$.

In the study of alternating current and voltage, in the analysis of vibration problems, and in fact in almost all advanced branches of applied mathematics, it is an

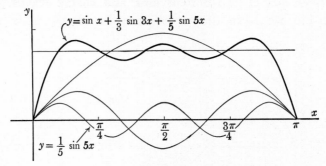

Fig. 134.

extremely important fact that a rather arbitrarily specified function $f(x)$ can be thus approximated by a proper "series" of sine and cosine terms. We cannot here enter into a discussion of this subject, but the student of analytic geometry should understand clearly how one goes about plotting the separate trigonometric terms and adding the ordinates to obtain the successive sum functions.

The method of addition of ordinates is of course also used in obtaining the graphs of equations such as

$$y = x + \sin x,$$

$y = x^2 - \cos x$, etc. If one thinks of making the separate graphs of $y = x$ and $y = \sin x$, and adding the ordinates, he can easily visualize the general character of the graph of $y = x + \sin x$.

## PROBLEMS

In each of the following, determine the amplitude and period; sketch the curve, marking the units on both axes:

**1.** $y = 3 \cos \frac{1}{2}x$.

**2.** $y = 2 \sin 2x$.

**3.** $y = \frac{3}{2} \sin \pi x$.

**4.** $y = \frac{1}{2} \cos \frac{\pi}{2} x$.

**5.** $y = 4 \cos \frac{2}{3}x$.

**6.** $y = 2 \sin \frac{1}{4}x$.

In each of the following, determine the amplitude, period, and lag or lead; sketch the curve, marking the units on both axes:

**7.** $y = \cos \left( x + \frac{\pi}{6} \right)$.

**8.** $y = 3 \sin \left( x - \frac{\pi}{4} \right)$.

**9.** $y = 2 \cos \left( 2x - \frac{\pi}{3} \right)$.

**10.** $y = 3 \cos (3x - \pi)$.

**11.** $y = \frac{3}{2} \sin (\pi x + \pi)$.

**12.** $y = 4 \cos \left( 2\pi x - \frac{\pi}{2} \right)$.

**13.** Draw on the same axes the graphs of $y = \sin x$, $y = \sin^2 x$, and $y = \sqrt{\sin x}$.

**14.** Show that the functions $\sin^2 x$ and $\cos^2 x$ are periodic with period $\pi$.

**15.** Show that the product of two even or odd functions is an even function while the product of an even and an odd function is odd.

Sketch the graphs of the following equations; use the method of addition of ordinates wherever convenient:

**16.** $y = 2 \cos x + \sin 2x$.

**17.** $y = 3 \sin x + 2 \cos 2x$.

**18.** $y = \frac{1}{2}x + \cos x$.

**19.** $y = x + \sin x$.

**20.** $y = 2 \sin^2 2x$.

**21.** $y = \cos^2 x$.

**22.** $y = \sin^2 \frac{1}{2}x$.

**23.** $y = \sin^3 x$.

**24.** $y^2 = \sin 2x$.

**25.** $y^2 = \cos x$.

**26.** $y = \sin^2 x + \cos^2 x$.

**27.** $y = \cos^2 x - \sin^2 x$.

**28.** $y = \sin x \cos x$.

**29.** $y = x^2 - \cos x$.

In each of the following, obtain the graph from $x = -\pi$ to $\pi$ by the method of addition of ordinates as illustrated by Figs. 133 and 134:

**30.** $y = 2(\sin x - \frac{1}{2} \sin 2x + \frac{1}{3} \sin 3x)$.

**31.** $y = \frac{\pi}{2} + 2(\sin x + \frac{1}{3} \sin 3x)$.

**32.** $y = \frac{\pi}{4} - \frac{2}{\pi} \left( \frac{\cos 2x}{1^2} + \frac{\cos 6x}{3^2} \right)$.

**33.** Plot carefully on the same axes the graphs of $y = \sin x$ and $y = x - \frac{x^3}{6}$ for $x = -\pi$ to $\pi$ and compare the curves. It is shown in more advanced mathematics that for all values of $x$ the value of $\sin x$ is given by

$$\sin x = x - \frac{x^3}{3!} + \frac{x^5}{5!} - \frac{x^7}{7!} + \cdots,$$

where the expression on the right is called an *infinite series*. For small values of $x$, the higher powers are negligible and the graph of $y = \sin x$ should therefore nearly coincide with that of $y = x - \frac{x^3}{6}$ in a range near the origin.

**34.** Same as Prob. 33 for the curves $y = \cos x$ and $y = 1 - \frac{x^2}{2}$. The equation for calculating $\cos x$, which corresponds to that given above for $\sin x$, is

$$\cos x = 1 - \frac{x^2}{2!} + \frac{x^4}{4!} - \frac{x^6}{6!} + \cdots.$$

The graph of $y = 1 - \frac{x^2}{2} + \frac{x^4}{24}$ would be a better approximation to that of $y = \cos x$ in a wider interval about the origin.

**78. Graphs of tan x, cot x, sec x, csc x.**—The graph of the equation $y = \tan x$ is shown in Fig. 135. This is an

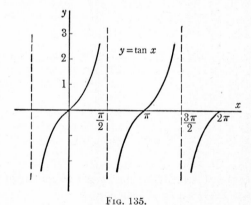

Fig. 135.

odd function, and it is of course periodic with period $\pi$. The lines $x = \pi/2$, $3\pi/2$, etc., are vertical asymptotes. The graph of $y = \cot x$ is similar and may be drawn by the student.

In Fig. 136 we have drawn the graph of $y = \sin x$, and

on the same axes that of $y = \csc x$. The latter graph was obtained by using the relation

$$\csc x = \frac{1}{\sin x};$$

thus, where $\sin x = 1$, $\csc x = 1$; where $\sin x = \frac{1}{2}$, $\csc x = 2$; where $\sin x$ approaches zero, $\csc x$ increases beyond bound. The lines $x = 0$, $x = \pi$, etc., are vertical asymptotes.

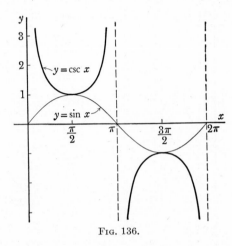

Fig. 136.

The same reciprocal relation exists between the functions sec $x$ and cos $x$. The student can easily draw the corresponding figure.

**79. The inverse trigonometric functions.**—We define the abbreviation

(1)　　　　　$y = \textbf{arcsin } x$　　or　　$y = \sin^{-1} x$

to mean *y is the radian measure of an angle whose sine is x.* We may assign to $x$ in (1) any value from $-1$ to $+1$, and to each such value of $x$ there will correspond an indefinite number of values of $y$. Thus if $x = \frac{1}{2}$ we have

$$y = \arcsin \tfrac{1}{2} = \text{an angle whose sine is } \tfrac{1}{2} = \frac{\pi}{6}, \frac{5\pi}{6}, -\frac{7\pi}{6}, \text{ etc.}$$

The function arcsin $x$ is thus a *multiple-valued* function defined over the interval $-1 \le x \le 1$.

If we solve (1) for $x$ in terms of $y$ we obtain the equation

$$x = \sin y;$$

the graph of $y = \arcsin x$ is therefore identical with that of $x = \sin y$, which in turn is simply that of $y = \sin x$ with the axes interchanged (Fig. 137).

The function can be made single-valued by agreeing to use for $y$ the value on the arc labeled $AB$ in the figure.

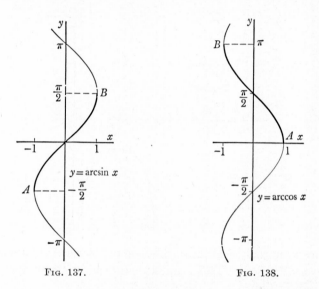

FIG. 137.    FIG. 138.

This part of the curve is called its *principal branch,* and the corresponding values of the function are called its *principal values.* Thus the principal value of arcsin $\frac{1}{2}$ is $\pi/6$; the principal value of arcsin $-1$ is $-\pi/2$ (**not 3$\pi$/2**). *The principal value of arcsin $x$ is the angle lying in the interval from $-\pi/2$ to $+\pi/2$ whose sine is $x$. There is one and only one such angle corresponding to each value of $x$ from $-1$ to $+1$.*

The inverse trigonometric functions arise rather often in integral calculus. They are encountered, for example, in the problem of finding the area of an ellipse. In order to handle such problems intelligently the student must

have a clear understanding of the graphs of these functions
and must be familiar with their principal values.

The graph of $y = \arccos x$ is shown in Fig. 138.  Since
this equation is equivalent to $x = \cos y$, the graph is simply
the curve $y = \cos x$ with the axes interchanged.  The
function is made single-valued by using, for each value of $x$,

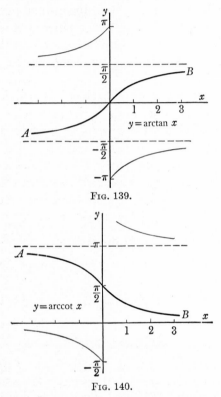

Fig. 139.

Fig. 140.

the value of $y$ on the arc $AB$.  Thus the principal value of
arccos $\frac{1}{2}$ is $\pi/3$; the principal value of arccos $-1$ is $\pi$, etc.
*The principal value of arccos $x$ is the angle lying in the interval
from 0 to $\pi$ whose cosine is $x$.  There is one and only one such
angle corresponding to each value of $x$ from $-1$ to $+1$.*

The graphs of $y = \arctan x$ and $y = \text{arccot } x$ are shown in
Figs. 139 and 140.  In each case the principal branch is the
arc $AB$.  Observe that the principal value of arctan $x$ lies

between $-\pi/2$ and $\pi/2$ and, in this sense, is like that of arcsin $x$. The principal value of arccot $x$ lies between 0 and $\pi$ and thus corresponds to that of arccos $x$. The principal value of arctan $-1$ is $-\pi/4$; the principal value of arccot $-1$ is $3\pi/4$.

Our selection of principal values appears to be perfectly arbitrary. One reason for choosing principal values at all is to give each of these functions a single definite value for each value of $x$. This is essential in operations of calculus. The student may conclude, after studying the graphs, that our choice is in each case the most natural one. There are certain advantages in our selections which will appear in the study of calculus.

We shall not discuss the graphs of arcsec $x$ and arccsc $x$. These functions are of course defined for $|x| \geqq 1$, and their graphs are identical with those of sec $x$ and csc $x$, respectively, with the axes interchanged. One can usually avoid the use of these functions by substituting arccos $(1/x)$ for arcsec $x$ and arcsin $(1/x)$ for arccsc $x$.

### PROBLEMS

Draw the graphs of the following equations; mark the units on both axes:

**1.** $y = \frac{1}{2} \cot x$.     **2.** $y = 2 \tan \frac{1}{2}x$.     **3.** $y = \tan 2x$.

**4.** $y = \cot\left(x + \dfrac{\pi}{4}\right)$.     **5.** $y = \sec x$.     **6.** $y = \csc \frac{1}{4}x$.

**7.** $y = \csc^2 x$.     **8.** $y \cos^2 x = 1$.

In each of the following, solve the given pair of equations simultaneously to find the coordinates of the points of intersection of the two graphs in the given interval; illustrate the result by drawing the graphs:

**9.** $y = \sin x$;     $y = \frac{1}{2} \tan x$; $0 \leqq x < 2\pi$.

**10.** $y = \sin 2x$;     $y = \cos x$;    $0 \leqq x < 2\pi$.

**11.** $y = 3 \tan \frac{1}{4}x$; $y = 2 \sin \frac{1}{2}x$; $0 \leqq x < 8\pi$.

**12.** $y = \cot 2x$;     $y = 2 \sin 4x$; $0 \leqq x \leqq \dfrac{\pi}{2}$.

**13.** Draw on the same axes the graphs of

(a) $y = \tan x$; $y = \cot x$.

(b) $y = \cos x$; $y = \sec x$.

What relation exists between the ordinates to the two curves?

In Probs. 14 to 22, only the principal values of the inverse trigonometric functions are to be considered:

**14.** sin arccos $\frac{1}{2}$ = ?            **15.** sin arccot $(-1)$ = ?

**16.** cos (arcsin 1 + arctan $\frac{3}{4}$) = ?   **17.** tan 2 arccos $\frac{12}{13}$ = ?

**18.** tan $\frac{1}{2}$ arccos $\frac{3}{5}$ = ?      **19.** cot $\left(\dfrac{\pi}{4} - \arcsin \frac{3}{5}\right)$ = ?

**20.** Show that arctan $\frac{1}{4}$ + arctan $\frac{3}{5}$ = $\pi/4$.  Hint: Take the tangent of both sides.

**21.** Show that arctan $\frac{1}{2}$ + arctan $\frac{1}{3}$ = $\pi/4$.

**22.** Show that arctan $\frac{1}{3}$ + arctan $\frac{1}{5}$ = arctan $\frac{4}{7}$.

**23.** The radius of the base of a right circular cone is 2 ft.  The height is 1 ft. when the time $t = 0$ and increases at a rate of $\frac{1}{4}$ ft. per minute. Express the vertex angle $\theta$ as a function of $t$.

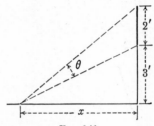

FIG. 141.

**24.** A picture 2 ft. high hangs on a wall with its lower edge 3 ft. above the observer's eye (Fig. 141).  Express the angle $\theta$ subtended by the picture at the eye as a function of the distance $x$ of the observer from the wall.  Sketch a graph showing approximately how this angle varies with $x$.

Draw the graphs of the following equations:

**25.** $y = 2 \arcsin \frac{1}{2}x$.             **26.** $y = \arccos 2x$.

**27.** $y = \operatorname{arcsec} x$.                  **28.** $y = \operatorname{arccsc} x$.

**29.** $y = \arcsin \left(x + \dfrac{\pi}{4}\right)$.          **30.** $y = \arctan \left(2x - \dfrac{\pi}{2}\right)$.

Solve the following equations for $x$ considering only the principal values of the angles:

**31.** arcsin $2x$ − arcsin $x$ = $\frac{1}{3}\pi$.

**32.** arctan $2x$ + arctan $3x$ = $\frac{1}{4}\pi$.

**33.** tan $\left(\dfrac{\pi}{4} + \arctan x\right)$ = 7.

**34.** arcsin $2x$ + arctan $\frac{3}{4}$ = $\frac{1}{2}\pi$.

# CHAPTER XI

## THE EXPONENTIAL
## AND LOGARITHMIC CURVES

**80. The graph of $y = a^x$.**—The graph of the equation $y = 2^x$ is shown in Fig. 142. The table of corresponding values of $x$ and $y$ is obtained in the usual way. Thus,

when $x = -3$, $\quad y = 2^{-3} = \dfrac{1}{2^3} = \dfrac{1}{8}$;

when $x = 2\frac{1}{2}$, $\quad y = 2^{2+\frac{1}{2}} = 2^2 \cdot 2^{\frac{1}{2}} = 4\sqrt{2} = 5.7.$*

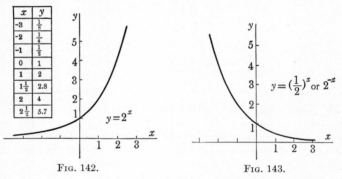

| $x$ | $y$ |
|-----|-----|
| -3 | $\frac{1}{8}$ |
| -2 | $\frac{1}{4}$ |
| -1 | $\frac{1}{2}$ |
| 0 | 1 |
| 1 | 2 |
| $1\frac{1}{2}$ | 2.8 |
| 2 | 4 |
| $2\frac{1}{2}$ | 5.7 |

FIG. 142.              FIG. 143.

The graph of the more general exponential equation

$$y = a^x \qquad (a > 0)$$

has the same general shape. If $a > 1$, $a^x$ increases as $x$ increases and the curve is like that in Fig. 142. If $0 < a < 1$, then $a^x$ *decreases* as $x$ increases and the curve is as shown in Fig. 143.

A very important special case of the exponential function is that in which the number $a$ in the expression $a^x$ is replaced by the special number $e(= 2.718$ approximately) which is

---

* Any student who is not thoroughly familiar with the rules for handling exponents, and with the use of negative and fractional exponents, should study the review of exponents, pages 4 to 5, before proceeding.

the base of natural logarithms.　The graph of the equation

$$y = e^x = 2.718^x$$

is shown in Fig. 144.　The values of $y$ can be obtained by using logarithms or by the use of tables that give directly the value of $e^x$.　See for example Table V, page 294, in this book.

A more general exponential equation is

$$y = ae^{bx}$$

where $a$ and $b$ are constants.　Equations of this form occur often in various branches of science.　Let, for example, $Q$ denote a variable quantity that has the value $Q_0$ when the time $t = 0$ and that increases (or decreases) with $t$ in such a way that its rate of increase (or decrease) is at every instant proportional to the

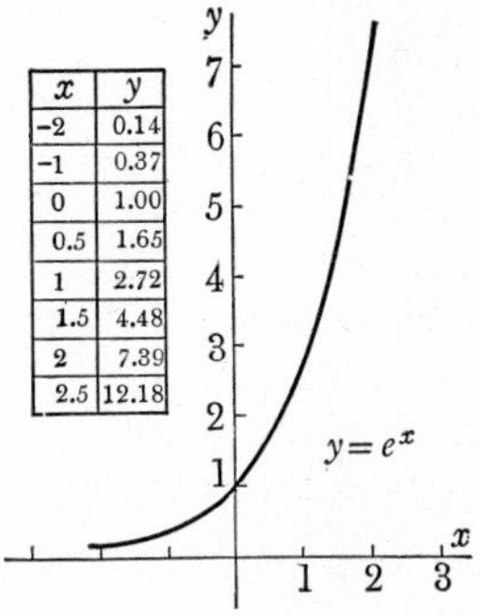

| $x$ | $y$ |
|-----|-----|
| -2 | 0.14 |
| -1 | 0.37 |
| 0 | 1.00 |
| 0.5 | 1.65 |
| 1 | 2.72 |
| 1.5 | 4.48 |
| 2 | 7.39 |
| 2.5 | 12.18 |

FIG. 144.

magnitude of $Q$ at that instant.　It can be shown that under such conditions the equation connecting $Q$ and $t$ is of the form

$$Q = Q_0 e^{bt}.$$

This equation is said to express the "compound-interest" law.　Money on which interest is compounded continuously obeys this law.　Certain chemical reactions also proceed in accordance with this equation.　The rate at which bacteria in a culture increase is proportional to the number present.　Consequently, the expression for the number present at any time is of this type.

In making the table of values for such equations it is convenient to use a form such as that shown below for the equation

$$Q = 1.5e^{0.4t}.$$

| $t$............... | $-3$ | $-2$ | $-1$ | 0 | 1 | 2 | 3 |
|---|---|---|---|---|---|---|---|
| $0.4t$........... | $-1.2$ | $-0.8$ | $-0.4$ | 0 | 0.4 | 0.8 | 1.2 |
| $e^{0.4t}$........... | 0.30 | 0.45 | 0.67 | 1 | 1.49 | 2.22 | 3.32 |
| $Q$.............. | 0.45 | 0.68 | 1.01 | 1.50 | 2.24 | 3.33 | 4.98 |

Here, the third row is obtained from a table of values of $e^x$, using for $x$ the values in the second row.   The fourth

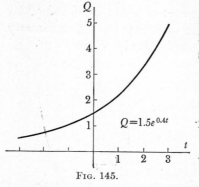

FIG. 145.

row is of course obtained from the third by multiplying by 1.5.  The graph is shown in Fig. 145.

**81.  The graph of $y = \log_a x$ $(a > 1)$.**—It   follows  from the definition of the logarithm of a number* that if

$$y = \log_a x,$$

then

$$x = a^y.$$

It is evident then that the graph of the equation $y = \log_a x$ is identical with that of $x = a^y$, which in turn is simply that of $y = a^x$ with the axes interchanged.   The graphs of $y = \log_2 x$ and $y = \log_e x$ are shown in Fig. 146.   That of $y = \log_{10} x$ is of course similar in form.   In fact, since

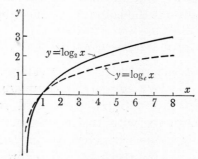

FIG. 146.

$$\log_{10} x = 0.43429 \cdot \log_e x,$$

each ordinate on this curve is approximately four-tenths of the corresponding ordinate on the graph of $y = \log_e x$.

**82.  Natural logarithms.   Use of tables.**—The student is of course familiar with the fact that if

$$\log_{10} 4.87 = 0.6875,$$

* See Introduction, page 5.

then,

$$\log_{10} 48.7 = 1.6875; \qquad \log_{10} 487 = 2.6875, \text{ etc.}$$

The "decimal part" or *mantissa* of the *common logarithm* of a number is thus independent of the position of the decimal point in the number. This property follows from the general law:

$$\log_a (MN) = \log_a M + \log_a N.$$

Thus since $48.7 = (4.87) \cdot (10)$ we have

$$\begin{aligned}
\log_{10} 48.7 &= \log_{10} 4.87 + \log_{10} 10 \\
&= 0.6875 + 1 \\
&= 1.6875.
\end{aligned}$$

The above property is thus seen to result from the fact that $\log_{10} 10 = 1$.

The corresponding formula for natural logarithms is

$$\log_e 48.7 = \log_e 4.87 + \log_e 10.$$

The value of $\log_e 10$ is **2.3026,** so we have

$$\log_e 48.7 = \log_e 4.87 + \mathbf{2.3026}.$$

Similarly,

$$\log_e 487 = \log_e 4.87 + 2(\mathbf{2.3026}), \text{ etc.}$$

Table IV, page 292, gives the natural logarithms of numbers from 1 to 10, to four places. Using it we readily find that

$$\log_e 4.87 = 1.5831.$$

Then,

$$\begin{aligned}
\log_e 48.7 &= 1.5831 + 2.3026 = 3.8857; \\
\log_e 487 &= 1.5831 + 2(2.3026) = 6.1883; \\
\log_e 0.487 &= 1.5831 - 2.3026 \\
&= 1.5831 + (7.6974 - 10) = 9.2805 - 10.
\end{aligned}$$

In this connection, note that the necessary multiples of $\log_e 10$ are given at the bottom of the page.

The problem of finding $N$ when $\log_e N$ is given is solved as indicated in the following:

*Example*

Given $\log_e N = 8.3465$, find $N$.

*Solution*

First subtract $3 \log_e 10$ from the given logarithm:

$$8.3465 - 6.9078 = 1.4387.$$

Next, find the number in the table whose natural logarithm is 1.4387. This number is 4.215. Now multiply this number by $10^3$ to obtain the final result, $N = 4215$.

When a table of natural logarithms of desired accuracy is not available, one computes $\log_e N$ from the formula

$$\log_e N = \log_{10} N \cdot \log_e 10 = 2.3026 \log_{10} N.*$$

This is of course a special case of the general formula

$$\log_b N = \frac{\log_a N}{\log_a b} = \log_a N \cdot \log_b a.$$

## PROBLEMS

Draw the graphs of the following equations:

**1.** $y = 4^x$.    **2.** $y = 2(3)^{-x}$.    **3.** $y = (1.6)^x$.

**4.** $y = (0.3)^x$.    **5.** $y = e^{0.1x}$.    **6.** $y = \frac{1}{2}e^{2x}$.

**7.** $y = 2.4e^{0.6x}$.    **8.** $y = e^{-x^2}$.

**9.** If \$500 is invested at a rate of 3 per cent per annum compounded continuously, the compound amount at the end of $t$ years is given by the formula

$$A = 500e^{0.03t}.$$

Draw the graph showing how the amount increases with the time; compare the amount at the end of 10 years with that obtained if the interest is compounded annually.

**10.** Draw the graph of $y = 2^{x-2}$. HINT: Since $2^{x-2} = 2^x 2^{-2} = \frac{1}{4}(2^x)$, the given equation is equivalent to $y = \frac{1}{4}(2^x)$.

**11.** Show that the equation $y = e^{ax+b}$ can be written in the form $y = ce^{ax}$ where $c = e^b$. See hint in Prob. 10.

**12.** Show that if two ordinates are drawn to the curve $y = e^x$ one unit apart the ratio of the longer to the shorter is approximately 2.7. HINT: $e^{x+1}/e^x = e$.

* To eight places the value of $\log_e 10$ is 2.30258509, and its reciprocal is 0.43429448.

**13.** Show from the definition of the logarithm of $N$ to the base $a$ that $a^{\log_a N} = N$.

**14.** If one should draw the graph of $y = \log_{10} x$ and then double all the ordinates, would he have the graph of $y = \log_{10} x^2$ or $y = \log_{10} (2x)$, or neither?  Explain.

**15.** Show that the graph of $y = \log_a (kx)$ is simply that of $y = \log_a x$ translated in the $y$-direction by an amount $\log_a k$.  $(k > 0.)$

Draw the graphs of the following equations:

**16.** $y = \log_{10} x$.

**17.** $y = \log_{10} (1 + x)$.

**18.** $y = \log_e (1 - x)$.

**19.** $y = \log_e (1 + x^2)$.

**20.** $y = \log_4 x^3$.

Construct the graphs of the following equations using the method of addition of ordinates:

**21.** $y = \dfrac{x}{2} + \dfrac{1}{2^x}$.

**22.** $y = e^x + e^{-x}$.

**23.** $y = \frac{1}{2}(2^x + 2^{-x})$.

**24.** $y = 1 - x + (1.5)^x$.

**25.** $y = 2^x - x^2$.

**26.** $y = 3^x - x^3$.

**27.** Show that $\log_b N = \log_a N \cdot \log_b a$.

**28.** Show that $\log_b a = \dfrac{1}{\log_a b}$.

**29.** Find the *natural* logarithms of the following numbers:

(a) 37.8          (b) 6564          (c) 828.6

(d) 0.437          (e) 0.085          (f) 0.000782

**30.** In each of the following, find the number $N$ whose *natural* logarithm is given:

(a) $\log_e N = 2.3468$          (b) $\log_e N = 5.8344$

(c) $\log_e N = 6.4365 - 10$          (d) $\log_e N = 8.2665 - 10$

**83. Boundary curves.   Damped vibrations.**—In Fig. 147 we have drawn lightly the graphs of $y = 3e^{-\frac{1}{4}x}$ and

$$y = \sin \frac{\pi x}{2}.$$

The latter curve has period 4, and there are therefore two complete cycles in the interval from $x = 0$ to $x = 8$.  By multiplying the ordinates to these two curves for each value of $x$, we have obtained the graph (heavy curve) of

$$(1) \qquad\qquad y = 3e^{-\frac{1}{4}x} \sin \frac{\pi x}{2}.$$

In connection with this multiplication of ordinates, the
following facts should be observed:

1. At every point where the factor sin $(\pi x/2) = 0$, the
product is zero; hence the graph of (1) crosses the $x$-axis
at $x = 0, 2, 4, 6, 8, \cdots$ .

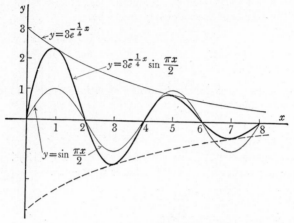

FIG. 147.

2. Since sin $(\pi x/2)$ is never greater than 1, the product
curve is never above the graph of $y = 3e^{-\frac{1}{4}x}$; at each point
where sin $(\pi x/2) = 1$, the product is *equal* to this other
factor. In fact, the graph of (1) is tangent to the
curve $y = 3e^{-\frac{1}{4}x}$ at $x = 1$, and 5.

3. At the points where sin $(\pi x/2) = -1$, the
product is equal numerically but opposite in sign
to the other factor. Thus at the points where $x =$
3 and 7 the graph of (1) is tangent to the dotted
curve whose equation is $y = -3e^{-\frac{1}{4}x}$. The two
curves $y = \pm 3e^{-\frac{1}{4}x}$ therefore form *boundaries*
between which the graph of (1) oscillates, its
"amplitude" decreasing as $x$ increases.

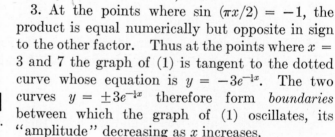

FIG. 148.

Figure 148 shows a weight $W$ which is supported by a
spring. If the weight is pulled down some additional distance and then released, it will oscillate up and down. It
can be shown that if the resistance of the medium to the
motion is proportional to the velocity, the equation govern-

ing the oscillations has the general form

$$y = A e^{-kt} \sin (nt + \alpha)$$

where $y$ is the vertical displacement of the weight (from its position of equilibrium) at time $t$, and the other letters represent constants whose values depend upon the stiffness of the spring, the viscosity of the medium, and the initial displacement and velocity of the weight. The curve shown in Fig. 147 is one of these "damped-vibration" curves. They are important not only in the study of mechanical vibrations in machines and structures, but also in certain electrical-circuit phenomena.

The method of multiplication of ordinates is often valuable. In the case of an equation like $y = x \cos x$, or $y = (1/x) \sin x$, or $y = xe^x$, one can usually visualize the general character of the graph by sketching the graphs of the separate factors and mentally multiplying the ordinates. Thus in Fig. 149 we have drawn the graphs of $y = x$ and $y = e^x$, and by multiplying the ordinates have obtained the graph of the equation

$$y = xe^x.$$

In connection with the use of this method observe that

1. *Where both factors are positive or negative, the product is positive; i.e.*, where both of the "factor" curves lie above or below the $x$-axis, the product curve is above. Where one is above and the other below, the product curve is below.

2. *Where either factor is zero, the product is zero if the other factor is finite.*

3. *Where either factor has the value 1, the product is equal to the other factor.* Thus in Fig. 149 the product curve crosses the graph of $y = e^x$ at $x = 1$ because at this point the other factor has the value 1.

4. *Where both factors are greater than 1 in absolute value, the absolute value of the product is larger than that of either factor; where the absolute value of one factor is larger than 1 and that of the other is smaller than 1, that of the product*

*is between the two.*   Thus in Fig. 149 the graph of $y = xe^x$ lies above that of either factor for $x > 1$ but lies between the two for $0 < x < 1$.   Finally, *where both factors are less than 1 in absolute value, the absolute value of the product is less than that of either factor.*   Thus in Fig 149 the ordinates to the curve $y = xe^x$ in the interval $-1 < x < 0$ are smaller

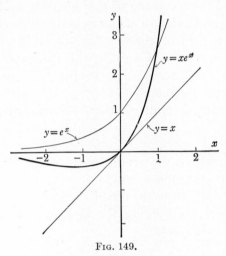

FIG. 149.

in absolute value than those to either the line $y = x$ or the curve $y = e^x$.

**84. The hyperbolic functions.**—Certain combinations of the exponential functions $e^x$ and $e^{-x}$ occur sufficiently often in various scientific applications to make it desirable to assign names to them and tabulate their values.   These functions are called *hyperbolic functions.*   It can be shown that they are related to the equilateral hyperbola in somewhat the same way that the trigonometric functions are related to the circle, and they are accordingly given similar names.   We shall not here discuss this relation but shall set up the definitions in an arbitrary way as follows:

$$\text{Hyperbolic sine } x \text{ (sinh } x) = \frac{e^x - e^{-x}}{2};$$

$$\text{Hyperbolic cosine } x \text{ (cosh } x) = \frac{e^x + e^{-x}}{2};$$

**Hyperbolic tangent $x$ (tanh $x$) $= \dfrac{e^x - e^{-x}}{e^x + e^{-x}}$.**

The hyperbolic cosecant (csch), secant (sech), and cotangent (coth) are defined, respectively, as the reciprocals of hyperbolic sine, cosine, and tangent. It should be emphasized that the hyperbolic functions are not new functions— they are simply names given to certain frequently occurring combinations of the exponential functions.

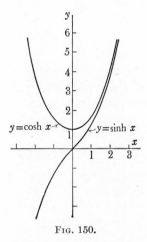

FIG. 150.

Table V, page 294, in this book gives the values of sinh $x$, cosh $x$, and tanh $x$, for values of $x$ from 0 to 10. The corresponding graphs can be made from this table. The graphs of $y = \sinh x$ and $y = \cosh x$, which are shown in Fig. 150, could be made by drawing the separate graphs of $y = \frac{1}{2}e^x$ and $y = \frac{1}{2}e^{-x}$, and adding and subtracting the ordinates. The student should draw the graph of $y = \tanh x$.

It can be shown, using principles of mechanics, that a uniform cable supported at the ends hangs in a curve whose equation is of the form

$$y = \frac{a}{2}\left(e^{\frac{x}{a}} + e^{-\frac{x}{a}}\right)$$

where $a$ is a constant whose value depends upon the amount of "sag" allowed. This curve is called a *catenary*, and it is easy to see that its equation can be written in the form

$$y = a \cosh \frac{x}{a}.$$

The graph of $y = \cosh x$ (Fig. 150) is then the catenary in which $a = 1$.

As indicated in the next set of exercises, there are relations between the hyperbolic functions that are quite similar to those between the trigonometric functions. Thus, corresponding to the relation $\cos^2 x + \sin^2 x = 1$, we have $\cosh^2 x - \sinh^2 x = 1$; corresponding to the formula $\sin 2x = 2 \sin x \cos x$, we have $\sinh 2x = 2 \sinh x \cosh x$. These relations may be proved by substituting for the hyperbolic functions the equivalent exponential expressions and carrying out the indicated operations. Thus to prove that $\cosh^2 x - \sinh^2 x = 1$ we proceed as follows:

$$\cosh^2 x - \sinh^2 x = \left(\frac{e^x + e^{-x}}{2}\right)^2 - \left(\frac{e^x - e^{-x}}{2}\right)^2$$
$$= \frac{e^{2x} + 2 + e^{-2x}}{4} - \frac{e^{2x} - 2 + e^{-2x}}{4}$$
$$= \tfrac{2}{4} + \tfrac{2}{4} = 1.$$

## PROBLEMS

Make the graphs of the following equations using the method of multiplication of ordinates:

**1.** $y = xe^{-x}$.  **2.** $y = x \sin x$; $(0 \leqq x \leqq 2\pi)$.

**3.** $y = x \cos \frac{1}{2}x$; $(0 \leqq x \leqq 4\pi)$.

**4.** $y = x \sin^2 x$; $(-2\pi \leqq x \leqq 2\pi)$.

**5.** $y = \dfrac{\sin x}{x}$; $(0 < x \leqq 2\pi)$.

**6.** $y = x \sin \dfrac{\pi}{x}$; $(0 < x \leqq 2)$.

**7.** $y = xe^{-x^2}$.  **8.** $y = e^{-x} \sin x$; $(0 \leqq x \leqq 2\pi)$.

**9.** $y = e^x \cos x$; $(0 \leqq x \leqq 2\pi)$.

**10.** $y = 4e^{0.1t} \sin t$; $(0 \leqq x \leqq 2\pi)$.

**11.** $y = 5e^{-0.2t} \sin \pi t$; $(-1 \leqq t \leqq 2)$.

**12.** Prove the identities:

(a) $\cosh^2 x - \sinh^2 x = 1$.

(b) $\tanh^2 x + \operatorname{sech}^2 x = 1$.

(c) $\coth^2 x - \operatorname{csch}^2 x = 1$.

**13.** Show that

(a) $\cosh x + \sinh x = e^x$.

(b) $\cosh x - \sinh x = e^{-x}$.

**14.** Show that $\sinh x$ and $\tanh x$ are odd functions and that $\cosh x$ is an even function by proving that

(a) $\sinh(-x) = -\sinh x$;

(b) $\cosh(-x) = \cosh x$;

(c) $\tanh(-x) = -\tanh x$.

**15.** Prove the relations:

(a) $\sinh 2x = 2 \sinh x \cosh x$.

(b) $\cosh 2x = \cosh^2 x + \sinh^2 x$.

(c) $\tanh 2x = \dfrac{2 \tanh x}{1 + \tanh^2 x}$.

**16.** Prove the relations:

(a) $\sinh(x \pm y) = \sinh x \cosh y \pm \cosh x \sinh y$.

(b) $\cosh(x \pm y) = \cosh x \cosh y \pm \sinh x \sinh y$.

(c) $\tanh(x \pm y) = \dfrac{\tanh x \pm \tanh y}{1 \pm \tanh x \tanh y}$.

Make the graphs of the following equations:

**17.** $y = \tanh x$.          **18.** $y = \coth x$.

**19.** $y = \operatorname{sech} x$.          **20.** $y = \operatorname{csch} x$.

**21.** Solve the equation $y = \frac{1}{2}(e^x - e^{-x})$ for $x$ in terms of $y$. This function of $y$ is called the *inverse hyperbolic sine* of $y$.

**22.** Solve the equation $y = \frac{1}{2}(e^x + e^{-x})$ for $x$ in terms of $y$. This function of $y$ is called the *inverse hyperbolic cosine* of $y$.

**23.** Solve the equation $y = (e^x - e^{-x})/(e^x + e^{-x})$ for $x$ in terms of $y$. This function of $y$ is called the *inverse hyperbolic tangent* of $y$.

# CHAPTER XII

## PARAMETRIC EQUATIONS

**85. Introduction.**—In previous chapters, our usual method of defining a curve has been to give a single equation connecting the variables $x$ and $y$. Sometimes it is more convenient to use *two* equations that express $x$ and $y$ as functions of a third variable. This third variable is called a *parameter*, and the equations are called *parametric equations* of the curve. Such equations may have the form

$$x = g(t); \qquad y = h(t).$$

The direct relation between $x$ and $y$ would result from the operation of eliminating the parameter $t$ between these equations.

### *Example*

Consider the equations

$$x = 2t - 1; \qquad y = 4t^2 + 6.$$

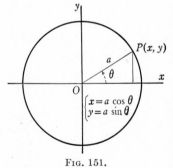

We can eliminate $t$ by solving the first equation for $t$ in terms of $x$, and substituting this for $t$ in the second; we thus obtain the equation

$$y = x^2 + 2x + 7.$$

The given equations are *parametric equations* of this parabola.

**86. Parametric equations of the circle.**—Let $P(x, y)$ be any point on the circle shown in Fig.

Fig. 151.

151, and let the angle that $OP$ makes with the positive $x$-axis be denoted by $\theta$. Then if $a$ is the radius of the circle, the coordinates of $P$ are

$$x = a \cos \theta; \qquad y = a \sin \theta.$$

These two equations, which express the coordinates of any point $P$ on the circle in terms of the parameter $\theta$, are parametric equations of the circle.

The direct relation between $x$ and $y$ results from eliminating $\theta$ between these equations. This can be done easily by squaring both members of each equation and then adding them. We thus have

$$x^2 = a^2 \cos^2 \theta; \qquad y^2 = a^2 \sin^2 \theta.$$
$$x^2 + y^2 = a^2 (\cos^2 \theta + \sin^2 \theta)$$

or

$$x^2 + y^2 = a^2.$$

This direct relation between $x$ and $y$ is often called the *rectangular equation* of the curve because it expresses the relation between the rectangular coordinates of the points on it.

When the rectangular equation of a certain curve is known, an indefinite number of pairs of parametric equations can easily be obtained. Thus if we take the equation

(1) $$y = x^2 + 4$$

and arbitrarily let $x = 3t + 5$, we find that

$$y = 9t^2 + 30t + 29.$$

The equations

$$x = 3t + 5, \qquad y = 9t^2 + 30t + 29,$$

then constitute a pair of parametric equations defining the parabola whose rectangular equation is $y = x^2 + 4$. If we let $x = \sin \theta$ in (1), we get $y = \sin^2 \theta + 4$. We thus have another pair of parametric equations; in this case they define only the arc of the parabola for which $|x| < 1$. Why?

**87. Parametric equations of the ellipse.**—It is easy to show that the equations

(2) $$x = a \cos \theta, \qquad y = b \sin \theta$$

are parametric equations of an ellipse with semiaxes $a$ and

$b$; for, if one writes the equations in the form

$$\frac{x}{a} = \cos \theta, \qquad \frac{y}{b} = \sin \theta$$

and then squares both members of each equation and adds, he gets the standard equation

$$\frac{x^2}{a^2} + \frac{y^2}{b^2} = 1.$$

From the parametric equations (2) it can be shown that the ellipse can be constructed, point by point, as follows:

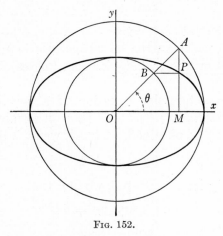

Fig. 152.

Draw two concentric circles having radii $a$ and $b$ $(a > b)$ as shown in Fig. 152; these are called the *major and minor auxiliary circles*, respectively. To determine a point on the ellipse, draw a line through $O$ at any angle $\theta$ with the positive $x$-axis, and cutting the major and minor circles at $A$ and $B$, respectively. Through $A$ draw a vertical line, and through $B$ draw a horizontal line. These intersect at $P$ which is a point on the ellipse; for if the coordinates of $P$ are $x$ and $y$ it is obvious that

$$x = OM = OA \cos \theta = a \cos \theta;$$
$$y = MP = OB \sin \theta = b \sin \theta.$$

**88. Path of a projectile.**—Using the fundamental principles of physics it can be shown that if a projectile is fired from the origin with an initial velocity $v_0$ ft. per second at an angle $\alpha$ with the horizontal $x$-axis (Fig. 153), and if it

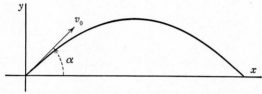

Fig. 153.

then moves under the action of the gravitational force only, its position at the end of $t$ sec. is given by the equations

$$x = (v_0 \cos \alpha)t, \qquad y = (v_0 \sin \alpha)t - \tfrac{1}{2}gt^2,$$

where $g$ is a constant whose value is approximately 32 These are of course parametric equations of the path of the projectile.

In order to find the corresponding rectangular equation we may eliminate $t$ by solving the first equation for $t$ in terms of $x$, substituting this in the second, and simplifying; the result is,

$$y = (\tan \alpha)x - \left(\frac{g}{2v_0{}^2 \cos^2 \alpha}\right) x^2.$$

This is an equation of the form $y = Ax - Bx^2$ and represents a parabola.

PROBLEMS

In each of the following, eliminate the parameter and identify the curve if possible. Draw the curve from the given parametric equations or from the rectangular equation:

**1.** $x = 2t,\ y = 4 - t$. 　　　　 **2.** $x = \tfrac{1}{2}t,\ y = \dfrac{4}{t}$.

**3.** $x = \cot \theta,\ y = 2 \tan^2 \theta$.

**4.** $x = 5t,\ y = \pm 3 \sqrt{1 - t^2}$.

**5.** $x = 4 \tan \theta,\ y = \sec \theta$.

**6.** $x = 1 + \sin \theta,\ y = \cos \theta - 2$.

**7.** $x = 2 + 5 \sin \theta,\ y = \cos \theta - 3$.

**8.** $x = 3 \cos \theta - 4 \sin \theta$, $y = 3 \sin \theta + 4 \cos \theta$.

**9.** $x = 3 \cos \theta + 4$, $y = 5 \sin \theta - 2$.

**10.** $x = 8(1 - \sin \theta)$, $y = 4 \cos \theta$.

**11.** $x = 4 \cot \theta$, $y = 4 \sin^2 \theta$.

**12.** $x = a \cos^4 \theta$, $y = a \sin^4 \theta$.

**13.** A baseball is thrown horizontally from a point 6 ft. above the ground with a speed of 120 ft. per second. Neglecting air resistance, find parametric equations of its path and sketch this curve. Assuming the ground to be level, determine how far the ball will travel horizontally before striking it. HINT: Put $v_0 = 120$ and $\alpha = 0$ in the equations of Art. 88. Find the time of flight by putting $y = -6$ and solving for $t$; compute the value of $x$ for this value of $t$.

**14.** From a point $O$ on the side of a hill, a ball is thrown as indicated in Fig. 154. Find the point at which it will strike the ground, air resistance being neglected.

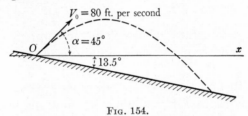

FIG. 154.

**89. The cycloid.**—*A cycloid is defined as the curve traced by a point $P$ fixed on the circumference of a circle, when the circle rolls along a fixed line.* The curve is shown in Fig. 155.

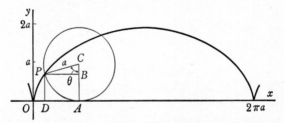

FIG. 155.

Choosing the coordinate system as shown, we shall derive expressions for the coordinates of $P$ in terms of the number of radians $\theta$ through which the wheel has turned from its position when this tracing point was at the origin:

If the radius of the rolling circle is $a$, then

$$OA = \text{arc } PA = a\theta.$$

The coordinates of $P$ are then

$$x = OD = OA - DA = OA - PB = a\theta - a \sin \theta;$$
$$y = DP = AB = AC - BC = a - a \cos \theta.$$

The parametric equations of the cycloid are therefore

$$x = a(\theta - \sin \theta); \qquad y = a(1 - \cos \theta).$$

It is possible to eliminate the parameter $\theta$ by solving the second equation for $\cos \theta$ in terms of $y$ and substituting this result into the first.    The resulting rectangular equation is quite complicated, and for this reason one always uses the parametric equations when dealing with the cycloid.

**90. The involute.**—A string is wound about the circumference of a circle, one end of the string being initially at $A$ in Fig. 156.   The string is then unwound while being held taut. *The curve traced by the end of the string as it unwinds is called the involute of the circle.*  We

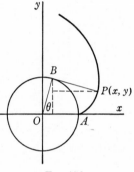

FIG. 156.

can derive parametric equations for this curve as follows:

When the piece of string that originally lay along the arc $AB$ has been unwound, the end of the string is at $P$ where $PB \perp OB$; also, if $\theta$ is the angle (radians) subtended at $O$ by arc $AB$ then

$$BP = \text{arc } AB = a\theta$$

where $a = OB$ is the radius of the circle.   If the coordinates of $P$ are $x$ and $y$, we then have

$$x = OB \cos \theta + BP \sin \theta = a \cos \theta + a\theta \sin \theta;$$
$$y = OB \sin \theta - BP \cos \theta = a \sin \theta - a\theta \cos \theta.$$

These equations give the coordinates of any point $P$ on the curve in terms of the angle $\theta$; the curve is accordingly defined by the parametric equations

$$x = a(\cos \theta + \theta \sin \theta); \qquad y = a(\sin \theta - \theta \cos \theta).$$

**91. Graphing from parametric equations.**—Parametric equations are often used to define curves that cannot be drawn readily from their rectangular equations. Consider, for example, the equation

$$(1) \qquad x^4 - 3xy^2 + 2y^3 = 0.$$

We easily deduce that the graph is not symmetrical to either axis or the origin. It has no horizontal or vertical asymptotes because the coefficients of the highest powers of both $x$ and $y$ are constants (see page 140). It goes through the origin, and the tangent lines to the curve at this point are $y = 0$ and $y = \frac{3}{2}x$. These are found by setting $2y^3 - 3xy^2 = 0$ (see page 142).

This information, while valuable, is hardly sufficient to enable us to sketch the curve. We may therefore try to obtain a few points on the graph. If we substitute values for $x$, we must in each case solve a cubic equation to find the corresponding value or values of $y$. If we substitute values for $y$, we have similar difficulties in solving for $x$.

We may obtain convenient parametric equations for the above curve by letting $y = tx$. Substituting $tx$ for $y$ in (1), and solving for $x$, we get $x = t^2(3 - 2t)$; then, since $y = tx$ we have

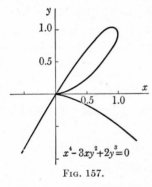

$$x = t^2(3 - 2t); \qquad y = t^3(3 - 2t).$$

It is now easy to substitute values for $t$, compute the corresponding values of $x$ and $y$, and make the graph. The result is shown in Fig. 157. It may be observed that when the curve is defined by the above parametric equations *there is one and only one point on the curve corresponding to each value of $t$*; i.e., we define a definite point on the curve by specifying the value of $t$. When the rectangular equation is used, there may be three different points on the curve corresponding to a given value of $x$. This is sometimes an important consideration.

In plotting a curve from its parametric equations it is usually necessary to vary the spacing of the values assigned to the parameter $t$ in order to obtain a desirable distribution of points along the curve. The table should be made out as in the following

### *Example*

Plot the curve defined by the equations

$$x = 4t - \tfrac{1}{2}t^3; \qquad y = \tfrac{1}{2}t^2 - 4.$$

### *Solution*

By assigning positive values to $t$ we obtain the following table:

| $t$ | 0 | 0.5 | 1 | 1.5 | 2 | 2.5 | $\sqrt{8}$ | 3 | 3.25 |
|---|---|---|---|---|---|---|---|---|---|
| $x$ | 0 | 1.94 | 3.5 | 4.31 | 4 | 2.19 | 0 | -1.5 | -4.16 |
| $y$ | -4 | -3.88 | -3.5 | -2.88 | -2 | -0.88 | 0 | 0.5 | 1.28 |

For the corresponding negative values of $t$, the values of $y$ are the same as those in the above table, while the values of $x$ are numerically the same but opposite in sign; the graph is therefore symmetrical with respect to the $y$-axis. By plotting the points we obtain the graph shown in Fig. 158. Observe that the values assigned to $t$ are not used in making the graph.

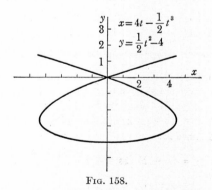

FIG. 158.

The student may show by eliminating $t$ that the rectangular equation of this curve is

$$x^2 - 2y^3 - 8y^2 = 0.$$

## PROBLEMS

**1.** Find the parametric equations of the cycloid when the origin is translated to the top of an arch.

**2.** Show that if the abscissas of two points on the cycloid differ by $2\pi a$, their ordinates are equal; hence infer that the parametric equations define $y$ as a *periodic* function of $x$ with period $2\pi a$. What is the physical interpretation of this fact?

**3.** If the tracing point on the rolling circle is at a distance $b \neq a$ from the center, show that the equations of its path are

$$x = a\theta - b\sin\theta; \quad y = a - b\cos\theta.$$

This curve is called a *prolate cycloid* if $b > a$, and a *curtate cycloid* if $b < a$.

**4.** Draw the curtate cycloid (see Prob. 3) for which $a = 8$, $b = 4$.

**5.** By eliminating the parameter $\theta$ from the equations

$$x = a(\theta - \sin\theta), \quad y = a(1 - \cos\theta),$$

show that the rectangular equation of the cycloid with axes as shown in Fig. 155 is

$$x = a\arccos\frac{a-y}{a} \pm \sqrt{2ay - y^2}.$$

**6.** A circle of radius $\frac{1}{4}a$ rolls inside a circle of radius $a$ as shown in Fig. 159. Show that the path traversed by a point $P$ on the rolling circle is defined by the equations

$$x = a\cos^3\theta, \quad y = a\sin^3\theta,$$

where $\theta$ is the angle shown. This curve is called the *hypocycloid of four cusps*. HINT: arc $AP$ = arc $AB$, hence $\angle ACP = 4\theta$. Then,

$$x = OD + LP \quad \text{and} \quad y = DC - LC;$$

but $OD = OC\cos\theta = \frac{3}{4}a\cos\theta$, etc. Observe that $\angle LCP = \frac{1}{2}\pi - 3\theta$.

**7.** The *hypocycloid* is the curve traced by a point fixed on the circumference of a circle of radius $b$ when this circle rolls on the *inside* of a circle of radius $a$; $(a > b)$. Using a figure similar to Fig. 159 show that the equations of this curve are

$$x = (a - b)\cos\theta + b\cos\frac{a-b}{b}\theta;$$

$$y = (a - b)\sin\theta - b\sin\frac{a-b}{b}\theta.$$

**8.** The *epicycloid* is the curve traced by a point fixed on the circumference of a circle of radius $b$ when this circle rolls on the *outside* of a circle of radius $a$.  Show that parametric equations of this curve are

$$x = (a + b) \cos \theta - b \cos \frac{a + b}{b} \theta;$$

$$y = (a + b) \sin \theta - b \sin \frac{a + b}{b} \theta.$$

Use a figure similar to Fig. 159 but having the rolling circle on the outside of the fixed circle.

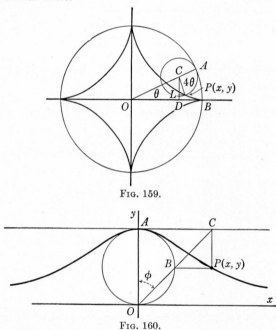

FIG. 159.

FIG. 160.

**9.** A circle of radius $a$ is drawn tangent to the $x$-axis at the origin and cutting the $y$-axis at $A$ (Fig. 160); the tangent to the circle at $A$ is then drawn.  Through the origin $O$ a secant line is drawn meeting the circle at $B$ and the tangent at $C$.  The horizontal line through $B$ and the vertical line through $C$ meet at $P(x, y)$.  Show that the coordinates of $P$ are

$$x = 2a \tan \phi, \qquad y = 2a \cos^2 \phi$$

where $\phi$ is the parameter shown in the figure.  The curve that is the locus of $P$ is called the *witch of Agnesi*.  By eliminating the parameter show that its rectangular equation is

$$y = \frac{8a^3}{x^2 + 4a^2}.$$

**10.** Show that a line through the origin with slope $m$ intersects the folium of Descartes $x^3 + y^3 = 3axy$ (Fig. 125) at the origin and at the point whose coordinates are

$$x = \frac{3am}{1 + m^3}; \qquad y = \frac{3am^2}{1 + m^3}.$$

These are then parametric equations of the folium, $m$ being the parameter. HINT: Let $y = mx$ in the equation $x^3 + y^3 = 3axy$.

**11.** Plot the folium whose equations are

$$x = \frac{6m}{1 + m^3}; \qquad y = \frac{6m^2}{1 + m^3}.$$

Draw each of the following curves from its parametric equations, showing in each case the table of values:

**12.** $x = t(4 - t^2); y = t^2(4 - t^2).$

**13.** $x = t(4 - t); y = \frac{1}{8}t^2(9 - t^2).$

**14.** $x = \frac{1}{8}t^3 + t; y = \frac{1}{8}t^3 - t.$

**15.** $x = 4 - 0.25t^2; y = 0.2t^3 - 1.8t.$

**16.** $x = 4t^3(2 - t); y = 4t^2(2 - t).$

**17.** $x = \dfrac{16t}{(1 + t^2)^2}; y = \dfrac{16t^2}{(1 + t^2)^2}.$

**18.** $x = \dfrac{4t^2 - 1}{1 - t^3}; y = \dfrac{4t^3 - t}{1 - t^3}.$

# CHAPTER XIII

## POLAR COORDINATES

**92. Introduction.**—In using the rectangular coordinate system we locate a point by giving its distances from two fixed lines, namely, the $x$- and $y$-axes. We consider now the *polar coordinate system* in which a point is located by specifying its *distance* and *direction* from a fixed point. One is using essentially this system when he says, for example, that a town $B$ is 30 miles northeast of a certain town $A$—he is giving the distance and direction of $B$ from $A$, instead of giving the distance east and the distance north.

**93. Polar coordinates.**—Choose a fixed point $O$, called the *origin* or *pole*, and a fixed line $OA$ through it as shown in Fig. 161. The line $OA$ is called the *polar axis;* it may be regarded as consisting of the positive "half" of the $x$-axis of the rectangular coordinate system.

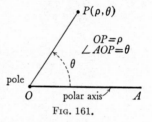

Fig. 161.

The position of any point $P$ in the plane is determined if we know the distance $OP$ and the angle $AOP$. The distance $OP$ is called the *radius vector* of $P$ and is denoted by $\varrho$; the angle $AOP$ is called the *vectorial angle* and is denoted by $\theta$. The polar coordinates of $P$ are then $(\varrho, \theta)$.

We may agree, as in trigonometry, that the radius vector $OP$ may rotate indefinitely about $O$ and that $\theta$ *is positive if the rotation is counterclockwise* and negative if clockwise. As to the sign of $\rho$, we may agree that *distances measured from the pole along the terminal side of $\theta$ are positive;* those measured in the opposite direction, along the terminal side produced through $O$, are negative. Accordingly, we plot a point $P(\rho, \theta)$ by the following procedure:

183

*Step 1.  Using the polar axis as the initial line, lay off the given vectorial angle θ, counterclockwise if positive and clockwise if negative.*

*Step 2.  Next, measure off the given radius vector ρ directly along the terminal side of θ if ρ is positive; if ρ is negative, extend the terminal side of θ through O and measure off ρ along this extension of the terminal side.*

The procedure is illustrated by Fig. 162 in which the points $P(3, 7\pi/6)$ and $Q(-4, -\pi/4)$ are plotted.

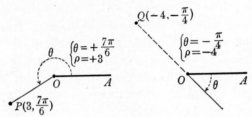

Fig. 162.

An important consequence of the above conventions regarding ρ and θ is the fact that *a given point has more than one pair of coordinates*.  Thus the point $Q(-4, -\pi/4)$ in Fig. 162 has also the coordinates $(+4, +3\pi/4)$, $(+4, -5\pi/4)$, and an indefinite number of other pairs.  The coordinates of the origin or pole are $ρ = 0$ with *any* value of θ.  In rectangular coordinates we have what is called a one-to-one correspondence between the pairs of numbers $(x, y)$ and the points of the plane; *i.e.*, a given pair of coordinates defines a single point, and conversely a given point has a single pair of coordinates.  In the polar coordinate system as defined above, this is not the case.  A given pair of coordinates $(ρ, θ)$ defines a single point, but a given point has indefinitely many pairs of coordinates.

Plotting in polar coordinates is facilitated by the use of polar coordinate paper.  This paper is ruled off in radial lines and concentric circles as shown in Fig. 163.

**94. Relations between rectangular and polar coordinates.**—In Fig. 164 we have taken the pole at the origin of the rectangular coordinate system, and the polar axis

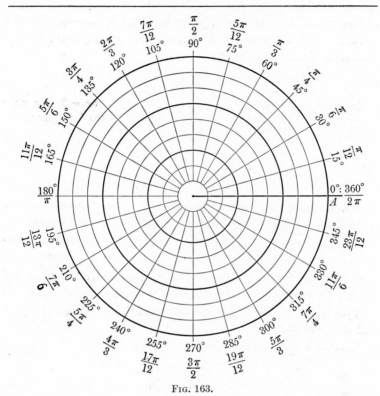

FIG. 163.

along the positive $x$-axis. From either figure it is evident
that we have the following relations between the rectangular
and polar coordinates of any point $P$ (for which $\rho \neq 0$):

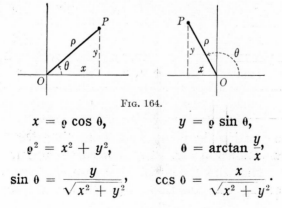

FIG. 164.

$$x = \rho \cos \theta, \qquad y = \rho \sin \theta,$$

$$\rho^2 = x^2 + y^2, \qquad \theta = \arctan \frac{y}{x},$$

$$\sin \theta = \frac{y}{\sqrt{x^2 + y^2}}, \qquad \cos \theta = \frac{x}{\sqrt{x^2 + y^2}}.$$

These relations enable one to transform the coordinates of a point or the equation of a curve from rectangular to polar coordinates, or vice versa.

### Example

In order to transform the equation $x^2 + y^2 - 6x = 0$ into polar coordinates, we replace $x^2 + y^2$ by $\rho^2$ and $6x$ by $6\rho \cos \theta$ and obtain the result

$$\rho^2 - 6\rho \cos \theta = 0,$$

or

$$\rho = 6 \cos \theta.$$

**95. Graphs in polar coordinates.**—The graph of an equation in polar coordinates is defined in essentially the same way as that of an equation in rectangular coordinates; *it is the locus of all points having a pair of polar coordinates that satisfy the equation.* The fundamental method of making the graph is to construct a table of corresponding values of $\rho$ and $\theta$, plot the points, and draw a smooth curve through them.

Consider, for example, the equation

$$\rho = \frac{8}{2 - \cos \theta}.$$

By substituting for $\theta$ the values from 0 to 360° at intervals of 30° we obtain the following table:

| $\theta$ | 0° | 30° | 60° | 90° | 120° | 150° | 180° |
|---|---|---|---|---|---|---|---|
| $\rho$ | 8 | 7.1 | 5.3 | 4 | 3.2 | 2.8 | 2.7 |

| $\theta$ | 210° | 240° | 270° | 300° | 330° | 360° |
|---|---|---|---|---|---|---|
| $\rho$ | 2.8 | 3.2 | 4 | 5.3 | 7.1 | 8 |

Upon plotting the points and connecting them we have the graph shown in Fig. 165. The curve appears to be an ellipse. That this is actually the case can be proved by transforming the equation into rectangular coordinates.

For this purpose we *replace $\rho$ by $\sqrt{x^2 + y^2}$; replace cos $\theta$ by $\dfrac{x}{\sqrt{x^2 + y^2}}$.* The equation obtained is

$$3x^2 + 4y^2 - 16x - 64 = 0.$$

This is of course the equation of an ellipse. By completing the square in $x$, the student may show that its center is at $(\frac{8}{3}, 0)$ and that $a = \frac{16}{3}$, $b = 8/\sqrt{3}$, and $c = \frac{8}{3}$. It follows immediately that this ellipse has one focus at the origin.

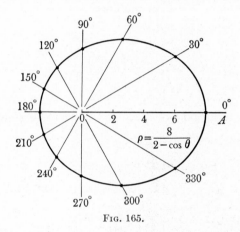

FIG. 165.

When we say that this ellipse is the graph of the polar equation $\rho = \dfrac{8}{2 - \cos \theta}$ we mean that every point on this curve has at least one pair of coordinates that satisfy the equation, and that the equation is not satisfied by any pair of coordinates of any point not on this curve. It is not necessary that all the pairs of coordinates of a given point on the graph satisfy the equation. Thus the point $(4, \pi/2)$ has also the coordinates $(-4, -\pi/2)$; the second pair does not satisfy the equation.

It should be observed here that *two different equations in polar coordinates* may have the *same* graph. This situation results from the fact that a given point has more than one pair of coordinates. In particular, the point whose coordinates are $(\rho, \theta)$ is identical with that whose coordinates are $(-\rho, \theta + \pi)$; it follows that if we replace $\rho$ by $-\rho$ and $\theta$ by $\theta + \pi$, in a given equation, the graph of the resulting equation coincides with that of the given one.  The student may thus show that the equations

$$\rho = \frac{8}{2 - \cos \theta} \quad \text{and} \quad \rho = \frac{-8}{2 + \cos \theta}$$

have the same graph (Fig. 165).

### PROBLEMS

**1.** Plot the following points:

(a) $P(4, -60°)$; $Q(-2, 180°)$; $R(-4, -90°)$.

(b) $P\left(-3, \dfrac{\pi}{6}\right)$; $Q(-4, \pi)$;   $R\left(2, \dfrac{5\pi}{3}\right)$.

(c) $P\left(-2, \dfrac{\pi}{2}\right)$; $Q\left(4, \dfrac{3\pi}{2}\right)$;   $R(-3, 0)$.

**2.** Find the rectangular coordinates of the following points:

(a) $P(-6, 120°)$; $Q(8, \pi)$;   $R\left(\sqrt{8}, -\dfrac{3\pi}{4}\right)$.

(b) $P\left(16, -\dfrac{\pi}{2}\right)$; $Q(-12, \pi)$; $R(10, 330°)$.

**3.** Find two pairs of polar coordinates for each of the following points:

(a) $P(4, -4)$; $Q(-3, 0)$; $R(-6\sqrt{3}, -6)$.

(b) $P(0, -2)$; $Q(5, 12)$; $R(-3, 4)$.

(c) $P(0, 0)$;   $Q(0, 4)$;   $R(-\sqrt{12}, 2)$.

**4.** Suppose that we should agree to restrict $\rho$ to positive values and $\theta$ to values in the interval $0 \leqq \theta < 2\pi$.  Would there then be a one-to-one correspondence between the points of the plane and the number pairs $(\rho, \theta)$, or would some point or points still have more than one pair of coordinates?

Make the graph of each of the following equations in polar coordinates, giving the table of values; then transform the equation to rectangular coordinates and name the curve:

**5.** $\rho = 4$.          **6.** $\theta = \dfrac{\pi}{4}$.          **7.** $\rho \cos \theta = 2$.

**8.** $\rho \sin \theta = 4$.          **9.** $\rho = 6 \sin \theta$.

**10.** $\rho = 8 \cos \theta$.          **11.** $\rho = 6 \sin \theta + 8 \cos \theta$.

**12.** $\rho = \dfrac{2}{1 + \cos \theta}$.          **13.** $\rho = \dfrac{6}{2 + \sin \theta}$.

**14.** $\rho = \dfrac{8}{1 - 2 \sin \theta}$.

**15.** $\rho^2 \sin 2\theta = 8$.

**16.** $\rho^2 \cos 2\theta = 4$.

**17.** By transforming to rectangular coordinates, show that the graph of $\rho = a \sec^2 \frac{1}{2}\theta$ is a parabola.

In each of the following, draw the curve from the given equation in rectangular coordinates and transform the equation into polar coordinates:

**18.** $y = 2x$.          **19.** $y = 4$.          **20.** $x + 2 = 0$.

**21.** $x^2 + y^2 = 9$.                    **22.** $x^2 + y^2 = 10x$.

**23.** $x^2 + y^2 + 9y = 0$.              **24.** $2xy = a^2$.

**25.** $x^2 - y^2 = a^2$.                 **26.** $x^2 + y^2 = 8x + 6y$.

**27.** $9x^2 + 25y^2 - 72x = 81$.

**28.** Derive a formula for the distance between two points in terms of their polar coordinates. HINT: Transform the distance formula from rectangular to polar coordinates. Note that the result is simply the cosine law of trigonometry.

## 96. Polar equations of the line.

—The general equation of the line in polar coordinates is more complicated than that in rectangular coordinates and is seldom used. For this reason it will not be discussed here. The special cases in which the line is parallel or perpendicular to the polar axis, or passes through the pole, lead to simple equations with which the student should be familiar.

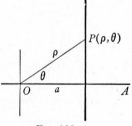

FIG. 166.

The line shown in Fig. 166 is perpendicular to the polar axis. In rectangular coordinates its equation is $x = a$. It is easily seen that in polar coordinates the equation is

$$\varrho \cos \theta = a.$$

Similarly, if the line is parallel to the polar axis and at a distance $b$ from it, the equation is

$$\varrho \sin \theta = b.$$

Finally, for a line passing through the pole with inclination

$\alpha$ we have the equation

$$\theta = \alpha.$$

**97. Polar equations of the circle.**—As in the case of the line, the general equation of the circle in polar coordinates is seldom useful. There are however certain special cases that arise frequently. They are

*Center at pole, radius r:* $\varrho = r.$
*Center at (r, 0), radius r:* $\varrho = 2r \cos \theta.$
*Center at (r, $\pi/2$), radius r:* $\varrho = 2r \sin \theta.$

The first of these needs no discussion. The second and third are easily derived from Figs. 167 and 168, respectively.

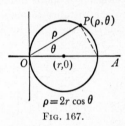

$\rho = 2r \cos \theta$

FIG. 167.

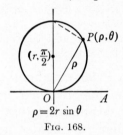

$\rho = 2r \sin \theta$

FIG. 168.

They can of course also be derived by transforming the corresponding rectangular equations into polar coordinates.

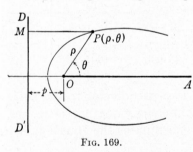

FIG. 169.

These equations are $x^2 + y^2 = 2rx$ and $x^2 + y^2 = 2ry$.

**98. Polar equations of the conics.**—In order to obtain a simple form of the equation of a conic in polar coordinates *we take the origin or pole at a focus and the polar axis perpendicular to the directrix DD' as shown in Fig.* 169. We use the definition of the conic given on page 136; in accordance with it, if $P(\rho, \theta)$ is any point on the conic then

$$OP = e \cdot MP \qquad (e > 0)$$

or

$$\rho = e(p + \rho \cos \theta).$$

Upon solving this equation for $\rho$ we get the *standard equation*

$$\rho = \frac{ep}{1 - e \cos \theta}.$$

This equation represents

> *An ellipse if* $0 < e < 1$;
> *A parabola if* $e = 1$;
> *A hyperbola if* $e > 1$.

The student can show that if the directrix is taken to the right of the pole instead of to the left as shown in the figure the equation is

$$\rho = \frac{ep}{1 + e \cos \theta};$$

finally, if the directrix is taken parallel to the polar axis the equation is

$$\rho = \frac{ep}{1 \pm e \sin \theta}.$$

The positive sign in the last equation applies if the directrix is above the pole and the negative sign if below.

Any equation of the form

$$\rho = \frac{k}{a \pm b \cos \theta \ (or\ sin\ \theta)}$$

can be put into one of the above forms by dividing numerator and denominator by $a$; *it accordingly represents a conic with one focus at the origin.*

### Example 1

Identify and sketch the conic whose equation $\rho = \dfrac{8}{2 - \cos \theta}$.

#### Solution

Dividing numerator and denominator by 2 we have the standard form

$$\rho = \frac{4}{1 - \tfrac{1}{2} \cos \theta}.$$

Since $e = \tfrac{1}{2}$, the equation is that of an ellipse for which $ep = 4$ or $p = 8$. The graph is shown in Fig. 165.

### Example 2

Identify and sketch the conic whose equation is $\rho = \dfrac{8}{5 + 5 \sin \theta}$.

*Solution*

Dividing numerator and denominator by 5, we have

$$\rho = \frac{1.6}{1 + \sin \theta}.$$

Since $e = 1$, the graph is a parabola.  It is shown in Fig. 170.

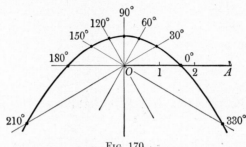

Fig. 170.

In making a rough sketch of a conic from an equation of the above form, it is often sufficient, after determining the nature of the conic, to plot only the points corresponding to $\theta = 0$, $\pi/2$, $\pi$, and $3\pi/2$.  Observe that the value of $\theta$ for which $\rho$ "becomes infinite" may be found immediately by setting the denominator of the right-hand member equal to zero.  This gives the direction of the axis in the case of the parabola and of the asymptotes in the case of the hyperbola.  Thus in example 2 above we may set $\sin \theta + 1 = 0$ to find that the axis is parallel to the line $\theta = 3\pi/2$.  Since the axis goes through the origin, it coincides with this line.  In the case of the hyperbola the asymptotes go through the center (not the origin) parallel to the lines determined by setting the denominator equal to zero.  See Prob. 25 in the next set.

### PROBLEMS

Draw the graphs of the following equations:

1. $\rho \cos \theta = -4$.          2. $\rho \sin \theta = 1.5$.
3. $\rho \sin \theta = -2$.          4. $\rho \cos \theta = 3$.

**5.** $\tan \theta = 0.7$.

**6.** $\theta = -\dfrac{\pi}{2}$.

**7.** $\rho = 6 \cos \theta$.

**8.** $\rho = -4 \cos \theta$.

**9.** $\rho = -2 \sin \theta$.

**10.** $\rho = -2.8 \sin \theta$.

**11.** $\rho = 4 \cos \left( \theta + \dfrac{\pi}{4} \right)$.

**12.** $\rho = -6$.

**13.** Show that the polar equation of the circle passing through the points $(0, 0)$, $(a, 0)$, and $(b, \pi/2)$, (Fig. 171) is $\rho = a \cos \theta + b \sin \theta$. HINT: Write the equation in rectangular coordinates and transform to polar.

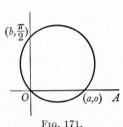

FIG. 171.

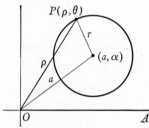

FIG. 172.

**14.** Show that the equation of the circle with center at $(a, \alpha)$ and radius $r$ is

$$\rho^2 + a^2 - 2a\rho \cos (\theta - \alpha) = r^2.$$

HINT: Use the cosine law on the triangle in Fig. 172.

Reduce each of the following equations to standard form; identify and draw the curve:

**15.** $\rho = \dfrac{10}{2 + \cos \theta}$.

**16.** $\rho = \dfrac{6}{\cos \theta - 1}$.

**17.** $\rho = \dfrac{6}{1 - 2 \sin \theta}$.

**18.** $\rho = \dfrac{8}{4 + 3 \sin \theta}$.

**19.** $\rho = \dfrac{10}{3 + 4 \cos \theta}$.

**20.** $\rho = \dfrac{8}{1 + 2 \sin \theta}$.

**21.** $\rho = \dfrac{8}{\sin \theta - 1}$.

**22.** $\rho = \dfrac{12}{4 + 5 \sin \theta}$.

**23.** $\rho = \dfrac{15}{4 \cos \theta - 3}$.

**24.** $\rho = \dfrac{-10}{2 + \cos \theta}$.

**25.** Show that the inclinations of the asymptotes to the hyperbola whose equation is $\rho = \dfrac{ep}{1 - e \cos \theta}$ $(e > 1)$ are given by $\theta = \arccos (\pm 1/e)$.

**26.** Show that the length of the major axis of the ellipse whose equation is $\rho = \dfrac{ep}{1 - e \cos \theta}$ $(e < 1)$ is $\dfrac{2ep}{1 - e^2}$.

**27.** Show that the major axis of an ellipse is longer than any other chord that can be drawn through a focus.

**28.** Identify and sketch the curve whose equation is $\rho \sin \theta \tan \theta = 2p$.

**29.** In defining the polar-coordinate system we could have restricted $\rho$ to positive values only. If this were done, what would be the graph of the equation $\rho = \dfrac{6}{1 + 2 \sin \theta}$?

**30.** Same as Prob. 29 for the equation $\rho = \dfrac{8}{1 - 2 \cos \theta}$.

## 99. Analysis of polar equations.

—The sketching of a polar curve is often facilitated by an appropriate analysis of the equation. This analysis may include the determination of its intercepts, tests for symmetry, and other items that were included in the discussion of equations in rectangular coordinates.

Of greatest value in this connection however is the information that one obtains by studying the way in which $\rho$ varies with $\theta$ as $\theta$ increases from 0 to 360° (or in some cases to some angle other than 360°). As an example we shall consider the equation

$$\rho = 2 + 4 \cos \theta.$$

When $\theta = 0$, $\rho = 6$, and we may regard the curve as "starting" at this point (Fig. 173); this is obviously the *largest* value that $\rho$ can have since $\cos \theta$ cannot exceed 1. Now as $\theta$ increases from 0 to 90°, $\cos \theta$ decreases continuously from 1 to 0, so $\rho$ *must decrease correspondingly from 6 to 2.* As $\theta$ continues to increase beyond 90°, $\cos \theta$ is negative and $\rho$ continues to decrease becoming 0 when $\cos \theta = -\frac{1}{2}$ which is at $\theta = 120°$; we thus have the direction of a tangent line at the origin as shown in the figure. As $\theta$ continues past 120°, $\rho$ becomes negative because the negative term ($4 \cos \theta$) is now numerically larger than the positive term (2). At $\theta = 180°$, $\cos \theta = -1$ and $\rho = -2$; this is the numerically largest negative value that $\rho$ can have. The student should continue the analysis along these lines for $\theta$ from 180 to 360° and complete the drawing of the curve.

In making the above type of analysis one must break the entire $\theta$ interval, usually 0 to 360°, into proper sub-intervals.   If the angle involved in the equation is $\theta$ itself, intervals of 90° are usually satisfactory; such intervals

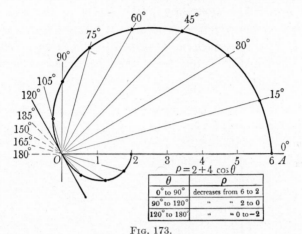

| $\theta$ | $\rho$ |
|---|---|
| 0° to 90° | decreases from 6 to 2 |
| 90° to 120° | "        " 2 to 0 |
| 120° to 180° | "        " 0 to −2 |

Fig. 173.

should however be subdivided again at any angles for which $\rho = 0$.   Thus in the above example we may use 90° intervals with additional subdivisions at 120° and 240° where $\rho = 0$.   If the angle involved in the equation is $2\theta$, it is necessary to take intervals of 45° for $\theta$ in order that the intervals for $2\theta$ may be 90°; if the angle involved is $3\theta$, the intervals for $\theta$ should be 30°.   In this connection see Figs. 178 and 179.   The results of the analysis can be put into a compact form as indicated in the figures.

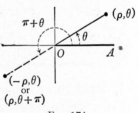

Fig. 174.

It is sometimes convenient to be able to test a polar equation for symmetry of the graph because this may enable one to draw the whole curve after sketching only a small part.   Tests are obtained as follows:

The point that is symmetrical to the point $(\rho, \theta)$ with respect to the origin has (among others) the coordinates $(-\rho, \theta)$ and $(\rho, \pi + \theta)$ (Fig. 174); it follows that *the graph of a polar equation has symmetry with respect to the pole if the equation is unaltered when ρ is replaced by −ρ, or if it is unaltered when θ is replaced by π + θ.*

It is left for the student to show in a similar way that

*The graph has symmetry with respect to the x-axis (0–180° line) if the equation is unaltered when θ is replaced by −θ. It has symmetry with respect to the y-axis (90–270° line) if the equation is unaltered when θ is replaced by π − θ.*

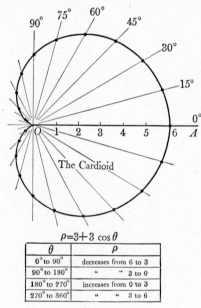

$\rho = 3 + 3 \cos \theta$

| θ | ρ |
|---|---|
| 0° to 90° | decreases from 6 to 3 |
| 90° to 180° | " " 3 to 0 |
| 180° to 270° | increases from 0 to 3 |
| 270° to 360° | " " 3 to 6 |

FIG. 175.

Each of these is a *sufficient* but not a *necessary* condition for the corresponding symmetry. Thus the last of the above tests means that the graph *must be* symmetrical with respect to the 90–270° line if the equation is unchanged when θ is replaced by π − θ; the curve *might be* symmetrical even if this substitution changes the equation.

We have considered the equation $\rho = 2 + 4 \cos \theta$. If θ is replaced by −θ, this equation is unaltered because cos (−θ) = cos θ. The graph is therefore symmetrical with respect to the 0–180° line. Half of the curve is shown in Fig. 173, and the other half can be drawn from symmetry.

**100. The cardioid and limaçon.**—We shall consider in the next few sections several polar equations whose graphs are curves that we have not previously encountered in rectangular coordinates. The first of these is the equation

$$\varrho = a + a \cos \theta$$

whose graph is illustrated by Fig. 175. Because of its heartlike shape this curve is called a *cardioid*. It is defined geometrically as follows:

Draw a circle of diameter $a$ (Fig. 176); from one end $O$ of a diameter draw any line cutting the circle at $Q$; on this line mark off two points $P$ and $P'$ such that $QP = QP' = a$. The locus of $P$ and $P'$ is the cardioid. The student may show that the points on the curve so constructed satisfy the above equation. He may also

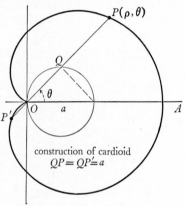

construction of cardioid
$QP = QP' = a$

Fig. 176.

show that other equations representing cardioids are $\rho = a (1 - \cos \theta)$ and $\rho = a (1 \pm \sin \theta)$.

The construction used in Fig. 176 may be generalized by making $QP = QP' = b$ where $b$ is in general not equal to $a$. This more general curve, of which the cardioid is of course a special case, has the equation

$$\varrho = b + a \cos \theta.$$

It is called the *limaçon*. If $b < a$, the curve has an inner loop as illustrated by Fig. 177. If $b > a$, $\rho$ is everywhere positive and the curve does not go through the origin. The construction of the figure for this case is left as an exercise in the next set.

It is now evident that Fig. 173 is the "half" of a limaçon

corresponding to values of $\theta$ from 0 to 180°.  Other equations representing limaçons are $\rho = b - a \cos \theta$ and $\rho = b \pm a \sin \theta$.

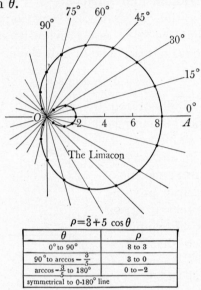

$$\rho = \bar{3} + 5 \cos \theta$$

| $\theta$ | $\rho$ |
|---|---|
| 0° to 90° | 8 to 3 |
| 90° to $\arccos -\frac{3}{5}$ | 3 to 0 |
| $\arccos -\frac{3}{5}$ to 180° | 0 to $-2$ |
| symmetrical to 0-180° line | |

Fig. 177.

## 101. The rose curves.—The graphs of the polar equations

$$\varrho = a \sin n\theta \qquad \text{and} \qquad \varrho = a \cos n\theta.$$

where $n$ is an integer are called *rose curves*.  They have the general character illustrated by Fig. 178.  Using the table given with the figure, the student should study carefully the way in which the curve is traced out as $\theta$ varies from 0 to 180°, noting particularly the directions of the tangent lines at the origin.  Observe that in this case the whole curve is obtained by letting $\theta$ vary only from 0 to 180°, and that it is traced over again when $\theta$ goes from 180 to 360°.

Each loop in the rose curve is called a *leaf*.  It can be shown that

*If n is **odd**, the number of leaves is equal to n;*

*If n is **even**, the number of leaves is equal to 2n.*

Thus the graph of $\rho = a \cos 3\theta$ has three leaves and that of $\rho = a \cos 2\theta$ has four.

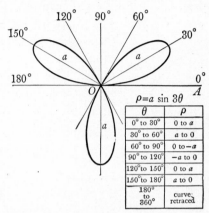

$$\rho = a \sin 3\theta$$

| $\theta$ | $\rho$ |
|---|---|
| $0°$ to $30°$ | 0 to $a$ |
| $30°$ to $60°$ | $a$ to 0 |
| $60°$ to $90°$ | 0 to $-a$ |
| $90°$ to $120°$ | $-a$ to 0 |
| $120°$ to $150°$ | 0 to $a$ |
| $150°$ to $180°$ | $a$ to 0 |
| $180°$ to $360°$ | curve retraced |

Fig. 178.

**102. The lemniscate.**—The polar equations studied so far have in each case defined $\rho$ as a *single-valued* function of $\theta$, *i.e.*, there has been only one value of $\rho$ for each value of $\theta$. An example of a *double-valued* function, which,

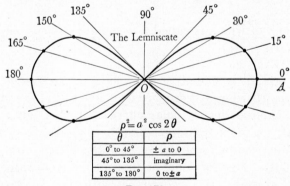

$$\rho^2 = a^2 \cos 2\theta$$

| $\theta$ | $\rho$ |
|---|---|
| $0°$ to $45°$ | $\pm a$ to 0 |
| $45°$ to $135°$ | imaginary |
| $135°$ to $180°$ | 0 to $\pm a$ |

Fig. 179.

incidentally, has an excluded interval for $\theta$, is given by the equation

$$\varrho^2 = a^2 \cos 2\theta.$$

Its graph (Fig. 179) is called a *lemniscate*. Observe that there are two values of $\rho$ (numerically equal but opposite in sign) for those values of $\theta$ for which cos $2\theta$ is positive, and that $\rho$ *is imaginary for the range of values of $\theta$ for which cos $2\theta$ is negative.* The $\theta$ interval from 45° to 135° is thus an *excluded interval.* There is no point on the curve corresponding to values of $\theta$ in this range.

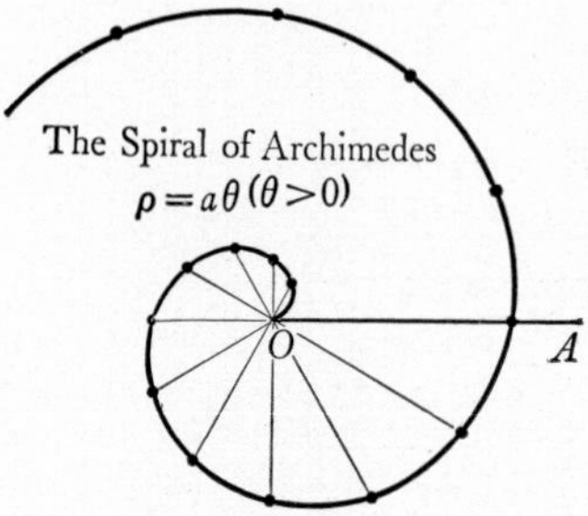

The Spiral of Archimedes
$\rho = a\theta \, (\theta > 0)$

Fig. 180.

**103. The spirals.**—The polar equation that corresponds to the equation $y = ax$ in rectangular coordinates is

$$\varrho = a\theta.$$

Its graph is called a *spiral of Archimedes.* The curve, for $\theta > 0$, is shown in Fig. 180. The student should draw the curve corresponding to $\theta < 0$ and show that it is symmetrical to that given in the figure with respect to the 90-270° line.

Other polar equations whose graphs are spiral curves are

$$\rho = e^{a\theta} \qquad \text{or} \qquad \log_e \rho = a\theta,$$

the graph of which is called a *logarithmic spiral,* and

$$\rho\theta = a,$$

whose graph is called a *hyperbolic* or *reciprocal spiral.* The construction of these curves is left to the exercises.

**104. Intersection of polar curves.**—If one solves simultaneously a given pair of equations in polar coordinates, he obtains the pairs of values of $\rho$ and $\theta$ that satisfy both equations. They of course represent points of intersection of the graphs. In accordance with the discussion of page 187, either or both curves may have equations other than those given, and the simultaneous solutions of any other such pair of equations also represent intersections of these same curves. It follows that in order to find analytically the coordinates of all intersections one may have to solve not only the given pair of equations, but also other pairs representing the same curves. In addition, it is necessary to determine by direct substitution whether or not the origin is a common point on the two curves—for the curves may have $\rho = 0$ for entirely different values of $\theta$.

### Example

Find the coordinates of the points of intersection of the circle

$$\rho = 3 \sin \theta$$

and the cardioid $\rho = 1 + \sin \theta$.

### Solution

Equating the right-hand members of the two equations we obtain

$$3 \sin \theta = 1 + \sin \theta.$$

Solving this equation we have

$$\sin \theta = \tfrac{1}{2}$$
$$\theta = 30° \text{ and } 150°.$$

The corresponding values of $\rho$ are equal to $\tfrac{3}{2}$, so the points $(\tfrac{3}{2}, \pi/6)$ and $(\tfrac{3}{2}, 5\pi/6)$ are intersections. On the circle we have $\rho = 0$ when $\theta = 0$ or $\pi$, and on the cardioid we have $\rho = 0$ when $\theta = 3\pi/2$. The origin is then a common point, but no pair of coordinates of the origin satisfies both equations. From the graphs (Fig. 181), we conclude that there are no other intersections.

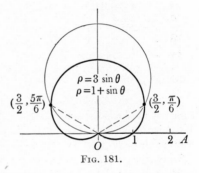

FIG. 181.

### PROBLEMS

**1.** Prove the test for symmetry with respect to the $x$-axis (0–180° line) given on page 196; work out another test.

**2.** Prove the test for symmetry with respect to the $y$-axis (90–270° line) given on page 196; work out another test.

**3.** Investigate each of the following equations for symmetry of the graph:

(a) $\rho = 4 \cos 2\theta$.

(b) $\rho = 2 - 3 \sin \theta$.

(c) $\rho = 2 \sin 3\theta$.

(d) $\rho = \dfrac{6}{3 - \cos \theta}$.

In each of the following problems make the graph of the given equation; in each case make a table similar to that in Figs. 177 and 178 showing how $\rho$ varies with $\theta$:

4. $\rho = 4(1 - \cos \theta)$.
6. $\rho = 1 - \sin \theta$.
8. $\rho = 3 + 6 \sin \theta$.
10. $\rho = 1 - 2 \sin \theta$.
12. $\rho = 2 + \sin \theta$.
14. $\rho = 4 - \sin \theta$.
16. $\rho = 4 \sin 2\theta$.
18. $\rho = a \cos 2\theta$.
20. $\rho = a \cos 5\theta$.
22. $\rho^2 = 4 \sin 2\theta$.
24. $\rho = 4\theta$.
26. $\rho\theta = 4$.

5. $\rho = 3(1 + \sin \theta)$.
7. $\rho = 2(\sin \theta - 1)$.
9. $\rho = 8 \cos \theta + 2$.
11. $\rho = 2 \cos \theta - 1$.
13. $\rho = 4 + 2 \cos \theta$.
15. $\rho = 4 - 3 \cos \theta$.
17. $\rho = a \cos 3\theta$.
19. $\rho = 3 \sin 5\theta$.
21. $\rho = 2 \sin 4\theta$.
23. $\rho^2 = 3 \cos 2\theta$.
25. $\rho\theta = \pi$.
27. $\rho = e^\theta$.

In each of the following problems draw only that part of the graph which corresponds to the given interval for $\theta$:

28. $\rho = 4 \cos 3\theta, \qquad 0 \leq \theta \leq \dfrac{\pi}{2}$.

29. $\rho = 2(1 - \sin \theta), 0 \leq \theta \leq \pi$.

30. $\rho = 1 - \cos \theta, \qquad 0 \leq \theta \leq \pi$.

31. $\rho = 3 - 6 \sin \theta, \quad 0 \leq \theta \leq \pi$.

32. $\rho^2 = 9 \cos 2\theta, \qquad 0 \leq \theta \leq \dfrac{\pi}{2}$.

33. Show by drawing a figure that the transformation equations for rotation of the polar axis through an angle $\alpha$ are $\rho = \rho'$, $\theta = \theta' + \alpha$. What is the new equation of the circle $\rho = 4 \cos \theta$ when the polar axis is rotated through $+45°$? Through $-90°$?

Draw the graphs of the following equations:

34. $\rho = a \tan^2 \theta \sec \theta$      (semicubical parabola).

35. $\rho = 2a \tan \theta \sin \theta$      (cissoid of Diocles).

36. $\rho^2\theta = a$ (lituus).

37. $\rho^2 = a^2\theta$ (parabolic spiral).

38. Show that when the equation

$$(x^2 + y^2)^2 = 4x(x^2 - 3y^2)$$

is transformed into polar coordinates it becomes $\rho = 4 \cos 3\theta$ and hence represents a three-leaved rose.

39. Investigate the nature of the graph of the equation

$$(x^2 + y^2 - y)^2 = x^2 + y^2$$

by transforming to polar coordinates.

In each of the following problems draw the two curves and find their points of intersection:

40. $\rho = 4 \sin \theta$; $\rho = 3 \cos \theta$.

41. $\rho \sin \theta = 3$; $\rho = 5$.

**42.** $\rho = 4 \sin \theta; \rho \sin \theta = 3$.

**43.** $\rho = 6 \cos \theta; \rho = 2(1 + \cos \theta)$.

**44.** $\rho = 2 \sin \theta; \rho = 2 + 4 \cos \theta$.

**45.** $\rho = \sin \theta; \quad \rho = \sin 2\theta$.

**46.** $\rho = \cos 2\theta; \rho = 1 + \sin \theta$.

**47.** $\rho^2 = \sin 2\theta; \rho = \sin \theta$.

**48.** Show that the parametric equations

$$x = \frac{4(1 - 3t^2)}{(1 + t^2)^2}, \qquad y = \frac{4t(1 - 3t^2)}{(1 + t^2)^2}$$

define the rose curve whose polar equation is $\rho = 4 \cos 3\theta$.

**49.** Show that the parametric equations

$$x = \frac{at(3 - t^2)}{(1 + t^2)^2}, \qquad y = \frac{at^2(3 - t^2)}{(1 + t^2)^2}$$

define the rose curve whose polar equation is $\rho = a \sin 3\theta$.

**50.** Transform the equation $x^2 - 2y^3 - 8y^2 = 0$ into polar coordinates and draw the graph from this polar equation. Compare with Fig. 158.

**51.** Transform the equation $x^4 - 3xy^2 + 2y^3 = 0$ into polar coordinates and draw the graph from this polar equation. Compare with Fig. 157.

# CHAPTER XIV

## CURVE FITTING

**105. Introduction.**—In various branches of science one often obtains a set of corresponding values of two variables by observation or experiment. It may then be important to find an equation that "fits" this table of values in a satisfactory way. Thus one might measure the atmospheric pressure at various altitudes in a given locality at a given time, and then try to devise an equation that would

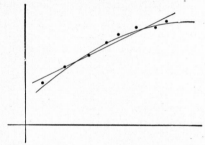

FIG. 182.

fit the observed data. Such an equation would express, at least in an approximate way, the atmospheric pressure as a function of the altitude.

A given set of corresponding values of two variables can of course be plotted as points on rectangular coordinate paper. The problem then becomes that of finding the equation of a curve that passes through or near these points in such a way as to indicate their general trend. An equation, when determined in such a manner, is called an *empirical equation* between the variables. The process of finding it is called *curve fitting*.

There is of course no unique solution to the problem of fitting a curve to a given set of points. Both the straight

line and the curve shown in Fig. 182 fit the given set of
points in an approximate way, and it is obvious that other
lines and curves could be drawn that might serve equally
well.

The first problem in fitting a curve to a given set of data
is to decide upon the type of curve to be employed.  In
some cases this is determined from theoretical considerations.  When this is not the case, one may make the
selection from considerations that appear later in this
chapter.  It is usually desirable to use the simplest type of
equation from which a reasonably good fit can be obtained.
The types to be considered in this chapter are

(1)  $$y = ax + b \qquad \text{(\textit{linear type})}$$
(2)  $$y = ax^2 + bx + c \quad \text{(\textit{parabolic type})}$$
(3)  $$y = ab^x \qquad \text{(\textit{exponential type})}$$
(4)  $$y = ax^n \qquad \text{(\textit{power type})}$$

After the type of equation has been chosen, the remaining
problem is to determine the values of the constants so that
the equation fits the given data in a satisfactory way.
Thus if the given points lay approximately along a straight
line, one would ordinarily choose the linear form $y = ax + b$
and proceed to determine $a$ and $b$ so as to secure a satisfactory fit.

We shall discuss two methods of evaluating the constants.
The first is the *method of average points*, and the second is
the *method of least squares*.  The first is simpler and easier
to apply, but the second ordinarily gives better results.

**106. Definition of average point.**—By the *average point*
of a given group of points we shall mean *the point whose
abscissa is the average of the abscissas of the group and whose
ordinate is the average of the ordinates*.  If the coordinates
of the given points are

$$(x_1, y_1), (x_2, y_2), (x_3, y_3), \cdots, (x_n, y_n),$$

and the coordinates of the average point for the group are
$(x_a, y_a)$, then

$$x_a = \frac{x_1 + x_2 + x_3 + \cdots + x_n}{n};$$

$$y_a = \frac{y_1 + y_2 + y_3 + \cdots + y_n}{n}.$$

**107. Linear type. Method of average points.**—When the given points lie approximately along a line, as shown in Fig. 182, a linear equation that will fit the data reasonably well can be obtained by the method of average points as follows: First divide the given set of points into two groups, putting approximately the same number of points in each group. Next, find the coordinates of the average point for each group and take the line determined by these two points as the required line.

*Example*

Find the equation of a line that fits the points shown in Fig. 183, their coordinates being

| $x$ | 1 | 2 | 3 | 4 | 5 | 6 | 7 | 8 | 9 | 10 |
|---|---|---|---|---|---|---|---|---|---|---|
| $y$ | 1.48 | 1.76 | 2.78 | 3.32 | 3.86 | 4.15 | 4.75 | 5.66 | 6.18 | 6.86 |

*Solution*

We may take the first five points as group 1; the average point for this group has the coordinates

$$x_a = \frac{1 + 2 + 3 + 4 + 5}{5} = 3;$$

$$y_a = \frac{1.48 + 1.76 + 2.78 + 3.32 + 3.86}{5} = 2.64.$$

We then take the remaining five points as group 2; the coordinates of the average point for this group are

$$x_a' = \frac{6 + 7 + 8 + 9 + 10}{5} = 8;$$

$$y_a' = \frac{4.15 + 4.75 + 5.66 + 6.18 + 6.86}{5} = 5.52.$$

The slope of the line through these two average points is

$$\frac{5.52 - 2.64}{8 - 3} = 0.576;$$

and its equation is

$$y - 2.64 = 0.576(x - 3)$$

or

$$y = 0.576x + 0.912.$$

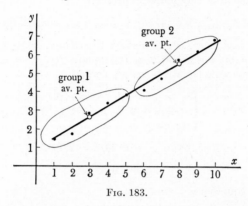

FIG. 183.

The result obtained by the above procedure depends, at least to some extent, upon the way in which we group the points. It is often necessary to choose the groups with care in order to obtain a good fit. It can be shown that the various choices of the groups result in lines all of which pass through the average point of the entire set.

**108. Parabolic type.**—The method of average points can be applied in a similar way to the problem of fitting a parabola

$$y = ax^2 + bx + c$$

to a given set of points. In this case there are three constants to determine. One accordingly divides the given set of points into three groups, finds the average point of each group, and passes the parabola through these three points.

*Example*

Fit a parabola of the form $y = ax^2 + bx + c$ to the following data:

| $x$ | $-2$ | $-1$ | 0 | 1 | 2 | 3 | 4 | 5 | 6 | 7 | 8 |
|---|---|---|---|---|---|---|---|---|---|---|---|
| $y$ | $-3.5$ | 0.4 | 2.5 | 4.2 | 5.8 | 6.6 | 7.8 | 8.0 | 8.6 | 7.6 | 6.2 |

*Solution*

We may take the first three points as group 1, the next four as group 2, and the last four as group 3. The coordinates of the corresponding average points are easily found to be

*group* 1: $(-1, -0.2)$; *group* 2: $(2.5, 6.1)$; *group* 3: $(6.5, 7.6)$.

In order to pass the parabola through these three points we substitute their coordinates for $x$ and $y$ in the equation $y = ax^2 + bx + c$ and obtain the following equations in $a$, $b$, and $c$:

$$\begin{cases} a - b + c = -0.2 \\ 6.25a + 2.5b + c = 6.1 \\ 42.25a + 6.5b + c = 7.6. \end{cases}$$

Solving these we find that $a = -0.190$, $b = 2.085$,

$$c = 2.075.$$

The desired equation is then

$$y = -0.190x^2 + 2.085x + 2.075.$$

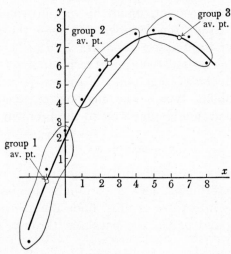

Fig. 184.

This curve and the given set of points are shown in Fig. 184. It is evident that a different choice of the groups might result in a parabola that differs appreciably from this one. One might conclude after studying the figure that a better fit would probably be obtained by taking the first four points as group 1, the next four as group 2, and the last three as group 3.

**109. Residuals.   Criteria for goodness of fit.**—Let us
assume that in Fig. 185 the curve $y = f(x)$ has been fitted
to the points $P_1(x_1, y_1)$, $P_2(x_2, y_2)$, etc.   We define the
*residual* of any one of the given points, for this curve, to
be the difference between the ordinate of the point and that
of the corresponding point on the curve.   Thus the residuals
of the points $P_1$, $P_2$, and $P_3$ are, respectively,

$$Q_1P_1 = y_1 - f(x_1);$$
$$Q_2P_2 = y_2 - f(x_2);$$
$$Q_3P_3 = y_3 - f(x_3).$$

*The residual of a point is positive if the point is above the
curve and negative if below.*

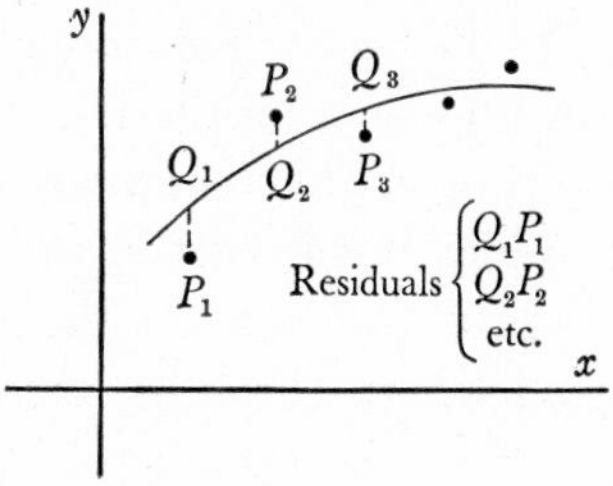

In connection with the fitting
of a curve to a given set of points
we have spoken in a general
way of securing a "good fit."
By a good fitting curve we have
meant a curve such that the absolute values of the residuals were
small.

Fig. 185.

It can easily be shown that when one fits a straight line
to a given set of points by the method of average points he
obtains, whatever the choice of groups, a line for which *the
algebraic sum of the residuals is zero.*   This does not mean
however that he necessarily has a good fit—for the residuals
could all be numerically large, the positive ones balancing
the negative ones.   Thus if one has only two points, the
best fitting line is the one passing through them.   The
perpendicular bisector of the segment joining them is also
a line for which the algebraic sum of the residuals is zero,
and this line would of course give a poor fit.   It is evident
then that we could not use the value of the algebraic sum
of the residuals as a criterion of the goodness of fit.

If we should consider the *squares* of the residuals instead
of the residuals themselves, we would be dealing with
*positive quantities*.   The sum of the squares of the residuals

could not be zero (unless the curve actually passed through all the points), but one would obviously have a good fit if this sum were small. In fitting a curve of a specified type to a given set of points one might try to determine the constants so that this sum is as small as possible and regard the result as the best fitting curve of the type. In fact we now set up the following:

**Definition:** *The best fitting curve of a given type is the one in which the constants are determined so that the sum of the squares of the residuals is a minimum.*

The justification for calling this the best fitting curve of the type lies in the theory of probability and will not be discussed.

The best fitting curve cannot, in general, be found by the method of average points but requires the method of least squares which is given at the end of this chapter. The calculations involved in this latter method are much longer, and for this reason the method of average points is often used where the best fitting curve is not required.

## PROBLEMS

In each of the following, fit a straight line to the given data by the method of average points using the subdivision indicated by the double bar. Compute the residuals at any three of the given points:

**1.**

| $x$ | 2 | 4 | 6 | 8 | 10 | 12 | 14 | 16 |
|---|---|---|---|---|---|---|---|---|
| $y$ | 6.4 | 7.1 | 8.0 | 9.1 | 9.8 | 10.8 | 11.6 | 12.2 |

**2.**

| $x$ | 1.4 | 2.6 | 3.0 | 3.8 | 4.4 | 4.8 | 5.8 | 7 | 8.2 |
|---|---|---|---|---|---|---|---|---|---|
| $y$ | 9.3 | 8.6 | 7.7 | 8.0 | 7.6 | 7.6 | 7.1 | 6.6 | 5.9 |

**3.**

| $x$ | $-2$ | $-1$ | 0 | 1 | 2 | 3 | 4 | 5 | 6 |
|---|---|---|---|---|---|---|---|---|---|
| $y$ | $-3.2$ | $-2.5$ | $-1.8$ | $-1.3$ | $-0.6$ | 0.1 | 0.4 | 1.0 | 1.5 |

**4.** The resistance $R$ (ohms) of a certain coil of copper wire at temperature $T$ (degrees centigrade) was found by measurement to be as follows:

| $T$ | 10.2° | 19.8° | 28.6° | 39.8° | 49.5° | 58.4° | 71.2° | 80.5° | 88.8° |
|---|---|---|---|---|---|---|---|---|---|
| $R$ | 13.12 | 13.54 | 14.08 | 14.72 | 15.06 | 15.58 | 16.24 | 16.66 | 17.24 |

Find the equation of a line to fit this data. Use the result to estimate the resistance at 45°.

**5.** The length $L$ (inches) of a certain coiled steel spring under the action of a tensile pull was found to increase with the pull $P$ (pounds) as shown below:

| $P$ | 0 | 5 | 10 | 15 | 20 | 25 | 30 | 35 | 40 | 45 |
|---|---|---|---|---|---|---|---|---|---|---|
| $L$ | 10.25 | 11.45 | 12.80 | 14.35 | 15.75 | 17.30 | 18.55 | 19.55 | 21.20 | 23.00 |

Find the equation of a straight line to fit this data. Use the result to estimate the length under a pull of 22 lb.

**6.** Show that every line for which the algebraic sum of the residuals is zero passes through the average point of the given set, and conversely. HINT: Let the given points be $(x_1, y_1)$, $(x_2, y_2)$, $\cdots$, $(x_n, y_n)$. Assuming the equation $y = ax + b$ and equating to zero the sum of the residuals we have

(1)　$[y_1 - (ax_1 + b)] + [y_2 - (ax_2 + b)] + \cdots + [y_n - (ax_n + b)]$
$$= 0.$$

Show that this reduces to

(2)　$$\frac{y_1 + y_2 + \cdots + y_n}{n} = a\,\frac{x_1 + x_2 + \cdots + x_n}{n} + b$$

which means that the point,

$$\left(\frac{x_1 + x_2 + \cdots + x_n}{n},\ \frac{y_1 + y_2 + \cdots + y_n}{n}\right)$$

must be on the line if (1) is to be satisfied. Conversely, show that (1) follows from (2).

**7.** Fit a parabola of the form $y = ax^2 + bx + c$ to the following data:

| $x$ | 0 | 1 | 2 | 3 | 4 | 5 | 6 | 7 |
|---|---|---|---|---|---|---|---|---|
| $y$ | $-5.4$ | $-5.2$ | $-4.4$ | $-2.8$ | $-1.2$ | 1.4 | 3.6 | 6.6 |

**8.** Fit a parabola of the form $y = ax^2 + bx + c$ to the following data:

| $x$ | $-1$ | 0 | 1 | 2 | 3 | 4 | 5 | 6 |
|---|---|---|---|---|---|---|---|---|
| $y$ | 3.2 | 4.2 | 4.1 | 3.8 | 2.8 | 1.4 | $-1.1$ | $-3.8$ |

**110. The power type.**—We consider now the problem of fitting an equation of the type

$$y = ax^n$$

to a given table of values of $x$ and $y$. If we take the common logarithm of both members of the equation, we obtain

$$\log y = \log a + n \log x.$$

This is obviously a *linear* relation between *log x* and *log y*, and if we let

$$\log x = u \quad \text{and} \quad \log y = v$$

it becomes

$$v = nu + \log a$$

where $\log a$ is a constant $(= L)$. It follows that *if the relation between x and y is of the form $y = ax^n$, the relation between log x and log y is linear.* We may then proceed as follows:

*Step* 1. *Make a new table in which the entries are the logarithms of the numbers in the given table; denote these new entries by u and v where u = log x and v = log y.*

*Step* 2. *Plot the points $(u, v)$ on rectangular coordinate paper. If they tend to lie along a straight line, the equation $y = ax^n$ is applicable.*

*Step* 3. *Fit a straight line $v = nu + L$ to this set of data using the method of average points (or the method of least squares which is discussed later). The value of n in the required equation $y = ax^n$ is the coefficient of u in this linear equation, and the value of a can be found from the fact that $L = \log a$.*

### Example

Show that an equation of the form $y = ax^n$ is suitable for the data given below and find proper values for $a$ and $n$.

| $x$ | 1 | 2 | 3 | 4 | 5 | 6 | 7 | 8 |
|-----|---|---|---|---|---|---|---|---|
| $y$ | 0.36 | 0.90 | 1.92 | 3.44 | 4.78 | 6.74 | 9.40 | 11.8 |

### Solution

Taking the common logarithms of the given numbers we construct the following table:

| $u = \log x$ | 0.0000 | 0.3010 | 0.4771 | 0.6021 | 0.6990 | 0.7782 | 0.8451 | 0.9031 |
|--------------|--------|--------|--------|--------|--------|--------|--------|--------|
| $v = \log y$ | $-0.4437$ | $-0.0458$ | 0.2833 | 0.5238 | 0.6794 | 0.8287 | 0.9731 | 1.0719 |

These points when plotted on rectangular coordinate paper tend to lie along a line as shown in Fig. 186. This means that an equation of the form $y = ax^n$ is applicable.

In order to fit a line to these points we choose the first four as group 1 and the last four as group 2. The corre-

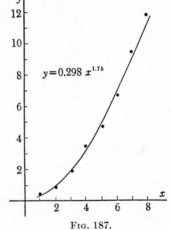

Fig. 186.                         Fig. 187.

sponding average points are (0.3450, 0.0794) and (0.8064, 0.8883); the line through these points has the equation

$$v = 1.753u - 0.5254.$$

This is of the form $v = nu + L$ where $n = 1.753$ and

$$L = \log a = -0.5254 = 9.4746 - 10;$$

from tables we find that $a = 0.2983$. The required empirical relation between $x$ and $y$ is then

$$\mathbf{y = 0.2983x^{1.753}.}$$

The graph of this curve and the given points are shown in Fig. 187.

The test for applicability of the formula $y = ax^n$ can be made more quickly by plotting the given data on *logarithmic coordinate paper* instead of looking up the logarithms and using ordinary paper.

Logarithmic coordinate paper, as shown in Fig. 188, has its horizontal and vertical rulings not at distances of

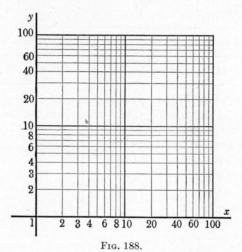

FIG. 188.

1, 2, 3, etc., from the origin, but at distances of log 1, log 2, log 3, and so on. The sample shown has two "cycles," the first going from 1 to 10 and the second from 10 to 100. The next cycle to the right along the $x$-axis would go from 100 to 1,000; the next one to the left would go from 1 down to 0.1.

Plotting the given data directly on this paper is of course equivalent to plotting the logarithms on ordinary paper. If the points tend to lie on a line, an equation of the form $y = ax^n$ is applicable.

**111. The exponential type.**—The problem of fitting an exponential equation of the form

$$y = a(10)^{kx}$$

to a given table of values of $x$ and $y$ is quite similar to that just discussed. We again take the common logarithms of both sides obtaining

$$\log y = \log a + kx.$$

This is a *linear* relation between $x$ and $\log y$, and if we let $\log y = v$ it becomes

$$v = kx + \log a$$

where again $\log a$ is a constant $(= L)$. It follows that *if the relation between $x$ and $y$ is of the form $y = a(10)^{kx}$, that between $x$ and $\log y$ is linear.* We may then proceed as follows:

*Step 1. Make a new table in which the entries are $x$ and $\log y$, denoting $\log y$ by $v$.*

*Step 2. Plot the points $(x, v)$ on rectangular coordinate paper. If they tend to lie in a straight line, the equation $y = a(10)^{kx}$ is applicable.*

*Step 3. Fit a straight line $v = kx + L$ to this set of data and then write down the required equation $y = a(10)^{kx}$ after determining $a$ from the relation $L = \log a$.*

### Example

Show that an equation of the form $y = a (10)^{kx}$ is suitable for the data given below and find proper values for $a$ and $k$.

| $x$ | 1 | 2 | 3 | 4 | 5 | 6 | 7 | 8 |
|---|---|---|---|---|---|---|---|---|
| $y$ | 0.72 | 1.08 | 1.68 | 3.24 | 5.28 | 8.64 | 13.8 | 22.6 |

### Solution

By taking the logarithms of the given values of $y$ we construct the table:

| $x$ | 1 | 2 | 3 | 4 | 5 | 6 | 7 | 8 |
|---|---|---|---|---|---|---|---|---|
| $v = \log y$ | $-0.1427$ | 0.0334 | 0.2253 | 0.5106 | 0.7226 | 0.9365 | 1.1399 | 1.3541 |

The student may verify that these points when plotted tend to lie along a line. We fit a line to them in the usual way obtaining

$$v = 0.2204x - 0.3944.$$

This is of the form $v = kx + L$ where $k = 0.2204$ and

$$L = \log a = -0.3944 = 9.6056 - 10.$$

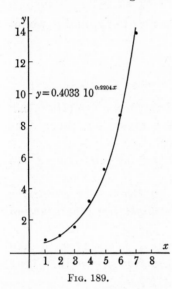

Fig. 189.

From tables we find that $a = 0.4033$. The required empirical relation between $x$ and $y$ is then

$$y = \mathbf{0.4033(10)}^{0.2204x}$$

The graph of this equation and the given points are shown in Fig. 189.

It is often convenient to use the exponential equation in the form $y = ae^{kx}$ where $e$ is the base of natural logarithms. In the above example we may replace 10 by $e^{2.303}$ and thus transform the result into the form

$$y = 0.4033(e^{2.303})^{0.2204x};$$

then, since $(e^m)^n = e^{mn}$ we obtain the result

$$y = \mathbf{0.4033}e^{0.5076x}.$$

Of course the result can also be easily expressed in the general exponential form $y = ab^x$. Thus since

$$10^{0.2204x} = (10^{0.2204})^x = 1.661^x$$

the above result can be written in the form

$$y = \mathbf{0.4033(1.661)}^x.$$

In practice it is usually desirable to use either 10 or $e$ as the base.

The test for applicability of the formula $y = a(10)^{kx}$

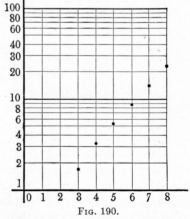

Fig. 190.

can be made more quickly by plotting the given data directly on *semilogarithmic coordinate paper*, as is done in Fig. 190, instead of looking up the logarithms of the given values of

$y$ and using ordinary paper.   As shown in the figure this paper has uniformly spaced vertical rulings but logarithmically spaced horizontal rulings.   Plotting the given points $(x, y)$ on it is of course equivalent to plotting the points $(x, \log y)$ on ordinary paper.   If the points tend to lie on a line, the equation $y = a(10)^{kx}$ (or $ae^{kx}$) is applicable.

## PROBLEMS

In Probs. 1, 2, and 3, show that an equation of the form $y = ax^n$ is applicable and find values for $a$ and $n$:

**1.**

| $x$ | 1 | 2 | 3 | 4 | 5 | 6 | 7 | 8 |
|---|---|---|---|---|---|---|---|---|
| $y$ | 0.54 | 1.42 | 2.68 | 3.92 | 5.66 | 7.34 | 9.28 | 11.4 |

**2.**

| $x$ | 2 | 4 | 6 | 8 | 10 | 12 | 14 | 16 |
|---|---|---|---|---|---|---|---|---|
| $y$ | 3.6 | 5.5 | 7.1 | 8.3 | 9.4 | 10.5 | 11.5 | 12.4 |

**3.**

| $x$ | 1 | 2 | 3 | 4 | 5 | 6 |
|---|---|---|---|---|---|---|
| $y$ | 26.4 | 9.3 | 5.2 | 3.6 | 2.5 | 1.9 |

In Probs. 4, 5, and 6, show that an equation of the form $y = a(10)^{kx}$ is applicable and find values for $a$ and $k$.   Express the final result also in the form $y = ae^{k'x}$;

**4.**

| $x$ | 1 | 2 | 3 | 4 | 5 | 6 |
|---|---|---|---|---|---|---|
| $y$ | 1.3 | 2.8 | 6.2 | 13.8 | 33.6 | 64.2 |

**5.**

| $x$ | 0 | 1 | 2 | 3 | 4 | 5 | 6 |
|---|---|---|---|---|---|---|---|
| $y$ | 42 | 26 | 16 | 10 | 7 | 4 | 3 |

**6.** .

| $x$ | 0 | 2 | 5 | 8 | 12 | 16 |
|---|---|---|---|---|---|---|
| $y$ | 80 | 59 | 35 | 21 | 10 | 5 |

**7.** The time $t$ (seconds) required for an object to fall a distance $s$ (feet) was observed and the data recorded as shown below. Show that an equation of the form $t = as^n$ is applicable and fit such an equation to the data:

| $s$ | 5 | 10 | 15 | 20 | 25 | 30 | 35 | 40 |
|---|---|---|---|---|---|---|---|---|
| $t$ | 0.58 | 0.84 | 1.03 | 1.19 | 1.34 | 1.47 | 1.60 | 1.71 |

**8.** In a certain chemical reaction it was found that out of an initial 60 grams of a certain substance the amount $M$ remaining after $t$ minutes was as given below. Show that an equation of the form $M = a(10)^{kt}$ is applicable and fit such an equation to the data. Express the result also in the form $M = ae^{k't}$.

| $t$ | 0 | 3 | 6 | 9 | 12 | 15 | 18 | 21 |
|---|---|---|---|---|---|---|---|---|
| $M$ | 60 | 38.2 | 24.4 | 15.6 | 9.9 | 6.4 | 4.1 | 2.6 |

**9.** The air resistance $R$ (pounds) against an automobile was found to vary with the speed $V$ (m.p.h.) as shown below. Show that an equation of the form $R = aV^n$ is applicable and find values for $a$ and $n$:

| $V$ | 10 | 20 | 30 | 40 | 50 | 60 |
|---|---|---|---|---|---|---|
| $R$ | 8 | 29 | 72 | 128 | 197 | 274 |

**10.** The number $N$ of bacteria per unit volume in a culture, at the end of $t$ hours, was found to be as follows:

| $t$ | 1 | 2 | 3 | 4 | 5 | 6 | 7 | 8 |
|---|---|---|---|---|---|---|---|---|
| $N$ | 52 | 64 | 76 | 95 | 114 | 130 | 158 | 187 |

Show that the equation $N = a(10)^{kt}$ is applicable and find values for $a$ and $k$. Use the result to estimate the value of $N$ when $t = 5.4$.

**11.** The pressure of a gas expanding adiabatically was found to vary with its volume as follows:

| $v$ | 2.0 | 2.6 | 4.2 | 4.6 | 5.2 | 6.0 |
|---|---|---|---|---|---|---|
| $P$ | 138 | 96 | 49 | 43 | 36 | 30 |

Show that a relation of the form $P = av^n$ is applicable and determine $a$ and $n$.

**112. Linear type.    Method of least squares.**—It has been pointed out in previous sections that when one fits a straight line to a given set of data by the method of average points he obtains a line for which the algebraic sum of the residuals is zero.    There are indefinitely many such lines; some of them give a good fit and some do not.    In accordance with the discussion on page 210, one may calculate the sum of the *squares* of the residuals and use the magnitude of this quantity as an indication of the goodness of fit.

The method of least squares gives the line for which *the sum of the squares of the residuals is a minimum.*    There is only one such line for a given set of points; so the result does not depend upon any choice of groups.    In this section we shall show how the equations for determining the constants are set up, reserving the proof for a later section.    We shall use in this illustration the data from the example on page 206 in order that we may be able to compare the results.    The data are as follows:

| $x$ | 1 | 2 | 3 | 4 | 5 | 6 | 7 | 8 | 9 | 10 |
|---|---|---|---|---|---|---|---|---|---|---|
| $y$ | 1.48 | 1.76 | 2.78 | 3.32 | 3.86 | 4.15 | 4.75 | 5.66 | 6.18 | 6.86 |

Assuming that $y = mx + b$ we write down two sets of equations: The first set, shown on the left below, is obtained by substituting the given coordinates for $x$ and $y$ in $y = mx + b$; the equations of the second set, shown on the right, are formed by multiplying each equation of the first set by the coefficient of $m$ in it.

$$
\begin{aligned}
1.48 &= m + b \\
1.76 &= 2m + b \\
2.78 &= 3m + b \\
3.32 &= 4m + b \\
3.86 &= 5m + b \\
4.15 &= 6m + b \\
4.75 &= 7m + b \\
5.66 &= 8m + b \\
6.18 &= 9m + b \\
\underline{6.86} &= \underline{10m + b} \\
40.80 &= 55m + 10b
\end{aligned}
\qquad
\begin{aligned}
1.48 &= m + b \\
3.52 &= 4m + 2b \\
8.34 &= 9m + 3b \\
13.28 &= 16m + 4b \\
19.30 &= 25m + 5b \\
24.90 &= 36m + 6b \\
33.25 &= 49m + 7b \\
45.28 &= 64m + 8b \\
55.62 &= 81m + 9b \\
\underline{68.60} &= \underline{100m + 10b} \\
273.57 &= 385m + 55b
\end{aligned}
$$

$$
\left.
\begin{aligned}
40.80 &= 55m + 10b \\
273.57 &= 385m + 55b
\end{aligned}
\right\}
m = 0.596, \qquad b = 0.802.
$$

We then add the two sets of equations, as indicated above, and solve the resulting two equations for $m$ and $b$. In this case the best fitting line has the equation

$$y = 0.596x + 0.802.$$

If we divide the equation $40.80 = 55m + 10b$ (which was obtained by adding the group on the left above) by 10, we get $4.08 = 5.5m + b$. The average point of the given set is of course $(5.5, 4.08)$, and this equation states the condition that the line $y = mx + b$ pass through this point. It follows that the line $y = 0.596x + 0.802$, which we have called the *best fitting line*, is one of the many lines for which the algebraic sum of the residuals is zero— it is the one for which, at the same time, the sum of the squares of the residuals is as small as possible. The student should plot the given points, draw this line, and compare the result with Fig. 183 which was obtained for the same data by the method of average points.

**113. The symbol $\Sigma$.**—In order to simplify the equations of the next section we introduce the following notation: Given a set of data $(x_1, y_1), (x_2, y_2), \cdots, (x_n, y_n)$, we shall denote the sum of all the $x$'s by $\Sigma x$ and the sum of all the $y$'s by $\Sigma y$; *i.e.,*

$$\Sigma x \equiv x_1 + x_2 + \cdots + x_n,$$
$$\Sigma y \equiv y_1 + y_2 + \cdots + y_n.$$

Using this convenient notation we may write the coordinates of the average point of the set as $(\Sigma x/n, \Sigma y/n)$.

Similarly, we shall denote the sum of the squares of the abscissas by $\Sigma x^2$, the sum of the products of the abscissas by the corresponding ordinates by $\Sigma xy$, etc.

**114. Derivation of equations for method of least squares.** If the points $(x_1, y_1)$, $(x_2, y_2)$, $\cdots$ , $(x_n, y_n)$ are fitted by the line $y = mx + b$, the residuals are

$$r_1 = y_1 - (mx_1 + b)$$
$$r_2 = y_2 - (mx_2 + b)$$
$$\cdots \cdots \cdots \cdots \cdots$$
$$r_n = y_n - (mx_n + b).$$

The squares of the residuals are

$$r_1{}^2 = y_1{}^2 - 2my_1x_1 - 2y_1b + m^2x_1{}^2 + 2mx_1b + b^2$$
$$r_2{}^2 = y_2{}^2 - 2my_2x_2 - 2y_2b + m^2x_2{}^2 + 2mx_2b + b^2$$
$$\cdots \cdots \cdots \cdots \cdots \cdots \cdots \cdots \cdots$$
$$r_n{}^2 = y_n{}^2 - 2my_nx_n - 2y_nb + m^2x_n{}^2 + 2mx_nb + b^2.$$

Adding these, and arranging the right-hand member in the form of a quadratic expression in $b$, we have

$$\Sigma r^2 = nb^2 + 2(m\Sigma x - \Sigma y)b + (m^2\Sigma x^2 - 2m\Sigma xy + \Sigma y^2).$$

If we should plot $\Sigma r^2$ against $b$, the graph would be a parabola lying entirely above the $b$-axis (since $\Sigma r^2$ is certainly positive); the parabola would open upward since the coefficient of $b^2$ is positive, and its minimum point would be at (see page 81)

$$b = -\frac{m\Sigma x - \Sigma y}{n}.$$

This implies that $b$ and $m$ must satisfy the relation

**(1)**                     $\Sigma y = m\Sigma x + nb$

in order that the sum of the squares of the residuals may be a minimum. Observe that this is precisely the equation obtained on page 220 by adding the equations in the left-hand column. Observe also that upon dividing the above equation by $n$ we have

$$\frac{\Sigma y}{n} = m\frac{\Sigma x}{n} + b,$$

which is the condition that the average point of the group $(\Sigma x/n, \Sigma y/n)$ be on the line.

If we arrange the expression for the sum of the squares of the residuals in the form of a quadratic in $m$, we have

$$\Sigma r^2 = (\Sigma x^2)m^2 + 2(b\Sigma x - \Sigma xy)m + (\Sigma y^2 - 2b\Sigma y + nb^2).$$

For a minimum value of $\Sigma r^2$ we must have

$$m = -\frac{b\Sigma x - \Sigma xy}{\Sigma x^2},$$

which implies that $m$ and $b$ must also satisfy the relation

$$\textbf{(2)} \qquad \boldsymbol{\Sigma xy = m\Sigma x^2 + b\Sigma x.}$$

This is the equation obtained by adding the right-hand column on page 220. The two equations (1) and (2) determine uniquely the values of $m$ and $b$ in the equation $y = mx + b$ in order that $\Sigma r^2$ shall be a minimum.

### PROBLEMS

For each of the following sets of data find the best fitting straight line using the method of least squares. Plot the points and draw the line:

**1.**

| $x$ | 1 | 2 | 3 | 4 | 5 | 6 |
|---|---|---|---|---|---|---|
| $y$ | $-2.9$ | $-1.5$ | $-0.4$ | $1.2$ | $2.5$ | $3.5$ |

**2.**

| $x$ | 1 | 2 | 3 | 4 | 5 | 6 | 7 |
|---|---|---|---|---|---|---|---|
| $y$ | 15.8 | 15.2 | 14.5 | 13.8 | 12.9 | 12.3 | 11.5 |

**3.**

| $x$ | 0 | 3 | 6 | 9 | 12 | 15 |
|---|---|---|---|---|---|---|
| $y$ | 2.4 | 4.0 | 5.8 | 7.8 | 9.3 | 11.2 |

**4.** The pressure $P$, in centimeters of mercury of a fixed quantity of gas, was found to vary with the centigrade temperature $T$, when its volume was held constant, as follows:

| $T$ | 20 | 30 | 40 | 50 | 60 | 70 | 80 |
|---|---|---|---|---|---|---|---|
| $P$ | 26.8 | 29.0 | 30.7 | 32.3 | 33.8 | 35.6 | 37.2 |

Express $P$ in terms of $T$ using the method of least squares.

In each of the following problems the given data can be fitted by an equation of the form $y = ax^n$ or $y = a(10)^{kx}$. Determine which equation is applicable and use the method of least squares to fit the data:

**5.**

| $x$ | 1 | 2 | 3 | 4 | 5 | 6 |
|---|---|---|---|---|---|---|
| $y$ | 2.5 | 7.7 | 15.2 | 24.8 | 35.2 | 48.0 |

**6.**

| $x$ | 2 | 5 | 7 | 8 | 10 | 12 |
|---|---|---|---|---|---|---|
| $y$ | 34 | 42 | 46 | 47 | 50 | 52 |

**7.**

| $x$ | 1 | 2 | 3 | 4 | 5 | 6 |
|---|---|---|---|---|---|---|
| $y$ | 3.96 | 5.92 | 9.18 | 13.7 | 20.8 | 31.6 |

**8.**

| $x$ | 5 | 10 | 15 | 20 | 25 | 30 |
|---|---|---|---|---|---|---|
| $y$ | 32 | 21 | 14 | 9 | 6 | 4 |

# SOLID
# ANALYTIC GEOMETRY

# CHAPTER XV

## PRELIMINARY DEFINITIONS AND FORMULAS

**115. Rectangular coordinates in space.**—We now wish to extend our rectangular coordinate system to three dimensions. For this purpose we take three mutually perpendicular lines through a point $O$ which we call the *origin*. These lines are called the $x$-, $y$-, and $z$-axes, respectively, and positive directions on them are chosen as indicated by the arrows in Fig. 191.

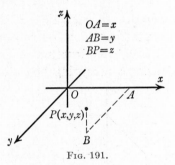

$OA = x$
$AB = y$
$BP = z$

Fig. 191.

For the present we may regard the $x$- and $y$-axes as *horizontal* lines and thus think of their plane, which is called the *xy-plane*, as a horizontal plane. We may then regard the $z$-axis as a *vertical* line. The plane determined by the $x$- and $z$-axes is called the *xz-plane*, and that determined by the $y$- and $z$-axes is called the *yz-plane*. These *coordinate planes*, which intersect at the origin, may be visualized by thinking of the floor and two adjacent walls of a room. The floor is the *xy*-plane and the two walls are the *xz*- and *yz*-planes. The walls intersect along the vertical $z$-axis.

We locate a point $P$ in space by giving its distances from the three coordinate planes. Its distance from the *yz*-plane, which is measured along or parallel to the $x$-axis, is its *x-coordinate*. Similar statements apply to the $y$- and $z$-coordinates. We write the coordinates of a point $P$ in the order $(x, y, z)$.

The coordinate planes divide space into eight octants

227

which are characterized by the signs of the coordinates. The octant in which all three coordinates are positive is called the *first octant*. The others are usually not num-

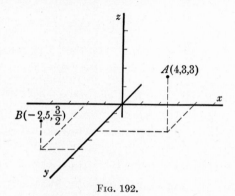

Fig. 192.

bered.  In Fig. 192, $A$ is in the first octant; $B$ is in the octant in which the coordinates have the signs $(- + +)$.

**116. Construction of figures.**—One of the most difficult tasks confronting the student of solid analytic geometry

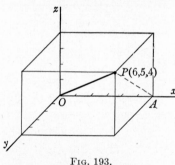

Fig. 193.

is that of drawing the figures. There are several ways of doing this, but none of them is entirely satisfactory. The method that we shall employ is illustrated by Fig. 193. The $x$- and $z$-axes are perpendicular to each other. The $y$-axis makes an angle of 135° with each of these in this figure, but it may be drawn at some other angle. Equal units are used on the $x$- and $z$-axes, but the unit on the $y$-axis is only about 0.7 as long. This "foreshortening" of the dimensions along this axis decreases the amount of distortion.

In the figure, we have plotted the point $P(6, 5, 4)$ and have drawn the rectangular box in which $OP$ is a diagonal. Observe now that while $OP$ is actually longer than $OA$ in space it appears shorter in the figure.   In space, the triangle $OAP$ is a right triangle in which $OP$ is the hypotenuse; the right angle is angle $OAP$.   It is thus evident that the student must learn to visualize the actual space relations by thinking of the figure in space. Any representation of a three-dimensional object by a drawing made upon a flat sheet of paper is somewhat of a makeshift and is intended to serve only as an aid in visualizing the true relations in space.

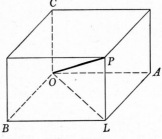

FIG. 194.

**117. The distance formula.—** Figure 194 represents a rectangular box whose edges are $OA$, $OB$, and $OC$.   In order to find the length of a diagonal $OP$ we note that in right triangle $OAL$

$$\overline{OL}^2 = \overline{OA}^2 + \overline{AL}^2.$$

Then, since $OP$ is the hypotenuse of right triangle $OLP$, we have

$$\overline{OP}^2 = \overline{OL}^2 + \overline{LP}^2$$
$$= \overline{OA}^2 + \overline{AL}^2 + \overline{LP}^2.$$

But $AL = OB$ and $LP = OC$.   Hence we can say that

$$\overline{OP}^2 = \overline{OA}^2 + \overline{OB}^2 + \overline{OC}^2.$$

*The square of the diagonal of a rectangular box is equal to the sum of the squares of its three edges.*   If $O$ is the origin and $P$ has coordinates $(x, y, z)$, then $OA = x$, $OB = y$, and $OC = z$.   The distance from $O$ to $P$ is then

$$OP = \sqrt{x^2 + y^2 + z^2}.$$

Now let $P_1(x_1, y_1, z_1)$ and $P_2(x_2, y_2, z_2)$ be any two points, and let it be required to find the undirected distance $P_1P_2$.   As shown in Fig. 195, the segment $P_1P_2$ may be regarded as a diagonal of a rectangular box whose edges have the lengths $x_2 - x_1$, $y_2 - y_1$, and $z_2 - z_1$, respectively. Denoting the required undirected distance by $d$, we have immediately

$$d = \sqrt{(x_2 - x_1)^2 + (y_2 - y_1)^2 + (z_2 - z_1)^2}.$$

**118. Direction angles and direction cosines of the radius vector $OP$.**—The directed segment $OP$ drawn from the

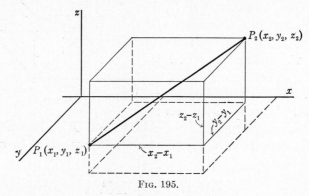

Fig. 195.

origin to any point $P(x, y, z)$ is called the *radius vector* of $P$. If we denote its directed length by $\rho$, then

$$\varrho = OP = \sqrt{x^2 + y^2 + z^2}.$$

The angles $\alpha$, $\beta$, and $\gamma$, which $OP$ makes with the positive directions on the $x$-, $y$-, and $z$-axes, respectively, are called the *direction angles* of $OP$. In Fig. 196 they are

$$\alpha = \angle AOP; \qquad \beta = \angle BOP; \qquad \gamma = \angle COP.$$

Each of these is a positive angle not greater than 180°.

The cosines of the direction angles are called the *direction cosines* of $OP$. They are

$$\cos \alpha = \frac{OA}{OP} = \frac{x}{\rho};$$

$$\cos \beta = \frac{OB}{OP} = \frac{y}{\rho};$$

$$\cos \gamma = \frac{OC}{OP} = \frac{z}{\rho}.$$

If we square the direction cosines, and add, we have

$$\cos^2 \alpha + \cos^2 \beta + \cos^2 \gamma = \frac{x^2}{\rho^2} + \frac{y^2}{\rho^2} + \frac{z^2}{\rho^2}$$
$$= \frac{x^2 + y^2 + z^2}{\rho^2} = \frac{\rho^2}{\rho^2} = 1.$$

*The sum of the squares of the direction cosines of OP is equal to one.*

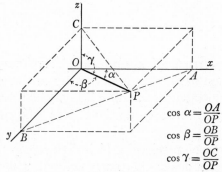

$$\cos \alpha = \frac{OA}{OP}$$
$$\cos \beta = \frac{OB}{OP}$$
$$\cos \gamma = \frac{OC}{OP}$$

Fig. 196.

If $P$ is in the first octant, its coordinates are all positive. In this case the direction cosines of $OP$ are all positive, and its direction angles are all less than 90°. If $P$ has one or more negative coordinates, the corresponding direction cosines are negative. The direction angles having negative cosines are between 90 and 180° (including the latter value).

### Example

In Fig. 197, the point $P$ has coordinates $(-3, 5, 4)$. The distance $OP$ is

$$\rho = \sqrt{(-3)^2 + 5^2 + 4^2} = \sqrt{50} = 5\sqrt{2}.$$

The direction cosines and direction angles of $OP$ are

$$\cos \alpha = \frac{x}{\rho} = \frac{-3}{5\sqrt{2}} = -0.42426; \qquad \alpha = 115° \ 6'.$$

$$\cos \beta = \frac{y}{\rho} = \frac{5}{5\sqrt{2}} = 0.70711; \qquad \beta = 45°.$$

$$\cos \gamma = \frac{z}{\rho} = \frac{4}{5\sqrt{2}} = 0.56568; \qquad \gamma = 55° \ 33'.$$

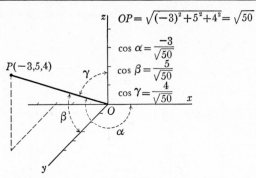

$$OP = \sqrt{(-3)^2 + 5^2 + 4^2} = \sqrt{50}$$

$$\cos \alpha = \frac{-3}{\sqrt{50}}$$

$$\cos \beta = \frac{5}{\sqrt{50}}$$

$$\cos \gamma = \frac{4}{\sqrt{50}}$$

Fig. 197.

**119. Components of a force.**—A force may be represented in magnitude and direction by an arrow or *vector*.
The vector is drawn in the direction of the force, its length
representing, to some convenient scale, the magnitude of
the force.

In problems of mechanics it is frequently necessary to
find the magnitudes of the components of a given force, in
the directions of the coordinate axes. The procedure is
illustrated by the following:

### Example

A pull of 50 lb. is exerted in the direction determined by the line $OP$
in Fig. 198. Find the components of this pull, in the directions of the
coordinate axes.

### Solution

The 50-lb. force along $OP$ is represented by the arrow or vector shown
in the figure, its length representing 50 lb. to some scale. The required
components are then represented by the lengths of the edges of the
rectangular box drawn as shown. If the magnitude of the given force
is $F$, and if the components are denoted by $F_x$, $F_y$, and $F_z$, respectively,
then

$$F_x = F \cos \alpha; \qquad F_y = F \cos \beta; \qquad F_z = F \cos \gamma.$$

In this case the direction cosines of $OP$ are found as follows:

$$OP = \sqrt{6^2 + 4^2 + 3^2} = \sqrt{61};$$

$$\cos \alpha = \frac{6}{\sqrt{61}}; \qquad \cos \beta = \frac{4}{\sqrt{61}}; \qquad \cos \gamma = \frac{3}{\sqrt{61}}.$$

The magnitudes of the components of the 50-lb. force are then

$$F_x = 50 \left( \frac{6}{\sqrt{61}} \right) = 38.4 \text{ lb.}$$

$$F_y = 50 \left( \frac{4}{\sqrt{61}} \right) = 25.6 \text{ lb.}$$

$$F_z = 50 \left( \frac{3}{\sqrt{61}} \right) = 19.2 \text{ lb.}$$

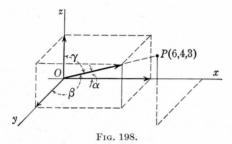

FIG. 198.

In various branches of science, one often deals with *vector quantities; i.e.,* quantities that have not magnitude alone (such as temperature) but that have both *magnitude and direction,* such as force or velocity. Such quantities can be represented by vectors, and it is often necessary to compute the component of such a vector in a given direction.

### PROBLEMS

**1.** In each of the following, plot the point $P$ and draw the radius vector $OP$; find its length, direction cosines, and direction angles:

(a) $P(2, 2, 4)$.　　(b) $P(-12, -3, 4)$.　　(c) $P(4, -3, 1)$.
(d) $P(5, 5, -5)$.　　(e) $P(-3, 2, -6)$.　　(f) $P(6, -3, -6)$.

**2.** For a certain radius vector $OP$, $\cos \alpha = \frac{2}{3}$ and $\cos \beta = \frac{1}{3}$. Find the two possible values for $\cos \gamma$ and draw the figure.

**3.** A line is drawn from the origin so as to make equal angles with the three coordinate axes. Find its direction cosines and draw the line. HINT: The point $(1, 1, 1)$ is on the line.

**4.** Describe and sketch the locus of points $(x, y, z)$ that satisfy the following conditions:

(a) $x = 4$.　(b) $x = 0$ and $z = 0$.　　(c) $x = 3$ and $y = 4$.
(d) $z = x$.　(e) $x + y = 4$.　　　　(f) $x + y = 4$ and $z = 0$.

**5.** Determine the coordinates of the point that is symmetrical with respect to the point $P(x, y, z)$ with respect to

(a) The origin.        (b) The $xy$-plane.        (c) The $x$-axis.

**6.** In each of the following, plot the given points and draw the line joining them and compute its length:

(a) $A(2, 6, 1)$        $B(8, 3, 7)$.        (b) $P(-4, 5, 2)$ $Q(2, 0, 5)$.
(c) $M(-4, -3, 2)$ $N(4, 1, -6)$.

**7.** Draw each of the following triangles and find the lengths of its sides:

(a) $A(0, 4, 1)$        $B(6, 5, 3)$ $C(10, 0, 6)$.
(b) $P(-3, -2, 3)$ $Q(0, 3, 0)$ $R(4, 0, 0)$.

**8.** Draw each of the following triangles and show that it is a right triangle:

(a) $A(2, 6, 2)$        $B(5, 8, 5)$        $C(8, 2, 6)$.
(b) $P(-4, -2, 5)$ $Q(4, -1, 8)$ $R(6, 4, 1)$.

**9.** Show that the coordinates of the mid-point of a segment

$$P_1(x_1, y_1, z_1) \, P_2(x_2, y_2, z_2)$$

are

$$\tfrac{1}{2}(x_1 + x_2), \qquad \tfrac{1}{2}(y_1 + y_2), \qquad \tfrac{1}{2}(z_1 + z_2).$$

**10.** Find the coordinates of the points that divide the segment $A(2, 7, 1)$ $B(8, -2, 5)$ into three equal parts.

**11.** Find the equation of the surface, all points of which are at a distance of 5 units from the origin. What is this surface?

**12.** Find the equation of the surface, all points of which are at a distance of 5 units from the point $C(3, 2, 5)$. Describe the surface.

**13.** A point $P(x, y, z)$ moves so that its distance from $F(4, 0, 0)$ is always equal to its distance from the $yz$-plane. Find the equation of the surface on which it moves. Describe the surface and try to sketch it.

**14.** A point $P(x, y, z)$ moves so that its distance from $A(2, 5, 1)$ is always equal to its distance from $B(8, 1, 6)$. Find the equation of the surface on which it moves and describe the surface.

**15.** Find the equation of the locus of a point, the sum of whose undirected distances from $(4, 0, 0)$ and $(-4, 0, 0)$ is equal to 10.

**16.** Find the coordinates of the point on the $x$-axis that is equidistant from $P(4, 3, 1)$ and $Q(-2, -6, 2)$.

**17.** In each of the following, a force of the given magnitude acts away from the origin along the line $OP$. Find its components along the axes:

(a) 100 lb.; $P(6, 6, 3)$.        (b) 70 lb.; $P(12, -4, -3)$.
(c) 60 lb.; $P(3, 0, -4)$.        (d) 200 lb.; $P(-6, 3, 5)$.

**18.** Pulls of 27 lb. and 35 lb. are applied to the block as shown in Fig. 199. Find the total vertical pull, and also the resultant pulls in the $x$- and $y$-directions. What is the magnitude, and what are the direction angles, of a single force that would produce the same effect as these two forces?

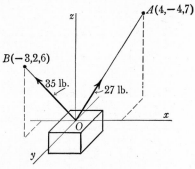

FIG. 199.

**19.** Same as Prob. 18 but with forces of 44 lb. and 20 lb. along $OA$ and $OB$, respectively, the coordinates of $A$ and $B$ being $(9, 6, 2)$ and $(-8, 6, 0)$.

**20.** Forces of 44 lb., 35 lb., and 30 lb. act away from the origin along the lines $OA$, $OB$, and $OC$, respectively. The coordinates of $A$, $B$, and $C$ are $A(9, -2, -6)$, $B(-6, 3, 2)$, $C(3, 4, 0)$. Find the algebraic sum of the components of these forces along each coordinate axis. Find the magnitude and direction angles of the single force having these components. This force is called the *resultant* of the given set of forces.

**120. Direction cosines of any directed line.**—Let $l$ (Fig. 200) be any directed line in space. The direction chosen as positive may be indicated by an arrowhead as shown in the figure. We define the *direction angles* of $l$ as follows:

Let $P_1(x_1, y_1, z_1)$ and $P_2(x_2, y_2, z_2)$ be any two points on $l$ such that the directed segment $P_1P_2$ is positive. Through $P_1$ draw lines $P_1x'$, $P_1y'$, and $P_1z'$ parallel to, and in the positive directions of, the $x$-, $y$-, and $z$-axes, respectively. Then the direction angles of $l$ are $\alpha$, $\beta$, and $\gamma$, where

$$\alpha = \angle x'P_1P_2; \qquad \beta = \angle y'P_1P_2; \qquad \gamma = \angle z'P_1P_2.$$

Each of these is a positive angle not greater than 180°.

The cosines of the above direction angles are called the

*direction cosines* of the directed line *l*. In order to compute their values we first find the distance $P_1P_2$ which we may denote by *d*

$$d = \sqrt{(x_2 - x_1)^2 + (y_2 - y_1)^2 + (z_2 - z_1)^2}.$$

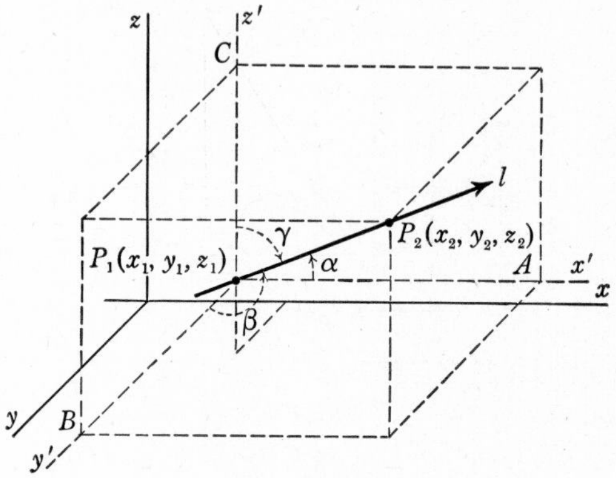

Fig. 200.

We then see from the figure that

$$\cos \alpha = \frac{P_1A}{P_1P_2} = \frac{x_2 - x_1}{d};$$

$$\cos \beta = \frac{P_1B}{P_1P_2} = \frac{y_2 - y_1}{d};$$

$$\cos \gamma = \frac{P_1C}{P_1P_2} = \frac{z_2 - z_1}{d}.$$

Since *d* is positive, each of the above direction cosines is positive or negative depending upon the sign of the numerator. It should be observed that the effect of reversing the positive direction on the line is to change the signs of all the direction cosines—and to replace the direction angles by their supplements.

Finally, if we square the direction cosines, and add, we have the important relation

$$\cos^2 \alpha + \cos^2 \beta + \cos^2 \gamma = 1.$$

### Example

Find the direction cosines of the line determined by the points $P_1(1, -2, 8)$ and $P_2(8, 2, 3)$ if the positive direction is from $P_1$ to $P_2$.

*Solution* (Fig. 201)

$$d = \sqrt{[8 - 1]^2 + [2 - (-2)]^2 + [3 - 8]^2} = \sqrt{90} = 3\sqrt{10};$$

$$\cos \alpha = \frac{8 - 1}{3\sqrt{10}} = \frac{7\sqrt{10}}{30} = 0.73786;$$

$$\cos \beta = \frac{2 - (-2)}{3\sqrt{10}} = \frac{4\sqrt{10}}{30} = 0.42164;$$

$$\cos \gamma = \frac{3 - 8}{3\sqrt{10}} = \frac{-5\sqrt{10}}{30} = -0.52705.$$

The value of $\cos \gamma$ is negative because $\gamma$ is between 90 and 180°. If the positive direction had been from $P_2$ to $P_1$, the signs of the direction cosines would have been reversed.

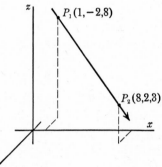

**121. Direction numbers.—** If a point moves from $A$ to $B$ along the line shown in Fig. 202, it moves 6 units in the positive $x$-direction, 3 units in the *negative* $y$-direction, and 2 units in the positive $z$-direction, as indicated by the dotted lines. The numbers 6, $-3$, and 2, written in the form

Fig. 201.

$$6 : -3 : 2$$

may be used to define the *direction* of the line. They fix its

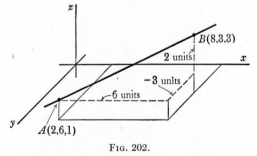

Fig. 202.

direction by indicating that for every 6 units moved in the $x$-direction a point traveling along the line must move $-3$

units in the $y$-direction and 2 units in the $z$-direction. Any set of three numbers proportional to these would serve equally well. Thus if the point moved 12 units in the $x$-direction, it would move $-6$ units in the $y$-direction and 4 units in the $z$-direction. The numbers $12: -6:4$ would then define the *same* direction. If the point travels from $B$ to $A$, instead of from $A$ to $B$, all the above distances have opposite signs; *i.e.*, the numbers $-6: +3: -2$ also fix the direction of the line determined by $A$ and $B$. We do not here specify whether $A$ to $B$ or $B$ to $A$ is positive.

Consider now the general case of a line determined by two points $P_1(x_1, y_1, z_1)$ and $P_2(x_2, y_2, z_2)$. The direction of the line in space is determined by the numbers

$$x_2 - x_1 : y_2 - y_1 : z_2 - z_1.$$

Any set of three numbers that could be obtained from these by multiplying each one by the same positive or negative constant $k(\neq 0)$ would serve equally well in fixing the direction of the line. Any such set of numbers is called a set of *direction numbers* of the line.

In the plane, we have determined a line by specifying two points on it, or by giving one point and its direction (inclination or slope). In space we may correspondingly fix a line by specifying two points on it, or by giving one point and a set of direction numbers.

### Example

Draw the line passing through $A(-2, 6, 5)$ with direction numbers $2: -1 : -1$.

#### Solution (Fig. 203)

Starting at $A$, we may obtain another point on the line by going 2 units in the $x$-direction, $-1$ units in the $y$-direction, and $-1$ units in the $z$-direction. Or, if more convenient, we may use any multiple of these distances. In the figure we have used 6, $-3$, and $-3$ units, respectively, thereby arriving at a point $B(4, 3, 2)$ which is on the required line.

It is obvious that any set of three numbers, not all zero,

may be regarded in the above way as defining the direction of a line in space. They are proportional to the direction cosines in accordance with the following theorem, proof of which is left to the student:

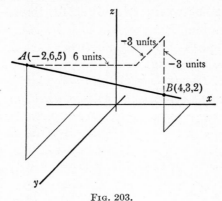

Fig. 203.

**Theorem :** *If a line has direction numbers a:b:c, its direction cosines are*

$$\cos \alpha = \frac{a}{\pm \sqrt{a^2 + b^2 + c^2}},$$

$$\cos \beta = \frac{b}{\pm \sqrt{a^2 + b^2 + c^2}},$$

$$\cos \gamma = \frac{c}{\pm \sqrt{a^2 + b^2 + c^2}},$$

*where the signs of the denominators are all + or all −, depending on which direction along the line is chosen as positive.*

### Example

The line shown in Fig. 202 has direction numbers $6: -3:2$. If the positive direction is from $A$ to $B$, the corresponding direction cosines are

$$\cos \alpha = \frac{6}{+ \sqrt{6^2 + (-3)^2 + 2^2}} = + \frac{6}{7};$$

$$\cos \beta = \frac{-3}{+7} = - \frac{3}{7};$$

$$\cos \gamma = \frac{2}{+7} = + \frac{2}{7}.$$

The positive sign was chosen for the radical because $\alpha$ and $\gamma$ are obviously less than 90° and their cosines are therefore positive. If the positive direction had been from $B$ to $A$, the negative sign would have been chosen.

**122. Angle between two directed lines.**—Two lines drawn at random in space do not, in general, intersect. We however speak of the angle between such lines in accordance with the following:

**Definition:** *The angle between two directed lines in space is equal to the angle between the positive directions of two lines that are parallel, respectively, to the given lines, have the same positive directions, and intersect at a point O.*

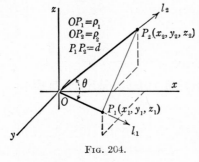

$OP_1 = \rho_1$
$OP_2 = \rho_2$
$P_1P_2 = d$
$P_2(x_2, y_2, z_2)$
$P_1(x_1, y_1, z_1)$

FIG. 204.

Without loss of generality we may take the point $O$ in the above definition as the origin. The problem of finding the angle between any two directed lines in space then reduces to that of finding the angle $\theta$ between the positive directions of two lines $l_1$ and $l_2$ through the origin, as shown in Fig. 204. The cosine of this angle may be expressed in terms of the direction cosines of $l_1$ and $l_2$ as follows:

Choose a point $P_1(x_1, y_1, z_1)$ on $l_1$, and a point $P_2(x_2, y_2, z_2)$ on $l_2$; let $OP_1 = \rho_1$, $OP_2 = \rho_2$, and $P_1P_2 = d$. Then, using the cosine law, we have the relation

$$d^2 = \rho_1{}^2 + \rho_2{}^2 - 2\rho_1\rho_2 \cos \theta.$$

Solving this equation for $\cos \theta$ we have

$$\cos \theta = \frac{\rho_1{}^2 + \rho_2{}^2 - d^2}{2\rho_1\rho_2}.$$

But,

$$\rho_1{}^2 = x_1{}^2 + y_1{}^2 + z_1{}^2; \qquad \rho_2{}^2 = x_2{}^2 + y_2{}^2 + z_2{}^2;$$
$$d^2 = (x_2 - x_1)^2 + (y_2 - y_1)^2 + (z_2 - z_1)^2.$$

Substituting these relations into the numerator of the above expression, and simplifying, we find that

$$\cos\theta = \frac{x_1x_2 + y_1y_2 + z_1z_2}{\rho_1\rho_2}.$$

$$= \frac{x_1}{\rho_1}\frac{x_2}{\rho_2} + \frac{y_1}{\rho_1}\frac{y_2}{\rho_2} + \frac{z_1}{\rho_1}\frac{z_2}{\rho_2}.$$

Now, if the direction angles of $l_1$ are $\alpha_1$, $\beta_1$, $\gamma_1$ and those of $l_2$ are $\alpha_2$, $\beta_2$, $\gamma_2$, it is obvious that

$$\frac{x_1}{\rho_1} = \cos\alpha_1 \quad \text{and} \quad \frac{x_2}{\rho_2} = \cos\alpha_2;$$

$$\frac{y_1}{\rho_1} = \cos\beta_1 \quad \text{and} \quad \frac{y_2}{\rho_2} = \cos\beta_2;$$

$$\frac{z_1}{\rho_1} = \cos\gamma_1 \quad \text{and} \quad \frac{z_2}{\rho_2} = \cos\gamma_2.$$

Making these substitutions we finally have the result

$$\textbf{cos } \theta = \textbf{cos } \alpha_1 \textbf{ cos } \alpha_2 + \textbf{cos } \beta_1 \textbf{ cos } \beta_2 + \textbf{cos } \gamma_1 \textbf{ cos } \gamma_2.$$

### *Example*

The directed line from $A(2, 3, 5)$ to $B(6, -2, 2)$ has the direction cosines

$$\cos\alpha_1 = \frac{4}{\sqrt{50}}; \quad \cos\beta_1 = \frac{-5}{\sqrt{50}}; \quad \cos\gamma_1 = \frac{-3}{\sqrt{50}}.$$

The directed line from $C(-2, -2, 8)$ to $D(4, 1, 6)$ has the direction cosines:

$$\cos\alpha_2 = \frac{6}{7}; \quad \cos\beta_2 = \frac{3}{7}; \quad \cos\gamma_2 = \frac{-2}{7}.$$

The cosine of the angle $\theta$ between these lines is

$$\cos\theta = \left(\frac{4}{\sqrt{50}}\right)\left(\frac{6}{7}\right) + \left(-\frac{5}{\sqrt{50}}\right)\left(\frac{3}{7}\right) + \left(-\frac{3}{\sqrt{50}}\right)\left(-\frac{2}{7}\right)$$

$$= \frac{3\sqrt{2}}{14} = 0.30304$$

$$\theta = 72° 22'.$$

Two lines in space are mutually perpendicular if and only if $\theta = 90°$. Since $\cos 90° = 0$, the condition for perpendicularity of $l_1$ and $l_2$ is

$$\textbf{cos } \alpha_1 \textbf{ cos } \alpha_2 + \textbf{cos } \beta_1 \textbf{ cos } \beta_2 + \textbf{cos } \gamma_1 \textbf{ cos } \gamma_2 = \textbf{0}.$$

If, instead of the direction cosines of $l_1$ and $l_2$, we have their direction numbers $a_1:b_1:c_1$ and $a_2:b_2:c_2$, respectively, we may first compute the direction cosines and then use the above formula, or we may use directly the equivalent formula

$$\cos \theta = \pm \frac{a_1 a_2 + b_1 b_2 + c_1 c_2}{\sqrt{a_1{}^2 + b_1{}^2 + c_1{}^2} \sqrt{a_2{}^2 + b_2{}^2 + c_2{}^2}}$$

The $+$ or $-$ sign is to be used depending on the choice of positive directions on $l_1$ and $l_z$. In terms of direction numbers the condition for perpendicularity becomes

$$a_1 a_2 + b_1 b_2 + c_1 c_2 = 0.$$

### Example

Two lines having direction numbers $2:6:-1$ and $4:-1:2$, respectively, are mutually perpendicular, because

$$(4) \cdot (2) + (-1) \cdot (6) + (2) \cdot (-1) = 0.$$

### PROBLEMS

**1.** Draw each of the following lines and find its direction numbers and direction cosines. The positive direction in each case is from the first given point to the second:

(a) $A(2, 1, 1)$    $B(6, 6, 4)$.      (b) $P(-2, 3, 4)$      $Q(0, 1, 3)$.
(c) $M(0, -3, 2)$ $N(0, 1, 5)$.      (d) $C(-3, -2, -2)$ $D(6, 0, 3)$.
(e) $L(0, 0, -2)$   $M(4, -4, 0)$.      (f) $R(7, 4, 1)$      $S(1, -2, 4)$.

**2.** In each of the following, a line is determined by the given point and direction numbers. In each case draw the line and find its direction cosines assuming the positive direction to be such that $\cos \gamma$ is positive:

(a) $A(2, 5, 1); 2:-2:1$.      (b) $A(-2, 2, 6); \quad 6:3:-2$.
(c) $A(0, 5, 0); 4:-4:3$.      (d) $A(-4, 0, -2); 2:0: \quad 1$.

**3.** Find the direction cosines of each of the coordinate axes.

**4.** Two of the direction angles of a certain line are $\alpha = 45°$ and $\beta = 60°$. Find its direction cosines if the positive direction is such that $\gamma$ is an acute angle.

**5.** A line goes through $A(-4, 6, 1)$ and has direction numbers $2:-2:1$. What are the coordinates of the point where this line pierces the $yz$-plane? The $xz$-plane?

**6.** A line goes through $P(4, 2, 3)$ and has direction numbers $3:2:-1$.

What are the coordinates of the point at which it pierces the $xy$-plane? The $xz$-plane?

**7.** A line goes through $P(4, 7, 2)$ and makes equal angles with the coordinate axes. What are the coordinates of the points at which it pierces the coordinate planes?

**8.** Find the cosine of the angle between the lines for which direction numbers are

(a) $2:1:-2; 3:-6:2.$          (b) $7:4:4;$     $6:-6:3.$

(c) $5:4:-3; 1:-1:0.$       (d) $3:-1:-4; 2:-3:1.$

**9.** Draw each of the following triangles and show that it is a right triangle; compute the cosine of the angle at $A$:

(a) $A(2, 7, 1)$     $B(8, 5, 5)$    $C(7, 3, 4).$

(b) $A(-2, 3, 2)$    $B(6, -3, 4)$ $C(1, 3, -1).$

(c) $A(-4, -2, 1)$ $B(5, -1, 5)$ $C(8, 4, -3).$

**10.** A line $l_1$ is drawn from the origin to $P(4, -2, 4)$, and from $P$ a line $l_2$ is drawn so as to make equal angles with the coordinate axes. Draw the figure and compute the angle between $l_1$ and $l_2$.

**11.** What relation must exist between the direction cosines of two lines if the lines are to be parallel?

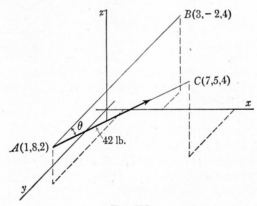

FIG. 205.

**12.** A force of 42 lb. acts along the line $AC$ as shown in Fig. 205. Find its component in the direction of $AB$. HINT: The required magnitude is equal to $42 \cos \theta$.

**13.** A force of 36 lb. acts along the line $OP$ drawn from the origin to $P(7, 4, 4)$. Find the component of this force in the direction of a line making equal angles with the coordinate axes.

**14.** Show that the direction numbers $a:b:c$ of a line $l$ that is perpendicular to each of two nonparallel lines $l_1$ and $l_2$ having direction numbers $a_1:b_1:c_1$ and $a_2:b_2:c_2$, respectively, are

$$a:b:c = \begin{vmatrix} b_1 & c_1 \\ b_2 & c_2 \end{vmatrix} : \begin{vmatrix} c_1 & a_1 \\ c_2 & a_2 \end{vmatrix} : \begin{vmatrix} a_1 & b_1 \\ a_2 & b_2 \end{vmatrix}$$

Hint: The condition that $l$ is perpendicular to both $l_1$ and $l_2$ is that $aa_1 + bb_1 + cc_1 = 0$ and $aa_2 + bb_2 + cc_2 = 0$. Solve these equations for $a/c$ and $b/c$ using determinants.

**15.** Find the direction numbers of the radius vector that is perpendicular to the plane of $OP$ and $OQ$ in Fig. 206.

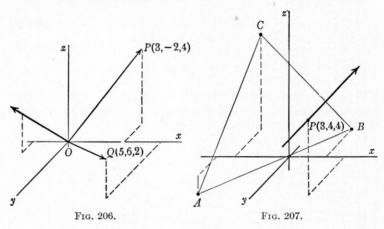

FIG. 206.          FIG. 207.

**16.** Draw each of the following triangles and find the direction numbers of the normals to its plane.   Draw the normal from the origin to the plane of the triangle:

(a) $A(8, 0, 0)$    $B(0, 12, 0)$ $C(0, 0, 8)$.

(b) $A(-5, 0, 0)$ $B(3, 8, 2)$   $C(-3, -4, 8)$.

(c) $A(2, 7, 1)$    $B(8, 2, 3)$   $C(3, 2, 8)$.

**17.** A line is to be drawn through $P(3, 4, 4)$ perpendicular to the plane determined by the points $A(-4, 2, -1)$ $B(2, -3, 0)$ and $C(-3, -3, 5)$ as shown in Fig. 207.   Find its direction numbers.

# CHAPTER XVI

## PLANES AND LINES

**123. Normal equation of a plane.**—A plane may be determined by specifying the length and direction of the normal $ON$ drawn from the origin to the plane. In Fig. 208 let the directed length $ON = p$, and let the direction angles of $ON$ be $\alpha$, $\beta$, and $\gamma$.

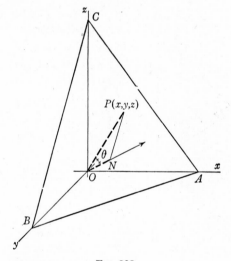

FIG. 208.

We wish now to determine the equation of the plane in terms of this data. For this purpose we let $P(x, y, z)$ be any point in the plane. We denote the directed length $OP$ by $\rho$ and let the direction angles of $OP$ be $\alpha_1$, $\beta_1$, and $\gamma_1$. Then, if $\theta$ is the angle between the directed segments $OP$ and $ON$, the triangle $OPN$ is a right triangle in which

$$OP \cos \theta = ON,$$

or

$$\rho \cos \theta = p.$$

245

Making use of the known formula for $\cos \theta$ we can write this in the form

$$\rho(\cos \alpha_1 \cos \alpha + \cos \beta_1 \cos \beta + \cos \gamma_1 \cos \gamma) = p.$$

Now since

$$\rho \cos \alpha_1 = x, \qquad \rho \cos \beta_1 = y, \qquad \text{and} \qquad \rho \cos \gamma_1 = z,$$

we have

(1)          $x \cos \alpha + y \cos \beta + z \cos \gamma = p.$

This is called the *normal form* of the equation of a plane, and it of course corresponds to the normal form of the equation of a line. It can be used for writing down the equation of a plane when the length and direction of its normal $ON$ are known.

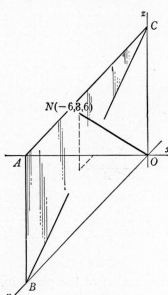

Fig. 209.

### Example

Find the equation of the plane through $N(-6, 3, 6)$ perpendicular to $ON$.

*Solution* (Fig. 209)

In this case

$$ON = p = \sqrt{(-6)^2 + 3^2 + 6^2} = 9;$$

$$\cos \alpha = -\tfrac{2}{3};$$
$$\cos \beta = \tfrac{1}{3};$$
$$\cos \gamma = \tfrac{2}{3}.$$

The normal form of the required equation is then

$$-\tfrac{2}{3}x + \tfrac{1}{3}y + \tfrac{2}{3}z = 9.$$

This can of course be reduced to

$$2x - y - 2z + 27 = 0.$$

**124. General form of the equation of a plane.**—The normal form of the equation of a plane is of first degree in $x$, $y$, and $z$. Every plane has an equation of this form, so we can say that *every plane has an equation that is of first degree.* We can easily prove, conversely, that *every equation of first degree in x, y, and z, represents a plane.* In fact we have the following:

**Theorem**: *The locus of every equation of the form*

(**2**) $$Ax + By + Cz + D = 0$$

*in which A, B, and C are not all zero, is a plane. Furthermore, the normal to the plane has direction numbers $A:B:C$.*

The proof is as follows: Without altering the locus of (2) we may divide by $\pm \sqrt{A^2 + B^2 + C^2}$, which is certainly not equal to zero. We thus obtain the equation

$$\frac{A}{\pm \sqrt{A^2 + B^2 + C^2}} x + \frac{B}{\pm \sqrt{A^2 + B^2 + C^2}} y$$
$$+ \frac{C}{\pm \sqrt{A^2 + B^2 + C^2}} z + \frac{D}{\pm \sqrt{A^2 + B^2 + C^2}} = 0.$$

Comparing this last equation with the normal form (1) we see that its locus, and hence that of (2), is a *plane* whose normal has the following direction cosines:

$$\cos \alpha = \frac{A}{\pm \sqrt{A^2 + B^2 + C^2}}$$
$$\cos \beta = \frac{B}{\pm \sqrt{A^2 + B^2 + C^2}}$$
$$\cos \gamma = \frac{C}{\pm \sqrt{A^2 + B^2 + C^2}}.$$

It follows that the numbers $A:B:C$ are direction numbers of the normal.

The equation $Ax + By + Cz + D = 0$ is called the *general form* of the equation of a plane. It can evidently be transformed into the normal form by dividing through by $\pm \sqrt{A^2 + B^2 + C^2}$. In doing this we choose the sign of the radical as follows: The distance from the origin to the plane is

$$p = \frac{-D}{\pm \sqrt{A^2 + B^2 + C^2}},$$

In order that $p$ may be positive we may agree to take the sign of the radical opposite to that of $D$ if $D \neq 0$. If $D = 0$, the plane goes through the origin and $p = 0$. In this case we agree to take the sign of the radical the same as that of $C$; this amounts to choosing the positive direction on the normal so that $\gamma$ is an acute angle. If $C = D = 0$, then $p = 0$ and $\gamma = 90°$. In this case we choose the sign of the radical to agree with that of $B$, thus making $\beta$ an acute angle.

**125. Drawing the plane and its normal.**—The line in which a given plane intersects a coordinate plane is called the *trace* of the given plane on that coordinate plane. Thus the trace of the plane whose equation is

$$5x + 8y + 10z = 40$$

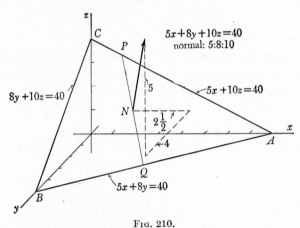

FIG. 210.

on the $xy$-plane is the line $AB$ in Fig. 210. Its equation, found by putting $z = 0$ in the equation of the given plane, is

$$5x + 8y = 40.$$

The equations of the traces on the other coordinate planes are found similarly. In making a drawing it is often convenient to represent a plane in space by its traces as illustrated by the figure.

Let it now be required to select a random point on the

plane and draw the normal to the plane through this
point.  If we draw a line from any point $P$ on one trace
to any point $Q$ on another trace, the line $PQ$ lies in the
plane.  If we choose a point $N$ on $PQ$, this point will lie
on the plane.

In order to draw the normal through $N$, we note that its
direction numbers are $5:8:10$ (or any set of numbers proportional to these).  In the figure we have obtained another
point on the normal by going $2\frac{1}{2}$ units in the $x$-direction,
4 units in the $y$-direction, and 5 units in the $z$-direction,
from $N$.

**126. Plane parallel to one or more coordinate axes.**—
The general equation of first degree in $x$, $y$, and $z$, is

$$Ax + By + Cz + D = 0$$

in which $A$, $B$, and $C$ are not all zero.  We have seen that
every such equation represents a plane whose normal has
the direction numbers $A:B:C$.  Suppose now that $C = 0$.
In this case $\cos \gamma = 0$, $\gamma = 90°$, and the plane is parallel
to the $z$-axis.

### Example

The equation $3x + 4y = 16$ represents a plane parallel to the $z$-axis,
and consequently perpendicular to the $xy$-plane, as shown in Fig. 211.

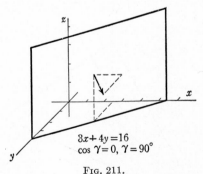

$3x + 4y = 16$
$\cos \gamma = 0, \gamma = 90°$

FIG. 211.

Similar considerations apply if $A$ or $B = 0$.  Discussion
of the case in which two of the coefficients are zero is left
to the student.

**127. Plane through a point perpendicular to a line.**—One and only one plane can be passed through a given point perpendicular to a given line. Its equation can be found as illustrated by the following:

### Example

Find the equation of the plane that passes through the point $P(1\frac{1}{2}, 5, 1)$ and is perpendicular to the line $A(-1\frac{1}{2}, -1, -1)$ $B(3\frac{1}{2}, 2, 6\frac{1}{2})$.

### Solution (Fig. 212)

Since the required plane is perpendicular to $AB$, *this line is a normal to the plane*. Its direction numbers can therefore be taken as the coefficients of $x$, $y$, and $z$, respectively, in the required equation. These direction numbers are $5:3:7\frac{1}{2}$.

The equation of the plane is then

$$5x + 3y + \tfrac{15}{2}z + D = 0$$

where $D$ is to be determined from the condition that the plane must pass through $P(1\frac{1}{2}, 5, 1)$. Substituting these coordinates into the above equation, and solving for $D$, we have

$$5(\tfrac{3}{2}) + 3(5) + \tfrac{15}{2}(1) + D = 0;$$
$$D = -30.$$

The required equation is then

$$5x + 3y + \tfrac{15}{2}z - 30 = 0$$

or

$$10x + 6y + 15z - 60 = 0.$$

The plane is represented by its traces in Fig. 212.

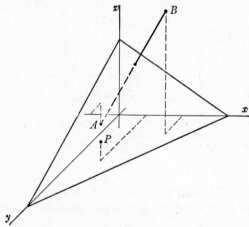

FIG. 212.

## PROBLEMS

**1.** Write the equation of the plane for which

(a) $\alpha = 60°$,  $\beta = 45°$,  $\gamma = 60°$, $p = 4$.

(b) $\alpha = 135°$, $\beta = 45°$,  $\gamma \approx 90°$, $p = 8$.

(c) $\alpha = 90°$,  $\beta = 120°$, $\gamma = 30°$, $p = 6$.

**2.** In each of the following, plot the point $P$ and draw the radius vector $OP$. Then find the equation of the plane through $P$ perpendicular to $OP$. Represent the plane in the drawing by its traces:

(a) $P(2, 4, 2)$.     (b) $P(-3, 1, 2)$.     (c) $P(-4, -3, 0)$.

(d) $P(4, -2, 1)$.    (e) $P(2, 2, -2)$.     (f) $P(0, 3, 0)$.

**3.** Reduce each of the following equations to the normal form. Find the direction cosines of the normal to the plane, and find the distance of the plane from the origin. Draw the figure, representing the plane by its traces:

(a) $2x + 3y + 6z + 21 = 0$.     (b) $2x - y + 2z = 12$.

(c) $8x + 4y - z = 27$.          (d) $x - y - 2z = -6$.

(e) $x + 2z - 6 = 0$.            (f) $y - 3 = 0$.

**4.** In each of the following, make a drawing in which the given plane is represented by its traces. Select a random point on the plane and draw the normal at this point:

(a) $5x + 6y + 10z = 30$.        (b) $3x - 2y + 2z - 12 = 0$.

(c) $3x - 4z + 12 = 0$.          (d) $x - 2y - 4z + 8 = 0$.

**5.** In each of the following, find the equation of the plane that passes through the point $P$ and is perpendicular to the line $AB$:

(a) $A(-2, 1, 1)$   $B(4, 5, 3)$;   $P(2, 1, 2)$.

(b) $A(-3, -2, 5)$ $B(3, 1, 1)$;   $P(1, 0, 0)$.

(c) $A(1, 5, 2)$     $B(4, -1, 5)$; $P(2, 2, 2)$.

**6.** A plane is passed through the mid-point of the segment

$$A(-2, 5, 1)\ B(6, 1, 5)$$

perpendicular to the line. Find its equation.

**7.** Find the coordinates of the point $P$ on the segment $A(-2, -1, 2)$ $B(7, 5, 5)$ that is $\frac{2}{3}$ of the way from $A$ to $B$. Find the equation of the plane through $P$ perpendicular to $AB$.

**8.** Find the equation of the locus of points equidistant from the two points $A(-3, -2, -1)$ and $B(7, 0, 5)$.

**9.** Find the point on the $y$-axis that is equidistant from the two points $A(1, -4, 4)$ and $B(7, 6, 2)$.

**10.** Find the center and radius of the sphere that passes through the points $A(10, -3, 4)$, $B(11, 7, -3)$, $C(-2, 0, 7)$, and $D(0, -4, 5)$. HINT: The center is the point in space that is equidistant from $A$, $B$, $C$, and $D$. Hence, find the equations of the planes that are the perpendicular bisectors of segments $AB$, $BC$, and $CD$, and solve these equations simultaneously.

**11.** Show that the distance from the plane

$$Ax + By + Cz + D = 0$$

to the point $P(x_1, y_1, z_1)$ is given by the formula

$$d = \frac{Ax_1 + By_1 + Cz_1 + D}{\pm \sqrt{A^2 + B^2 + C^2}}.$$

The method is analogous to that used in finding the distance from a line to a point. (If the sign of the radical is chosen as specified on page 248 when $D \neq 0$, then $d$ is positive if $P$ and the origin are on opposite sides of the plane.)

**12.** In each of the following, find the distance from the given plane to the given point (see Prob. 11).

(a) $2x + 2y + z = 15$; $P(5, 4, 6)$.

(b) $2x - 3y + 6z - 18 = 0$; $P(1, -1, 1)$.

(c) $4x - 5y - 3z + 24 = 0$; $P(-3, 5, 5)$.

**13.** Show that direction numbers of the line of intersection of the two planes

$$\begin{cases} A_1x + B_1y + C_1z + D_1 = 0 \\ A_2x + B_2y + C_2z + D_2 = 0 \end{cases}$$

are

$$\begin{vmatrix} B_1 & C_1 \\ B_2 & C_2 \end{vmatrix} : \begin{vmatrix} C_1 & A_1 \\ C_2 & A_2 \end{vmatrix} : \begin{vmatrix} A_1 & B_1 \\ A_2 & B_2 \end{vmatrix}$$

HINT: The line of intersection is perpendicular to the normals to both planes. Use Prob. 14, page 243.

**14.** Find the equation of the plane that passes through $P(1, 3, 2)$ and is perpendicular to the two planes $2x + y - z + 12 = 0$ and

$$x - y + z + 4 = 0.$$

HINT: If a plane is perpendicular to each of two given planes it is perpendicular to their line of intersection (see Prob. 13).

**15.** A plane is determined by the points $A(-3, 7, -2)$, $B(8, 1, 3)$, and $P(4, 6, 1)$. A second plane is determined by $A$, $B$, and $Q(-3, 7, 2)$. A third plane passes through the point $R(2, 3\frac{1}{2}, -1)$ and is perpendicular to the first two planes. What is its equation?

**128. Plane determined by three points.**—Of the four constants in the equation

$$Ax + By + Cz + D = 0$$

only three are *essential;* for we may divide through by any one (whose value is not zero) and thus reduce the number to three. Thus if $A \neq 0$, the above equation may be written in the form

$$x + by + cz + d = 0$$

where

$$b = \frac{B}{A}, \qquad c = \frac{C}{A}, \qquad \text{and} \qquad d = \frac{D}{A}.$$

Since the equation contains three essential constants, the plane is determined by three independent conditions. One such set of conditions is the requirement that the plane shall pass through three given points, not all on the same line. A procedure for finding the equation of the plane from these data is illustrated by the following:

### Example

Find the equation of the plane passing through the points $(-1, 2, 4)$, $(3, 3, \frac{1}{2})$, and $(4, 1, 1\frac{1}{2})$.

### Solution

Assuming that the plane determined by these points is such that $A \neq 0$ in the equation $Ax + By + Cz + D = 0$, we may write its equation in the form

$$x + by + cz + d = 0.$$

Substituting the coordinates of the given points for $x$, $y$, and $z$, we obtain the following three equations in $b$, $c$, and $d$:

$$\left\{ \begin{array}{l} -1 + 2b + 4c + d = 0 \\ 3 + 3b + \frac{1}{2}c + d = 0 \\ 4 + b + \frac{3}{2}c + d = 0. \end{array} \right.$$

Solving these we find that

$$b = \tfrac{5}{4}; \qquad c = \tfrac{3}{2}; \qquad d = -\tfrac{15}{2}.$$

The required equation is then

$$x + \tfrac{5}{4}y + \tfrac{3}{2}z - \tfrac{15}{2} = 0$$

or

$$4x + 5y + 6z - 30 = 0.$$

If the plane determined by the three points had been parallel to the $x$-axis (so that $A = 0$), the above set of equations would have been inconsistent. In this case we might have divided through by $B$ or $C$. Since $A$, $B$, and $C$ are not all zero, we can always divide by one of them.

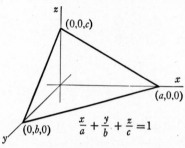

Fig. 213.

**129. Intercept equation of a plane.**—The *intercept* of a plane on a coordinate axis is the directed distance from the origin to the point of intersection of the plane and the axis. The plane shown in Fig. 213 has intercepts $a$, $b$, and $c$, on the $x$-, $y$-, and $z$-axes, respectively. The student may easily show that the plane has the equation

$$\frac{x}{a} + \frac{y}{b} + \frac{z}{c} = 1.$$

This is called the *intercept form* of the equation. It corresponds to the intercept form of the equation of a line that was studied in Chap. III.

**130. Angle between two planes.**—Let two planes intersect along a line as shown in Fig. 214. There are two supplementary angles of intersection, $\theta$ and $\pi - \theta$. *These angles are equal, respectively, to the two angles between the normals drawn to the planes from any point $P$ in space.* The problem of finding the angle between two planes thus reduces to that of finding the angle between two lines, namely, their normals. If the equations of the planes are

$$A_1x + B_1y + C_1z + D_1 = 0$$

and

$$A_2x + B_2y + C_2z + D_2 = 0,$$

then the normals have direction numbers

$$A_1 : B_1 : C_1 \qquad \text{and} \qquad A_2 : B_2 : C_2.$$

The angle between these normals, and consequently that between the planes, is given by the formula (Art. 122)

$$\cos\theta = \pm\frac{A_1A_2 + B_1B_2 + C_1C_2}{\sqrt{A_1{}^2 + B_1{}^2 + C_1{}^2}\,\sqrt{A_2{}^2 + B_2{}^2 + C_2{}^2}}.$$

If positive directions are chosen on the normals we may, if we wish, define the angle between the planes as that

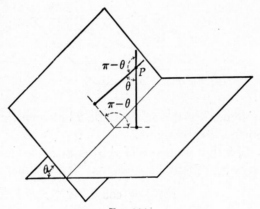

Fig. 214.

between the positive directions of the normals and choose the sign in the above formula accordingly. If we prefer, we may agree to choose the sign in each case so as to make $\cos\theta$ positive; in this case the formula gives the cosine of the acute angle.

The planes are mutually perpendicular if and only if $\cos\theta = 0$. Hence the condition for perpendicularity of the planes is

$$A_1A_2 + B_1B_2 + C_1C_2 = 0.$$

The planes are parallel if and only if their normals are parallel, in which case the direction numbers of the normals are proportional. The condition for parallelism of the planes is then

$$\frac{A_1}{A_2} = \frac{B_1}{B_2} = \frac{C_1}{C_2}.$$

**131. Angle between a line and a plane.**—We may define the angle that a line $AB$ in space makes with a plane as the angle $\phi$ (not greater than 90°) between $AB$ and its projection $A'B'$ on the plane. As shown in Fig. 215 this angle

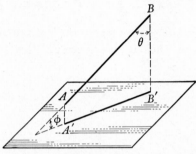

FIG. 215.

is the complement of the acute angle $\theta$ between the line $AB$ and the normal to the plane.

Let the direction numbers of $AB$ be $a_1:b_1:c_1$ and those of the normal to the plane be $a_2:b_2:c_2$. Then since

$$\sin \phi = \cos \theta,$$

we have

$$\sin \phi = \pm \frac{a_1a_2 + b_1b_2 + c_1c_2}{\sqrt{a_1{}^2 + b_1{}^2 + c_1{}^2} \sqrt{a_2{}^2 + b_2{}^2 + c_2{}^2}}.$$

The sign is to be chosen so that $\sin \phi$ is positive. This stipulation is of course equivalent to saying that $\sin \phi$ is equal to the *absolute value* of the right-hand member of the above equation.

### PROBLEMS

**1.** In each of the following, find the equation of the plane determined by $P$, $Q$, and $R$; find the intercepts of the plane on the axes and draw the figure:

(a) $P(4, 2, 3)$    $Q(1, 1, 5)$    $R(2, 6, 2)$.

(b) $P(-1, 1, \frac{7}{3})$ $Q(\frac{3}{2}, 8, 1)$   $R(-3, 4, 0)$.

(c) $P(3, 2, 0)$   $Q(1, 0, -5)$ $R(4, 2, 1)$.

**2.** A plane passes through the points $(3, 1, 7)$ and $(-3, -2, 3)$ and has its $x$-intercept equal to three times its $z$-intercept. What is its equation?

**3.** A plane has its $y$-intercept equal to $-4$ and passes through the points $(5, 1, 5)$ and $(-1, -2, 4)$. What is its equation?

**4.** A plane passes through the points $(-3, 5, 4)$ and $(8, -4, -2)$ and is perpendicular to the plane $2x - y - z = 3$. Find its equation.

**5.** The $x$- and $z$-intercepts of a plane are $-4$ and 6, respectively. The plane is perpendicular to the plane $x + 2y - 2z = 12$. What is its equation?

**6.** Find the acute angle between the two given planes:

(a) $2x - y + 2z - 10 = 0; 4x + y + z - 7 = 0$.

(b) $5x + 3y - 4z + 14 = 0; x - 4y - z + 12 = 0$.

(c) $3x + 4y = 16; 4y - 2z = 5$.

**7.** One corner of the rectangular block shown in Fig. 216 is cut off by a plane passing through $A$, $B$, and $C$. What angle does this plane make with the horizontal top plane $(BCD)$ of the block?

**8.** The base of a right pyramid 12 in. high is a rectangle 8 in. long and 6 in. wide. Compute the dihedral angle between two of its faces.

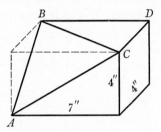

Fig. 216.

**9.** One end of a roof has the construction shown in Fig. 217. Compute the angle between the planes that intersect along $BC$.

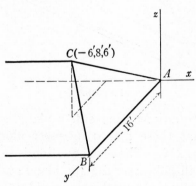

Fig. 217.

**10.** A plane passes through the point $P(-4, -2, 3)$ and is parallel to the plane $3x + y - 2z = 5$. Find its equation.

**11.** For what value of $k$ are the planes $x - 6y + 8z - 4 = 0$ and $4x + ky + z - 7 = 0$ mutually perpendicular?

**12.** In each of the following, find the angle that the line $PQ$ makes with the given plane:

(a) $P(-2, 3, 1)$ $Q(4, 6, 7)$; $x + 4y + z - 10 = 0$.

(b) $P(6, 8, 5)$ $Q(-4, 3, 0)$; $2x - 4y + 4z - 11 = 0$.

(c) $P(3, 5, -2)$ $Q(0, 0, 2)$; $8x - 4y + z + 16 = 0$.

**13.** A line segment is to be drawn from $P(10, 4, 4)$ to a point $Q$ on the $z$-axis. $PQ$ is to be parallel to the plane $2x + 3y + 4z = 30$. What are the coordinates of $Q$?

## 132. Equations of a line in space. General form.—We

have seen that the locus of any linear equation in $x$, $y$, and $z$ is a plane. We shall now see that a *line* in space can be defined by *two* such equations, regarded as a simultaneous system. Consider the pair of equations

$$\begin{cases} A_1x + B_1y + C_1z + D_1 = 0 \\ A_2x + B_2y + C_2z + D_2 = 0. \end{cases}$$

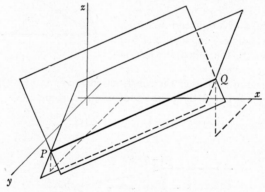

FIG. 218.

Each of these equations represents a plane, and let it now be assumed that these planes intersect along a line $PQ$ as shown in Fig. 218. The first equation is satisfied by the coordinates of all points on the one plane and by no other points. Similarly, the second is satisfied by the coordinates of all points on the other plane and by no other points. It is immediately evident that *the line of intersection of the*

*planes is the locus of all points whose coordinates satisfy* **both**
*equations.* The *two* equations therefore *define* this line.

In order to make the graph of the line we may locate two
points on it as follows: Substitute any convenient value for
$z$ into the two equations and then solve them simultaneously
for the corresponding values of $x$ and $y$. This of course
gives the coordinates of one point on the line. Obtain a
second point in the same way, using a different value for $z$.
The line can then be drawn through the two points.

### *Example*

Draw the line defined by the equations

$$\begin{cases} 3x - 2y + z - 8 = 0 \\ 2x - 2y - z + 2 = 0. \end{cases}$$

### *Solution*

Putting $z = 2$ we obtain the equations $3x - 2y = 6$ and $x - y = 0$.
Solving these we find $x = 6$, $y = 6$. Putting $z = 4$ we similarly find
$x = 2$, $y = 1$. Two points on the line are then (6, 6, 2) and (2, 1, 4).
The line is shown in Fig. 219.

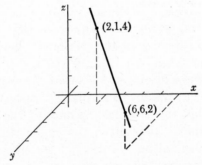

FIG. 219.

It is obvious that we could have substituted arbitrary values for $x$ or
$y$ instead of for $z$. In particular, we could have put $y = 0$, thus locating
the point where the line pierces the $xz$-plane; or we could have put
$x = 0$ to find the point where it pierces the $yz$-plane.

Two equations of the type discussed above constitute the
*general form* of the equations of a line. Other forms in

which the equations may be given are discussed in the following sections.

**133. The projection form.**—Let a line $l$ be defined by the two equations

(1) $$A_1x + B_1y + C_1z + D_1 = 0$$
(2) $$A_2x + B_2y + C_2z + D_2 = 0.$$

Each of these equations represents a plane through $l$ as indicated in Fig. 218 where $l$ is the line $PQ$. Consider now the equation

(3) $$(A_1x + B_1y + C_1z + D_1)$$
$$+ k(A_2x + B_2y + C_2z + D_2) = 0,$$

where $k$ is any constant. This equation represents a plane because it is of first degree. Furthermore, it is satisfied by the coordinates of every point on line $l$ because for every such point the quantities in both parentheses are equal to zero. Hence, for every value of $k$, (3) represents a plane through the line $l$. It is the equation of the *family* of planes through $l$, one of these planes corresponding to each value assigned to $k$.

Suppose now that $k$ is chosen in (3) so as to eliminate $z$. The resulting equation in $x$ and $y$ is that of the plane through $l$ perpendicular to the $xy$-plane. Similarly, if $k$ is chosen so as to eliminate $x$ or $y$ from (3), the resulting equation in $y$ and $z$ or in $x$ and $z$ is that of the plane through $l$ perpendicular to the $yz$- or $xz$-plane, respectively. These planes are called the *projecting planes* of the line $l$ on the coordinate planes. It is often convenient to define a line by giving the equations of two of its projecting planes instead of two general planes.

### Example

The equations $\begin{cases} 4x + 7y - 64 = 0 \\ 2x - 7z + 3 = 0 \end{cases}$ define the line $PQ$ shown in Fig. 220. The first equation is that of the plane through $PQ$ perpendicular to the $xy$-plane. The second is that of the plane through $PQ$ perpendicular to the $xz$-plane. $ST$ and $MN$ are the projections of $PQ$ on these coordinate planes.

The above equations are called the *projection form* of the equations of a line.    If the equations of a line are given in

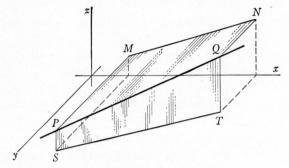

Fig. 220.

the general form, the corresponding projection form can be obtained as illustrated by the following:

### Example

A line is defined by the equations

$$\begin{cases} x + 5y + 6z = 10 \\ 3x + y - 2z = 4. \end{cases}$$

If we eliminate $z$ by multiplying both sides of the second equation by 3, and adding, we obtain the equation $10x + 8y = 22$ or

$$5x + 4y - 11 = 0.$$

If we similarly eliminate $y$ we get $7x - 8z - 5 = 0$.    The equations

$$\begin{cases} 5x + 4y - 11 = 0 \\ 7x - 8z - 5 \;\;\;= 0 \end{cases}$$

then constitute the projection form of the equations of the line.    (We could of course have eliminated $x$ and used the resulting equation in $y$ and $z$ together with either of the above two.)

**134. The symmetric form.**—A line may be determined by specifying the coordinates of two points on it, or by giving one point on it and its direction cosines or direction numbers.    From such data its equations can easily be written down in the *symmetric form* which we shall now derive.

Let $P_1(x_1,\ y_1,\ z_1)$ be one point on a line $l$ (Fig. 221) whose direction angles are $\alpha$, $\beta$, and $\gamma$.    Let $P(x,\ y,\ z)$ be any other point on the line and denote the directed distance $P_1P$ by $d$.   Then

$$\cos\alpha = \frac{x - x_1}{d}; \qquad \cos\beta = \frac{y - y_1}{d}; \qquad \cos\gamma = \frac{z - z_1}{d}.$$

If we solve each of these equations for $d$, and equate the values so obtained, we have the equations

$$\frac{x - x_1}{\cos\alpha} = \frac{y - y_1}{\cos\beta} = \frac{z - z_1}{\cos\gamma}.$$

These equations constitute the *symmetric form* of the equations of a line.   They can be used for writing down the

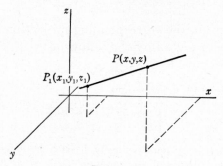

Fig. 221.

equations when the coordinates of one point on the line, and its direction cosines, are known (provided, of course, that none of the direction cosines is zero).

The above equalities still hold if we multiply all the denominators by any nonzero constant. *We may thus replace the direction cosines by a set of direction numbers.* The equations of the line through the point $(x_1, y_1, z_1)$ with direction numbers $a:b:c$ are then

$$\frac{x - x_1}{a} = \frac{y - y_1}{b} = \frac{z - z_1}{c}.$$

This is also called the symmetric form.   It is of course equivalent to the two equations

$$\frac{x - x_1}{a} = \frac{y - y_1}{b}; \qquad \frac{x - x_1}{a} = \frac{z - z_1}{c}.$$

These equations, when simplified, obviously constitute the projection form. The first is the equation of the plane that contains the line and is ⊥ to the $xy$-plane. The second represents the $xz$-projecting plane.

We consider finally the case of a line determined by two points $(x_1, y_1, z_1)$ and $(x_2, y_2, z_2)$. To find its equations we first note that it has the direction numbers

$$x_2 - x_1 : y_2 - y_1 : z_2 - z_1.$$

We can then write down its equations in the above symmetric form.

### Example

Find the symmetric and projection equations of the line through $A(2, 2, 4)$ and $B(8, 6\frac{1}{2}, 2\frac{1}{2})$.

*Solution* (Fig. 222)

Direction numbers of the line are $6 : 4\frac{1}{2} : -1\frac{1}{2}$ or $4 : 3 : -1$. The symmetric equations are then

$$\frac{x - 2}{4} = \frac{y - 2}{3} = \frac{z - 4}{-1}.$$

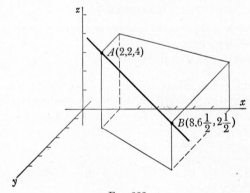

FIG. 222.

The equation $\dfrac{x - 2}{4} = \dfrac{y - 2}{3}$ reduces to $3x - 4y + 2 = 0$; the equation $\dfrac{x - 2}{4} = \dfrac{z - 4}{-1}$ reduces to $x + 4z - 18 = 0$. The projection form of the equations is then

$$\begin{cases} 3x - 4y + 2 = 0 \\ x + 4z - 18 = 0. \end{cases}$$

These equations represent the two projecting planes shown in the figure.

**135. The parametric form.**—If we let $t$ denote the value of each of the three fractions in the symmetric form, we may write

$$\frac{x - x_1}{a} = t; \qquad \frac{y - y_1}{b} = t; \qquad \frac{z - z_1}{c} = t.$$

Solving these equations for $x$, $y$, and $z$, respectively, we obtain the equations

$$x = x_1 + at; \qquad y = y_1 + bt; \qquad z = z_1 + ct.$$

These are *parametric equations* of the line, $t$ being the parameter.

### Example

The equations

$$x = 2 + 4t, \qquad y = 2 + 3t, \qquad z = 4 - t$$

represent the line shown in Fig. 222. We may obtain the coordinates of a point on the line by assigning any value to $t$. Thus if we let $t = -1$ we find that $x = -2$, $y = -1$, $z = 5$. This point is on the line.

### PROBLEMS

**1.** Locate two points on the line defined by the given pair of equations and draw the line:

(a) $x + 3y + z = 18$; $2x + y - 3z = 6$.

(b) $x - y + z - 2 = 0$; $8x - 9y + 4z + 10 = 0$.

**2.** Find the points where the line defined by the given equations pierces the $xy$- and $xz$-planes; draw the line through these points:

(a) $6x - y + 3z = 18$; $2x - 3y - 3z + 10 = 0$.

(b) $x + y - z = 2$; $x + 3y + z = 10$.

(c) $2x + 6y - 6z = 35$; $x - 4y + 8z + 21 = 0$.

**3.** Find the direction cosines of the line defined by the equations $2x - 3y - 2z + 11 = 0$, $x - 6y + 2z + 10 = 0$, if the positive direction is such that $\gamma$ is acute.

**4.** Write the symmetric equations of the line satisfying the given conditions; reduce the equations to the projection form:

(a) Through $(2, 1, 6)$; direction numbers $4:3:-2$.

(b) Through $(-1, 8, 1)$; direction numbers $2:-1:2$.

(c) Through $(-2, -5, -2)$ and $(4, -1, 2)$.

(d) Through $(-2, 0, 0)$ and $(4, 5, 3)$.

(e) Through $(6, 2, -2)$ parallel to the line through $(4, -4, 2)$ and $(1, -2, -1)$.

**5.** Find equations of the line through the given point perpendicular to the given plane:

(a) $A(8, 10, 8); x + y + 2z = 6.$

(b) $P(2, 1, 4); 4x - 3y + 2z = 12.$

**6.** What angle does the line $\dfrac{x - 4}{7} = \dfrac{y - 1}{4} = \dfrac{z + 3}{4}$ make with the plane $x - 2y - 2z = 8$?

**7.** Show that the lines $\dfrac{x + 5}{3} = \dfrac{y - 7}{4} = \dfrac{z + 2}{2}$ and

$$\frac{x - 3}{6} = \frac{y + 5}{-5} = \frac{z - 2}{1}$$

are mutually perpendicular.

**8.** A line is drawn through $P(0, 4, 0)$ with direction numbers $6:4:5$. Write its equations. Another line is to be drawn from $P$ to a point $A$ on the $z$-axis, and this second line is to be perpendicular to the first. Find the coordinates of $A$.

**9.** Find the angle between the lines $\dfrac{x - 2}{4} = \dfrac{y - 1}{7} = \dfrac{z}{-4}$ and $\dfrac{x}{3} = \dfrac{y - 1}{4} = \dfrac{z + 4}{-5}.$

**10.** At what point does the line $\dfrac{2x - 9}{6} = \dfrac{y - 3}{1} = \dfrac{z - 5}{4}$ pierce the plane $2x + 3y + 3z - 12 = 0$?

**11.** Draw the line whose parametric equations are $x = 2 - 3t$, $y = 1 + 4t, z = 6 - t.$ Find its projection equations.

**12.** A line is drawn from $A(3, -1, 4)$ to meet the line $x = 4t + 1$, $y = 6 - t, z = 1 + t$ at right angles. Find the point of intersection.

**13.** Compute the shortest distance from $P(7, 2, 3)$ to the line $A(2, 3, 1)$ $B(6, -4, 5)$. HINT: In Fig. 223, $PL = AP \sin \theta$.

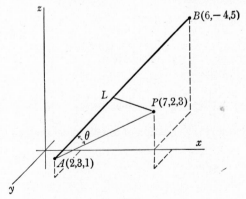

FIG. 223.

**14.** Compute the shortest distance from $P(0, 4, 0)$ to the line that passes through $A(2, 1, 6)$ and has direction numbers $6:2:-3$.

**15.** At a point on the plane $2x + 3y + 6z = 18$ a force of 70 lb. is applied along the line whose projection equations are $3x - 4y + 2 = 0$, $3x - 6z + 2 = 0$. Compute the component of the force normal to the plane (see Fig. 224).

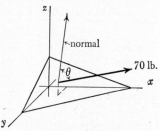

FIG. 224.

**16.** Find the equation of the plane through $P(-4, 6, 1)$ perpendicular to the line whose projection equations are $x - 2z + 2 = 0$ and $2y + z + 5 = 0$.

**17.** Find the equation of the plane that passes through the point $(2, -3, 4)$ and contains the line whose projection equations are

$$2x - y - 3 = 0$$

and $x + 3z - 6 = 0$. HINT: First write the equation of the family of planes containing the line.

**18.** Find the equation of the plane that passes through the origin and contains the line $\dfrac{x + 1}{3} = \dfrac{2y + 3}{4} = \dfrac{z + 6}{-2}$.

**19.** Show that the lines

$$\frac{x - 1}{3} = \frac{y + 2}{5} = \frac{z + 6}{13} \quad \text{and} \quad \frac{x - 4}{9} = \frac{y - 3}{5} = \frac{z - 7}{4}$$

determine a plane and find its equation.

**20.** Show that the lines

$$\frac{x + 2}{2} = \frac{y - 1}{-3} = \frac{z + 5}{4} \quad \text{and} \quad \frac{x - 3}{1} = \frac{2y + 5}{-3} = \frac{z + 3}{2}$$

are parallel and find the equation of the plane determined by them.

# CHAPTER XVII

## SURFACES AND CURVES

**136. Introduction.**—We have seen that the locus of an equation of first degree in $x$, $y$, and $z$ is a plane, and that two such equations may define a line. In the present chapter we shall study the loci of several equations of higher degree. We shall find that the locus of a single such equation is, in general, a surface. Two equations, each representing a surface, will be used to define a curve in space, namely, the curve of intersection.

**137. The sphere.**—The student can easily show, by using the distance formula, that the equation of a sphere with center at $(h, k, l)$ and radius $r$ is

$$(1) \qquad (x - h)^2 + (y - k)^2 + (z - l)^2 = r^2.$$

This is called the *standard equation* of the sphere. By performing the indicated operations on the left-hand member, the equation can be reduced to the *general form*

$$(2) \qquad x^2 + y^2 + z^2 + Gx + Hy + Iz + K = 0.$$

Conversely, any equation of the form (2) can be transformed into form (1) by completing the squares. Such an equation therefore represents a sphere, a point sphere, or no locus, depending upon whether the constant that constitutes the right-hand member when the equation has been put into form (1) is positive, zero, or negative. The situation is entirely analogous to that of the circle.

**138. Cylindrical surfaces.**—A surface generated by a line which moves so that it is always parallel to a fixed line and always intersects a fixed curve is called a *cylindrical surface* or *cylinder*. Any position of the generating line is called an *element* of the cylinder, and the fixed curve is called a *directrix*.

267

Consider now the equation

$$y^2 = 4x.$$

In the $xy$-plane the graph of this equation is the parabola shown in Fig. 225.   Now let a cylindrical surface be generated by a line which moves so that it always intersects this parabola and remains parallel to the $z$-axis.   It is easy to show that the equation $y^2 = 4x$ is satisfied by the coordinates of every point on this surface.   Thus, let

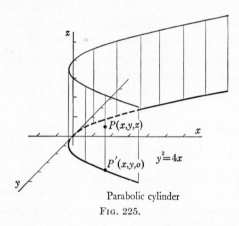

Parabolic cylinder

FIG. 225.

$P(x, y, z)$ be any point on the surface and let $P'(x, y, 0)$ be the projection of $P$ on the $xy$-plane.   Then, if the coordinates of $P'$ satisfy the equation $y^2 = 4x$, those of $P$ must do likewise because *both points have the same x- and y-coordinates.*   Conversely, every point whose coordinates satisfy the equation lies on the cylindrical surface.   *The equation $y^2 = 4x$ is then the equation of the surface.*

Observe that the parabola in the $xy$-plane is the locus of points whose coordinates satisfy the *two* equations $y^2 = 4x$ and $z = 0$.   This is the *trace* of the surface in the $xy$-plane. The upper parabola shown in the figure is the section of the surface cut by a plane parallel to the $xy$-plane and 4 units above it.   All points on this parabola satisfy the two equations $y^2 = 4x$ and $z = 4$

By applying the above method of reasoning to the general case of an equation $\varphi(x, y) = 0$ we may prove the following:

**Theorem:** *If an equation that represents a surface does not contain the variable z, then the surface is a cylinder with elements parallel to the z-axis. Its directrix is the curve in the xy-plane which is the locus of the given equation.*

Similarly, if the variable $x$(or $y$) is absent, the locus is a cylindrical surface whose elements are parallel to the $x$-(or $y$-) axis.

### Example

In the $xz$-plane the locus of the equation

$$4x^2 + 9z^2 = 36$$

is an ellipse.  In space, the locus of this equation is the *elliptic cylinder* having this ellipse as its directrix, and having its elements parallel to the $y$-axis (see Fig. 226).

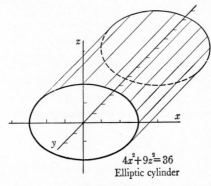

$$4x^2 + 9z^2 = 36$$
Elliptic cylinder

Fig. 226.

**139. Surfaces of revolution.**—The surface generated by revolving a plane curve about a line in its plane is called a *surface of revolution*.  The line about which the curve is revolved is the *axis of revolution*.

We shall consider now the problem of finding the equation of the surface generated when a curve lying in one of the coordinate planes is revolved about a coordinate axis.  As an example, let us revolve the parabola

$$3z = 24 - x^2$$

about the $z$-axis and find the equation of the surface thus generated. As shown in Fig. 227, any point such as $A$ travels in a circle of radius $r = QA$. For any point $P$ on this circle we have immediately

$$x^2 + y^2 = r^2.$$

The coordinates $(r, z)$ must satisfy the equation

$$3z = 24 - r^2;$$

hence

$$r^2 = 24 - 3z.$$

Substituting this for $r^2$ in the above equation we have

$$x^2 + y^2 = \mathbf{24 - 3}z.$$

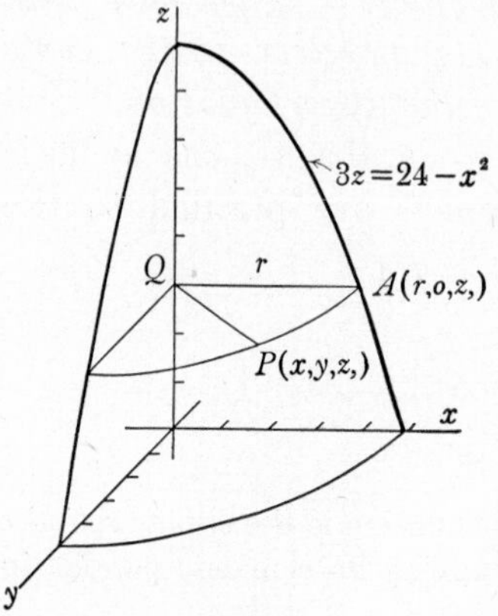

FIG. 227.

This is the equation of the surface. It may be observed that our procedure for finding it amounts to replacing $x$ in the equation of the given curve by $\sqrt{x^2 + y^2}$. The surface is called a *paraboloid of revolution*. The figure shows only one-fourth of the part lying above the $xy$-plane.

**140. Sections parallel to a coordinate plane.**—Let us take the equation

$$x^2 + y^2 = 24 - 3z$$

and put $z = 3$. The resulting equation is $x^2 + y^2 = 15$. This is the equation of the curve cut from the surface by the plane $z = 3$. In this case the section is the circle with center at $Q$ in Fig. 227.

In order to determine the nature of the surface defined by a given equation in $x$, $y$, and $z$, it is often necessary to study the sections cut from it by planes parallel to the coordinate planes. As indicated above, *the equations of sections parallel to the xy-plane may be found by putting z = k in the equation of the surface.* Thus if we put $z = k$ in the equation $x^2 + y^2 = 24 - 3z$ we have

$$x^2 + y^2 = 24 - 3k.$$

It is clear that these sections are circles of radius $\sqrt{24 - 3k}$.
Similarly, if we put $x = k$, we have the equation

$$y^2 = 24 - 3z - k^2.$$

Thus the sections of the surface cut by planes parallel to the $yz$-plane are parabolas. In particular the trace in the $yz$-plane is the parabola $y^2 = 24 - 3z$. If one recalls that the shape of the parabola $z = ay^2 + by + c$ is completely determined by the value of $a$ alone, he can immediately conclude that the above sections are all *congruent* parabolas.

Sections parallel to the $xz$-plane can be investigated similarly by putting $y = k$.

### PROBLEMS

**1.** Find the equation of the sphere satisfying the following conditions:

(a) Center at $(4, -2, 1)$, radius 6.

(b) Center at $(2, 0, 0)$, radius 2.

(c) Having the points $(-4, 5, 1)$ and $(4, 1, 7)$ as ends of a diameter.

(d) Center at $(4, 2, 5)$ and tangent to the $xy$-plane.

**2.** Show that the center and radius of the sphere represented by equation (2) are, respectively,

Center $(-\tfrac{1}{2}G, -\tfrac{1}{2}H, -\tfrac{1}{2}I)$;  radius $= \tfrac{1}{2}\sqrt{G^2 + H^2 + I^2 - 4K}$.

What are the conditions under which the equation represents a real sphere, a point sphere, and an imaginary sphere?

**3.** Find the equation of the plane that is tangent to the sphere $x^2 + y^2 + z^2 - 4x + 6y - 4z - 32 = 0$ at $(8, -1, 5)$. HINT: The tangent plane is perpendicular to the radius.

**4.** A sphere has its center at $(0, 4, 0)$ and it passes through the point $(7, 0, 4)$. Write the equation of its tangent plane and normal line at this point. (The normal line is the line perpendicular to the tangent plane.)

**5.** Sketch the following cylindrical surfaces:

(a) $y^2 + z^2 = 25$.  (b) $x^2 + y^2 = 8x$.  (c) $x^2 + z = 4$.

(d) $xy + 4 = 0$.  (e) $z = e^{-x^2}$.  (f) $y + \log z = 0$.

In each of the following problems the equations of a curve lying in one of the coordinate planes are given. Find the equation of the surface generated when the curve is revolved about the specified coordinate axis. Draw the figure:

**6.** $x^2 = 4z$, $y = 0$; $z$-axis.

**7.** $x^2 + z^2 = a^2$, $y = 0$; $x$-axis.

**8.** $z = 4x$, $y = 0$; $z$-axis.

**9.** $y = 2x,\ z = 0;\ y$-axis.

**10.** $z^2 + 1 = x,\ y = 0;\ x$-axis.

**11.** $\dfrac{x^2}{25} + \dfrac{z^2}{9} = 1,\ y = 0;\ z$-axis.

**12.** $\dfrac{x^2}{a^2} + \dfrac{y^2}{b^2} = 1,\ z = 0;\ x$-axis.

**13.** $z = e^{-x^2},\ y = 0;\ z$-axis.

**14.** $z = \sin x,\ y = 0;\ x$-axis.

In each of the following problems determine the nature of the curves cut from the given surface by planes parallel to the coordinate planes. Determine in each case whether or not the given surface could be generated by revolving a curve about one of the coordinate axes:

**15.** $x^2 + 2y^2 + 2z^2 = 16.$          **16.** $4x^2 + 4y^2 - z^2 = 0.$

**17.** $2x^2 + 3y^2 + 4z^2 = 12.$          **18.** $x^2 + z^2 - y = 4.$

**141. Quadric surfaces.**—The locus of an equation of second degree in $x$, $y$, and $z$ is called a *quadric surface*. One such surface is the sphere which we have already considered. In the following sections we shall discuss briefly the *standard equations* of several other quadric surfaces.

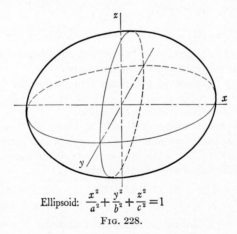

Ellipsoid: $\dfrac{x^2}{a^2} + \dfrac{y^2}{b^2} + \dfrac{z^2}{c^2} = 1$

Fig. 228.

**142. The ellipsoid.**—The surface defined by the equation

$$\frac{x^2}{a^2} + \frac{y^2}{b^2} + \frac{z^2}{c^2} = 1$$

is called an *ellipsoid* (Fig. 228). It has certain obvious

properties of symmetry, and its sections parallel to the coordinate planes are ellipses.

If any two of the three constants $a$, $b$, and $c$, are equal, the surface is an ellipsoid of revolution, which is sometimes called a *spheroid*. If $a = b = c$, the surface is a sphere.

**143. The hyperboloid of one sheet.**—The surface defined by the equation

$$\frac{x^2}{a^2} + \frac{y^2}{b^2} - \frac{z^2}{c^2} = 1$$

is called a *hyperboloid of one sheet* (Fig. 229). Its trace in the $xy$-plane is the ellipse $\frac{x^2}{a^2} + \frac{y^2}{b^2} = 1$. Sections parallel

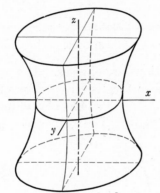

Hyperboloid of One Sheet: $\frac{x^2}{a^2} + \frac{y^2}{b^2} - \frac{z^2}{c^2} = 1$

Fig. 229.

to the $xy$-plane are also ellipses, while those parallel to the other two coordinate planes are hyperbolas. If $a = b$, the surface is a hyperboloid of revolution, the sections parallel to the $xy$-plane being circles.

**144. The hyperboloid of two sheets.**—The locus of the equation

$$\frac{x^2}{a^2} - \frac{y^2}{b^2} - \frac{z^2}{c^2} = 1$$

is called a *hyperboloid of two sheets* (Fig. 230). It is evident from the equation that sections parallel to the $xy$- and

$xz$-planes are hyperbolas. The trace in the $yz$-plane is the "imaginary ellipse" $\dfrac{y^2}{b^2} + \dfrac{z^2}{c^2} = -1$. The section cut by the plane $x = a$ is a "point ellipse," while for $|x| > a$ the

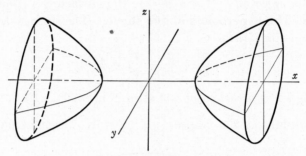

Hyperboloid of Two Sheets: $\dfrac{x^2}{a^2} - \dfrac{y^2}{b^2} - \dfrac{z^2}{c^2} = 1$

FIG. 230.

corresponding sections are ellipses. If $b = c$, these ellipses are circles and the surface is a hyperboloid of revolution.

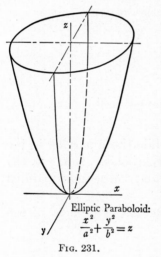

Elliptic Paraboloid:
$\dfrac{x^2}{a^2} + \dfrac{y^2}{b^2} = z$

FIG. 231.

**145. The elliptic paraboloid.—** The surface defined by the equation

$$\frac{x^2}{a^2} + \frac{y^2}{b^2} = z$$

is an *elliptic paraboloid* (Fig. 231). Sections parallel to and above the $xy$-plane are ellipses. Sections parallel to the other coordinate planes are parabolas. If $a = b$, the elliptic sections are circles and the surface is a paraboloid of revolution.

**146. The hyperbolic paraboloid.—** The surface whose equation is

$$\frac{x^2}{a^2} - \frac{y^2}{b^2} = z$$

is called a *hyperbolic paraboloid* (Fig. 232). Its trace in the $xy$-plane consists of the two lines $\dfrac{x^2}{a^2} - \dfrac{y^2}{b^2} = 0$; sections

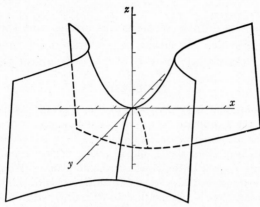

Hyperbolic Paraboloid: $\dfrac{x^2}{a^2} - \dfrac{y^2}{b^2} = z$

FIG. 232.

parallel to and above the $xy$-plane are hyperbolas with transverse axes parallel to the $x$-axis; sections parallel to and below the $xy$-plane are hyperbolas with transverse axes parallel to the $y$-axis.

Sections parallel to the other two coordinate planes are parabolas. Those parallel to the $xz$-plane open upward, while those parallel to the $yz$-plane open downward.

**147. The elliptic cone.**—The locus of the equation

$$\frac{x^2}{a^2} + \frac{y^2}{b^2} - \frac{z^2}{c^2} = 0$$

is an *elliptic cone* (Fig. 233). Its trace in the $xy$-plane is the "point ellipse" $\dfrac{x^2}{a^2} + \dfrac{y^2}{b^2} = 0$. Sections

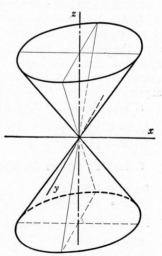

Elliptic Cone: $\dfrac{x^2}{a^2} + \dfrac{y^2}{b^2} - \dfrac{z^2}{c^2} = 0$

FIG. 233.

parallel to the $xy$-plane are ellipses.   Its trace in each of the other two coordinate planes is a pair of lines through the origin; sections parallel to these coordinate planes are hyperbolas.

If $a = b$, the elliptic sections are circles and the surface is a *circular cone*.   It could be generated by revolving a line having the equations $z = mx$, $y = 0$, about the $z$-axis.

### PROBLEMS

**1.** The point that is symmetrical to $P(x, y, z)$ with respect to the $xy$-plane has the coordinate $(x, y, -z)$.   It follows that if the equation of a surface is unaltered when $z$ is replaced by $-z$, the surface is symmetrical with respect to the $xy$-plane.   State corresponding tests for symmetry with respect to the other coordinate planes.   Which quadric surfaces are symmetrical with respect to all three coordinate planes?

**2.** The point that is symmetrical to $P(x, y, z)$ with respect to the $x$-axis has the coordinates $(x, -y, -z)$.   It follows that if the equation of a surface is unaltered when $y$ and $z$ are replaced by $-y$ and $-z$, respectively, the surface is symmetrical with respect to the $x$-axis. State corresponding tests for symmetry with respect to the other coordinate axes.   Is the hyperbolic paraboloid symmetrical with respect to one of the axes?

**3.** State a test for symmetry of a surface with respect to the origin.

**4.** Are the above tests for symmetry both necessary and sufficient, or are they merely sufficient?   HINT: If replacing $z$ by $-z$ does not alter the equation, the surface is symmetrical with respect to the $xy$-plane.   Hence the test is *sufficient*.   But if replacing $z$ by $-z$ *does* change the equation, might the surface be symmetrical to the $xy$-plane anyway?

**5.** Identify each of the following surfaces:

(a) $x^2 - 3y^2 - z^2 + 4 = 0$.          (b) $9x^2 + 16z^2 - 36y = 0$.
(c) $x^2 + y^2 = z^2$.                           (d) $3x^2 + 4y^2 + 6z = 0$.

**6.** Identify each of the following surfaces:

(a) $x^2 + 3y^2 = z^2$.                          (b) $4x^2 = 25(y^2 + z)$.
(c) $x^2 = 4(z - y^2)$.                          (d) $x^2 + 6(y^2 + z^2) = 24$.

Identify and sketch each of the following surfaces:

**7.** $z = x^2 + y^2$.                                   **8.** $x^2 + 4y^2 + 4z = 0$.
**9.** $z + 8 = 2(x^2 + y^2)$.                   **10.** $y^2 + z^2 = 8 - x$.
**11.** $4x^2 - y = 4 - z^2$.                     **12.** $4x^2 + 4y^2 - z^2 = 0$.
**13.** $2y^2 + 4z^2 = x^2$.                       **14.** $y^2 - 9x^2 = 4z^2$.

**15.** $4x^2 + 4y^2 - z^2 = 16.$     **16.** $2x^2 + 3y^2 - 4z^2 = 24.$
**17.** $y^2 + z^2 = x^2 + 4.$        **18.** $x^2 - 2y^2 - z^2 = 4.$
**19.** $y^2 + z^2 = 2(x^2 - 8).$     **20.** $2x^2 + y^2 = 16 - 2z^2.$
**21.** $x^2 + 2y^2 = 4(4 - z^2).$    **22.** $x^2 + 5y^2 + 5z^2 = 25.$
**23.** $2x^2 + 4y^2 + z^2 = 16.$     **24.** $x^2 + 4y^2 + 4z^2 = 8x.$
**25.** $x^2 - 2y^2 = 2z.$            **26.** $x^2 - y^2 = 4z.$

**27.** Discuss the sections of the hyperboloid $\dfrac{x^2}{a^2} + \dfrac{y^2}{b^2} - \dfrac{z^2}{c^2} = 1$ made by the plane $x = k$. Show in particular that the transverse axis of this hyperbola is parallel to the $y$-axis for $|k| < a$ but parallel to the $z$-axis for $|k| > a$. Discuss the case in which $k = a$.

**148. Curves in space.**—Consider the two equations

$$\begin{cases} x^2 + y^2 - 4z = 0 \\ \quad x - y + 2z = 12. \end{cases}$$

The locus of the first equation is a paraboloid, while that of the second is a plane that intersects the paraboloid in a curve. The points whose coordinates satisfy *both* equations are those lying on this curve. We may therefore regard the above pair of equations as the equations of this curve in space.

We may project this space curve onto the $xy$-plane by dropping a perpendicular from each point of the curve to the plane. These perpendiculars or projectors form a cylindrical surface whose equation is obtained by eliminating $z$ between the given equations. In the above case, the equation of this *projecting cylinder* is

$$x^2 + y^2 + 2x - 2y - 24 = 0.$$

The projecting cylinders on the $xz$- and $yz$-planes can be obtained similarly by eliminating $y$ and $x$, respectively. A curve in space is often defined by giving the equations of two of its projecting cylinders. This corresponds to our method of defining a line in space by giving the equations of two of its projecting planes.

**149. Parametric equations of a curve in space.**—We have already seen that the line through $(x_1, y_1, z_1)$ with the direction numbers $a:b:c$ has the parametric equations

$$x = x_1 + at, \qquad y = y_1 + bt, \qquad z = z_1 + ct.$$

In each of these equations the right-hand member is a *linear* function of $t$.

In general, the three equations

$$x = f_1(t), \qquad y = f_2(t), \qquad z = f_3(t),$$

are parametric equations of a *curve* in space, $t$ being the

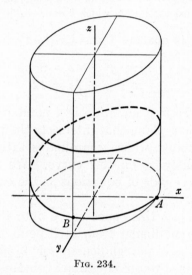

Fig. 234.

parameter. The result of eliminating $t$ between the first two equations is the *xy*-projecting cylinder of the curve, and the other projecting cylinders are similarly obtained.

As an example, consider the equations

$$x = 4 \cos t, \qquad y = 4 \sin t, \qquad z = \tfrac{2}{3}t.$$

When $t = 0$, we have $x = 4$, $y = 0$, $z = 0$. These are the coordinates of point $A$ in Fig. 234. If we let $t = \tfrac{1}{2}\pi$, we have $x = 0$, $y = 4$, $z = \tfrac{1}{3}\pi$. The corresponding point is $B$ in the figure. By continuing in this manner we may plot the curve as shown.

If we eliminate $t$ between the first two of the given

equations, we have the relation

$$x^2 + y^2 = 16.$$

Since the $x$- and $y$-coordinates of every point on the curve satisfy this equation, the curve must lie upon this cylinder. It is called a *helix*, and its parametric equations have the general form

$$x = a \cos t, \qquad y = a \sin t, \qquad z = bt.$$

The thread on a bolt, or the handrailing on a circular staircase, is a curve of this kind.

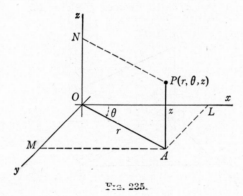

Fig. 225.

### 150. Cylindrical coordinates.

—In our study of plane analytic geometry we saw that some types of curves have simpler equations in polar than in rectangular coordinates. Similarly, some of the problems of space geometry can be handled more easily by means of coordinate systems other than the rectangular one that we have been using. In this section, and in the following one, we shall discuss briefly the *cylindrical* and *spherical* coordinate systems. Both of these systems are of great value in the study of more advanced topics in mathematics.

Let $P$ be a point in space whose rectangular coordinates are $(x, y, z)$, and let $A$ be the foot of the perpendicular from $P$ to the $xy$-plane. Let $(r, \theta)$ be the polar coordinates in the $xy$-plane of the point $A$.*    Then the three numbers $(r,\,\theta,\,z)$ are called the *cylindrical coordinates* of $P$.

The relations that enable one to change the equation of a surface from rectangular to cylindrical coordinates are easily seen from Fig. 235 to be

$$x = r \cos \theta; \qquad y = r \sin \theta; \qquad z = z.$$

Those for making the reverse transformation are equally obvious.

### Example

The equation $x^2 + y^2 - z^2 = 0$, which represents a circular cone, becomes $r^2 - z^2 = 0$ or $z = \pm r$ in cylindrical coordinates. Similarly, the equation $x^2 + y^2 + z^2 = 16$ becomes $r^2 + z^2 = \mathbf{16}$.

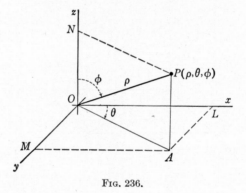

FIG. 236.

**151. Spherical coordinates.**—Let $P$ be a point in space whose rectangular coordinates are $(x,\,y,\,z)$, and let $A$ be the foot of the perpendicular from $P$ to the $xy$-plane. Then, as shown in Fig. 236, let

$$OP = \varrho; \qquad \text{angle } LOA = \theta; \qquad \text{angle } NOP = \phi.$$

The three numbers $(\rho,\,\theta,\,\phi)$ are the *spherical coordinates* of $P$. This coordinate system is similar to that used in locating points on the earth's surface by means of longitude and latitude. The angle $\theta$ corresponds to the longitude and $\phi$ to the colatitude, the latitude being the angle $AOP$.

---

* We use $(r,\,\theta)$ instead of $(\rho,\,\theta)$ here because we still wish to denote the radius vector $OP$ by $\rho$.

In the spherical coordinate system, $\theta$ may have any positive or negative value; $\phi$ is identical with the direction angle $\gamma$ and is restricted to positive values not greater than $\pi$. It is customary to restrict $\rho$ to positive values, but if we wish we may agree to interpret negative values of $\rho$ as we did in dealing with polar coordinates in the plane.

The relations that enable one to transform the equation of a surface from rectangular to spherical coordinates are easily found: Noting that $OA = NP = \rho \sin \phi$, while $ON = \rho \cos \phi$, we deduce immediately that

$$x = \rho \sin \phi \cos \theta;$$
$$y = \rho \sin \phi \sin \theta;$$
$$z = \rho \cos \phi.$$

### Example

The equation $x^2 + y^2 = 4z$ represents a paraboloid of revolution. Upon making the above substitutions for $x$, $y$, and $z$, we obtain the equation of this surface in spherical coordinates as follows:

$$\rho^2 \sin^2 \phi \, (\cos^2 \theta + \sin^2 \theta) = 4\rho \cos \phi;$$
$$\rho \sin^2 \phi = 4 \cos \phi;$$
$$\rho = 4 \cos \phi \csc^2 \phi.$$

### PROBLEMS

Draw the following curves:

**1.** $x^2 + y^2 = 25; z = x.$      **2.** $x^2 + y^2 = 10x; z = \frac{1}{2}x.$

**3.** $2z = x^2 + y^2; x - y + 2z = 6.$

**4.** $x^2 + y^2 + z^2 = 25; x^2 + y^2 = 9.$

**5.** $x^2 + y^2 + z^2 = 36; x^2 + y^2 = 6x.$

**6.** $x^2 + y^2 + z^2 = 32; x^2 + y^2 = 4z.$

**7.** $x^2 + y^2 + z^2 = 25; 9z^2 = 16(x^2 + y^2).$

**8.** $x = 5 \cos t; y = 5 \sin t; z = t.$

**9.** $x = 5 \sin t; y = 4 \cos t; z = \frac{1}{2}t.$

**10.** $x = t - 4; y = t; z = \frac{1}{2}t^2.$

**11.** $x = 4 \cos^2 t; y = 4 \sin^2 t; z = t^2.$

**12.** $x = 4 \cos t; y = 4 \sin t; z = 8 \sin t.$

Transform each of the following equations into both cylindrical and spherical coordinates; sketch the locus:

**13.** $x^2 + y^2 = 6.$      **14.** $x^2 + y^2 = 8y.$      **15.** $xy = 2.$

**16.** $x^2 + y^2 - \frac{1}{2}z^2 = 0.$     **17.** $x^2 + y^2 + z^2 = 16.$
**18.** $x^2 + y^2 + z^2 = 6z.$     **19.** $x^2 - y^2 - 2z^2 = 4.$

**20.** $4z = x^2 - y^2.$

**21.** Derive a formula for the distance between two points in terms of their spherical coordinates.

**22.** Describe the locus in spherical coordinates of each of the following equations: $\rho = k;\ \theta = k;\ \phi = k.$

**23.** Describe the locus in spherical coordinates of each of the following equations: $\rho \sin \phi = k;\ \rho \cos \phi = k.$

**24.** Write the equations expressing the cylindrical coordinates $r$, $\theta$, and $z$ in terms of $\rho$, $\theta$, and $\phi$.

**25.** Which one or ones of the three systems of space coordinates establishes a one-to-one correspondence between points of space and triplets of numbers?

# NUMERICAL TABLES

TABLE I.—COMMON LOGARITHMS

| N | 0 | 1 | 2 | 3 | 4 | 5 | 6 | 7 | 8 | 9 |
|---|---|---|---|---|---|---|---|---|---|---|
| 10 | 0000 | 0043 | 0086 | 0128 | 0170 | 0212 | 0253 | 0294 | 0334 | 0374 |
| 11 | 0414 | 0453 | 0492 | 0531 | 0569 | 0607 | 0645 | 0682 | 0719 | 0755 |
| 12 | 0792 | 0828 | 0864 | 0899 | 0934 | 0969 | 1004 | 1038 | 1072 | 1106 |
| 13 | 1139 | 1173 | 1206 | 1239 | 1271 | 1303 | 1335 | 1367 | 1399 | 1430 |
| 14 | 1461 | 1492 | 1523 | 1553 | 1584 | 1614 | 1644 | 1673 | 1703 | 1732 |
| 15 | 1761 | 1790 | 1818 | 1847 | 1875 | 1903 | 1931 | 1959 | 1987 | 2014 |
| 16 | 2041 | 2068 | 2095 | 2122 | 2148 | 2175 | 2201 | 2227 | 2253 | 2279 |
| 17 | 2304 | 2330 | 2355 | 2380 | 2405 | 2430 | 2455 | 2480 | 2504 | 2529 |
| 18 | 2553 | 2577 | 2601 | 2625 | 2648 | 2672 | 2695 | 2718 | 2742 | 2765 |
| 19 | 2788 | 2810 | 2833 | 2856 | 2878 | 2900 | 2923 | 2945 | 2967 | 2989 |
| 20 | 3010 | 3032 | 3054 | 3075 | 3096 | 3118 | 3139 | 3160 | 3181 | 3201 |
| 21 | 3222 | 3243 | 3263 | 3284 | 3304 | 3324 | 3345 | 3365 | 3385 | 3404 |
| 22 | 3424 | 3444 | 3464 | 3483 | 3502 | 3522 | 3541 | 3560 | 3579 | 3598 |
| 23 | 3617 | 3636 | 3655 | 3674 | 3692 | 3711 | 3729 | 3747 | 3766 | 3784 |
| 24 | 3802 | 3820 | 3838 | 3856 | 3874 | 3892 | 3909 | 3927 | 3945 | 3962 |
| 25 | 3979 | 3997 | 4014 | 4031 | 4048 | 4065 | 4082 | 4099 | 4116 | 4133 |
| 26 | 4150 | 4166 | 4183 | 4200 | 4216 | 4232 | 4249 | 4265 | 4281 | 4298 |
| 27 | 4314 | 4330 | 4346 | 4362 | 4378 | 4393 | 4409 | 4425 | 4440 | 4456 |
| 28 | 4472 | 4487 | 4502 | 4518 | 4533 | 4548 | 4564 | 4579 | 4594 | 4609 |
| 29 | 4624 | 4639 | 4654 | 4669 | 4683 | 4698 | 4713 | 4728 | 4742 | 4757 |
| 30 | 4771 | 4786 | 4800 | 4814 | 4829 | 4843 | 4857 | 4871 | 4886 | 4900 |
| 31 | 4914 | 4928 | 4942 | 4955 | 4969 | 4983 | 4997 | 5011 | 5024 | 5038 |
| 32 | 5051 | 5065 | 5079 | 5092 | 5105 | 5119 | 5132 | 5145 | 5159 | 5172 |
| 33 | 5185 | 5198 | 5211 | 5224 | 5237 | 5250 | 5263 | 5276 | 5289 | 5302 |
| 34 | 5315 | 5328 | 5340 | 5353 | 5366 | 5378 | 5391 | 5403 | 5416 | 5428 |
| 35 | 5441 | 5453 | 5465 | 5478 | 5490 | 5502 | 5514 | 5527 | 5539 | 5551 |
| 36 | 5563 | 5575 | 5587 | 5599 | 5611 | 5623 | 5635 | 5647 | 5658 | 5670 |
| 37 | 5682 | 5694 | 5705 | 5717 | 5729 | 5740 | 5752 | 5763 | 5775 | 5786 |
| 38 | 5798 | 5809 | 5821 | 5832 | 5843 | 5855 | 5866 | 5877 | 5888 | 5899 |
| 39 | 5911 | 5922 | 5933 | 5944 | 5955 | 5966 | 5977 | 5988 | 5999 | 6010 |
| 40 | 6021 | 6031 | 6042 | 6053 | 6064 | 6075 | 6085 | 6096 | 6107 | 6117 |
| 41 | 6128 | 6138 | 6149 | 6160 | 6170 | 6180 | 6191 | 6201 | 6212 | 6222 |
| 42 | 6232 | 6243 | 6253 | 6263 | 6274 | 6284 | 6294 | 6304 | 6314 | 6325 |
| 43 | 6335 | 6345 | 6355 | 6365 | 6375 | 6385 | 6395 | 6405 | 6415 | 6425 |
| 44 | 6435 | 6444 | 6454 | 6464 | 6474 | 6484 | 6493 | 6503 | 6513 | 6522 |
| 45 | 6532 | 6542 | 6551 | 6561 | 6571 | 6580 | 6590 | 6599 | 6609 | 6618 |
| 46 | 6628 | 6637 | 6646 | 6656 | 6665 | 6675 | 6684 | 6693 | 6702 | 6712 |
| 47 | 6721 | 6730 | 6739 | 6749 | 6758 | 6767 | 6776 | 6785 | 6794 | 6803 |
| 48 | 6812 | 6821 | 6830 | 6839 | 6848 | 6857 | 6866 | 6875 | 6884 | 6893 |
| 49 | 6902 | 6911 | 6920 | 6928 | 6937 | 6946 | 6955 | 6964 | 6972 | 6981 |
| 50 | 6990 | 6998 | 7007 | 7016 | 7024 | 7033 | 7042 | 7050 | 7059 | 7067 |
| 51 | 7076 | 7084 | 7093 | 7101 | 7110 | 7118 | 7126 | 7135 | 7143 | 7152 |
| 52 | 7160 | 7168 | 7177 | 7185 | 7193 | 7202 | 7210 | 7218 | 7226 | 7235 |
| 53 | 7243 | 7251 | 7259 | 7267 | 7275 | 7284 | 7292 | 7300 | 7308 | 7316 |
| 54 | 7324 | 7332 | 7340 | 7348 | 7356 | 7364 | 7372 | 7380 | 7388 | 7396 |
| N | 0 | 1 | 2 | 3 | 4 | 5 | 6 | 7 | 8 | 9 |

TABLE I.—COMMON LOGARITHMS.—(*Continued*)

| N | 0 | 1 | 2 | 3 | 4 | 5 | 6 | 7 | 8 | 9 |
|---|---|---|---|---|---|---|---|---|---|---|
| 55 | 7404 | 7412 | 7419 | 7427 | 7435 | 7443 | 7451 | 7459 | 7466 | 7474 |
| 56 | 7482 | 7490 | 7497 | 7505 | 7513 | 7520 | 7528 | 7536 | 7543 | 7551 |
| 57 | 7559 | 7566 | 7574 | 7582 | 7589 | 7597 | 7604 | 7612 | 7619 | 7627 |
| 58 | 7634 | 7642 | 7649 | 7657 | 7664 | 7672 | 7679 | 7686 | 7694 | 7701 |
| 59 | 7709 | 7716 | 7723 | 7731 | 7738 | 7745 | 7752 | 7760 | 7767 | 7774 |
| 60 | 7782 | 7789 | 7796 | 7803 | 7810 | 7818 | 7825 | 7832 | 7839 | 7846 |
| 61 | 7853 | 7860 | 7868 | 7875 | 7882 | 7889 | 7896 | 7903 | 7910 | 7917 |
| 62 | 7924 | 7931 | 7938 | 7945 | 7952 | 7959 | 7966 | 7973 | 7980 | 7987 |
| 63 | 7993 | 8000 | 8007 | 8014 | 8021 | 8028 | 8035 | 8041 | 8048 | 8055 |
| 64 | 8062 | 8069 | 8075 | 8082 | 8089 | 8096 | 8102 | 8109 | 8116 | 8122 |
| 65 | 8129 | 8136 | 8142 | 8149 | 8156 | 8162 | 8169 | 8176 | 8182 | 8189 |
| 66 | 8195 | 8202 | 8209 | 8215 | 8222 | 8228 | 8235 | 8241 | 8248 | 8254 |
| 67 | 8261 | 8267 | 8274 | 8280 | 8287 | 8293 | 8299 | 8306 | 8312 | 8319 |
| 68 | 8325 | 8331 | 8338 | 8344 | 8351 | 8357 | 8363 | 8370 | 8376 | 8382 |
| 69 | 8388 | 8395 | 8401 | 8407 | 8414 | 8420 | 8426 | 8432 | 8439 | 8445 |
| 70 | 8451 | 8457 | 8463 | 8470 | 8476 | 8482 | 8488 | 8494 | 8500 | 8506 |
| 71 | 8513 | 8519 | 8525 | 8531 | 8537 | 8543 | 8549 | 8555 | 8561 | 8567 |
| 72 | 8573 | 8579 | 8585 | 8591 | 8597 | 8603 | 8609 | 8615 | 8621 | 8627 |
| 73 | 8633 | 8639 | 8645 | 8651 | 8657 | 8663 | 8669 | 8675 | 8681 | 8686 |
| 74 | 8692 | 8698 | 8704 | 8710 | 8716 | 8722 | 8727 | 8733 | 8739 | 8745 |
| 75 | 8751 | 8756 | 8762 | 8768 | 8774 | 8779 | 8785 | 8791 | 8797 | 8802 |
| 76 | 8808 | 8814 | 8820 | 8825 | 8831 | 8837 | 8842 | 8848 | 8854 | 8859 |
| 77 | 8865 | 8871 | 8876 | 8882 | 8887 | 8893 | 8899 | 8904 | 8910 | 8915 |
| 78 | 8921 | 8927 | 8932 | 8938 | 8943 | 8949 | 8954 | 8960 | 8965 | 8971 |
| 79 | 8976 | 8982 | 8987 | 8993 | 8998 | 9004 | 9009 | 9015 | 9020 | 9025 |
| 80 | 9031 | 9036 | 9042 | 9047 | 9053 | 9058 | 9063 | 9069 | 9074 | 9079 |
| 81 | 9085 | 9090 | 9096 | 9101 | 9106 | 9112 | 9117 | 9122 | 9128 | 9133 |
| 82 | 9138 | 9143 | 9149 | 9154 | 9159 | 9165 | 9170 | 9175 | 9180 | 9186 |
| 83 | 9191 | 9196 | 9201 | 9206 | 9212 | 9217 | 9222 | 9227 | 9232 | 9238 |
| 84 | 9243 | 9248 | 9253 | 9258 | 9263 | 9269 | 9274 | 9279 | 9284 | 9289 |
| 85 | 9294 | 9299 | 9304 | 9309 | 9315 | 9320 | 9325 | 9330 | 9335 | 9340 |
| 86 | 9345 | 9350 | 9355 | 9360 | 9365 | 9370 | 9375 | 9380 | 9385 | 9390 |
| 87 | 9395 | 9400 | 9405 | 9410 | 9415 | 9420 | 9425 | 9430 | 9435 | 9440 |
| 88 | 9445 | 9450 | 9455 | 9460 | 9465 | 9469 | 9474 | 9479 | 9484 | 9489 |
| 89 | 9494 | 9499 | 9504 | 9509 | 9513 | 9518 | 9523 | 9528 | 9533 | 9538 |
| 90 | 9542 | 9547 | 9552 | 9557 | 9562 | 9566 | 9571 | 9576 | 9581 | 9586 |
| 91 | 9590 | 9595 | 9600 | 9605 | 9609 | 9614 | 9619 | 9624 | 9628 | 9633 |
| 92 | 9638 | 9643 | 9647 | 9652 | 9657 | 9661 | 9666 | 9671 | 9675 | 9680 |
| 93 | 9685 | 9689 | 9694 | 9699 | 9703 | 9708 | 9713 | 9717 | 9722 | 9727 |
| 94 | 9731 | 9736 | 9741 | 9745 | 9750 | 9754 | 9759 | 9763 | 9768 | 9773 |
| 95 | 9777 | 9782 | 9786 | 9791 | 9795 | 9800 | 9805 | 9809 | 9814 | 9818 |
| 96 | 9823 | 9827 | 9832 | 9836 | 9841 | 9845 | 9850 | 9854 | 9859 | 9863 |
| 97 | 9868 | 9872 | 9877 | 9881 | 9886 | 9890 | 9894 | 9899 | 9903 | 9908 |
| 98 | 9912 | 9917 | 9921 | 9926 | 9930 | 9934 | 9939 | 9943 | 9948 | 9952 |
| 99 | 9956 | 9961 | 9965 | 9969 | 9974 | 9978 | 9983 | 9987 | 9991 | 9996 |
| N | 0 | 1 | 2 | 3 | 4 | 5 | 6 | 7 | 8 | 9 |

## TABLE II.—TRIGONOMETRIC FUNCTIONS

| Angles | Sines | | Cosines | | Tangents | | Cotangents | | Angles |
|---|---|---|---|---|---|---|---|---|---|
| | Nat. | Log. | Nat. | Log. | Nat. | Log. | Nat. | Log. | |
| 0° 00′ | .0000 | ∞ | 1.0000 | 0.0000 | .0000 | ∞ | ∞ | ∞ | 90° 00′ |
| 10 | .0029 | **7.**4637 | 1.0000 | 0000 | .0029 | **7.**4637 | 343.77 | **2.**5363 | 50 |
| 20 | .0058 | 7648 | 1.0000 | 0000 | .0058 | 7648 | 171.89 | 2352 | 40 |
| 30 | .0087 | 9408 | 1.0000 | 0000 | .0087 | 9409 | 114.59 | 0591 | 30 |
| 40 | .0116 | **8.**0658 | .9999 | 0000 | .0116 | **8.**0658 | 85.940 | **1.**9342 | 20 |
| 50 | .0145 | 1627 | .9999 | 0000 | .0145 | 1627 | 68.750 | 8373 | 10 |
| 1° 00′ | .0175 | **8.**2419 | .9998 | **9.**9999 | .0175 | **8.**2419 | 57.290 | **1.**7581 | 89° 00′ |
| 10 | .0204 | 3088 | .9998 | 9999 | .0204 | 3089 | 49.104 | 6911 | 50 |
| 20 | .0233 | 3668 | .9997 | 9999 | .0233 | 3669 | 42.964 | 6331 | 40 |
| 30 | .0262 | 4179 | .9997 | 9999 | .0262 | 4181 | 38.188 | 5819 | 30 |
| 40 | .0291 | 4637 | .9996 | 9998 | .0291 | 4638 | 34.368 | 5362 | 20 |
| 50 | .0320 | 5050 | .9995 | 9998 | .0320 | 5053 | 31.242 | 4947 | 10 |
| 2° 00′ | .0349 | **8.**5428 | .9994 | **9.**9997 | .0349 | **8.**5431 | 28.636 | **1.**4569 | 88° 00′ |
| 10 | .0378 | 5776 | .9993 | 9997 | .0378 | 5779 | 26.432 | 4221 | 50 |
| 20 | .0407 | 6097 | .9992 | 9996 | .0407 | 6101 | 24.542 | 3899 | 40 |
| 30 | .0436 | 6397 | .9990 | 9996 | .0437 | 6401 | 22.904 | 3599 | 30 |
| 40 | .0465 | 6677 | .9989 | 9995 | .0466 | 6682 | 21.470 | 3318 | 20 |
| 50 | .0494 | 6940 | .9988 | 9995 | .0495 | 6945 | 20.206 | 3055 | 10 |
| 3° 00′ | .0523 | **8.**7188 | .9986 | **9.**9994 | .0524 | **8.**7194 | 19.081 | **1.**2806 | 87° 00′ |
| 10 | .0552 | 7423 | .9985 | 9993 | .0553 | 7429 | 18.075 | 2571 | 50 |
| 20 | .0581 | 7645 | .9983 | 9993 | .0582 | 7652 | 17.169 | 2348 | 40 |
| 30 | .0610 | 7857 | .9981 | 9992 | .0612 | 7865 | 16.350 | 2135 | 30 |
| 40 | .0640 | 8059 | .9980 | 9991 | .0641 | 8067 | 15.605 | 1933 | 20 |
| 50 | .0669 | 8251 | .9978 | 9990 | .0670 | 8261 | 14.924 | 1739 | 10 |
| 4° 00′ | .0698 | **8.**8436 | .9976 | **9.**9989 | .0699 | **8.**8446 | 14.301 | **1.**1554 | 86° 00′ |
| 10 | .0727 | 8613 | .9974 | 9989 | .0729 | 8624 | 13.727 | 1376 | 50 |
| 20 | .0756 | 8783 | .9971 | 9988 | .0758 | 8795 | 13.197 | 1205 | 40 |
| 30 | .0785 | 8946 | .9969 | 9987 | .0787 | 8960 | 12.706 | 1040 | 30 |
| 40 | .0814 | 9104 | .9967 | 9986 | .0816 | 9118 | 12.251 | 0882 | 20 |
| 50 | .0843 | 9256 | .9964 | 9985 | .0846 | 9272 | 11.826 | 0728 | 10 |
| 5° 00′ | .0872 | **8.**9403 | .9962 | **9.**9983 | .0875 | **8.**9420 | 11.430 | **1.**0580 | 85° 00′ |
| 10 | .0901 | 9545 | .9959 | 9982 | .0904 | 9563 | 11.059 | 0437 | 50 |
| 20 | .0929 | 9682 | .9957 | 9981 | .0934 | 9701 | 10.712 | 0299 | 40 |
| 30 | .0958 | 9816 | .9954 | 9980 | .0963 | 9836 | 10.385 | 0164 | 30 |
| 40 | .0987 | 9945 | .9951 | 9979 | .0992 | 9966 | 10.078 | 0034 | 20 |
| 50 | .1016 | **9.**0070 | .9948 | 9977 | .1022 | **9.**0093 | 9.7882 | **0.**9907 | 10 |
| 6° 00′ | .1045 | **9.**0192 | .9945 | **9.**9976 | .1051 | **9.**0216 | 9.5144 | **0.**9784 | 84° 00′ |
| 10 | .1074 | 0311 | .9942 | 9975 | .1080 | 0336 | 9.2553 | 9664 | 50 |
| 20 | .1103 | 0426 | .9939 | 9973 | .1110 | 0453 | 9.0098 | 9547 | 40 |
| 30 | .1132 | 0539 | .9936 | 9972 | .1139 | 0567 | 8.7769 | 9433 | 30 |
| 40 | .1161 | 0648 | .9932 | 9971 | .1169 | 0678 | 8.5555 | 9322 | 20 |
| 50 | .1190 | 0755 | .9929 | 9969 | .1198 | 0786 | 8.3450 | 9214 | 10 |
| 7° 00′ | .1219 | **9.**0859 | .9925 | **9.**9968 | .1228 | **9.**0891 | 8.1443 | **0.**9109 | 83° 00′ |
| 10 | .1248 | 0961 | .9922 | 9966 | .1257 | 0995 | 7.9530 | 9005 | 50 |
| 20 | .1276 | 1060 | .9918 | 9964 | .1287 | 1096 | 7.7704 | 8904 | 40 |
| 30 | .1305 | 1157 | .9914 | 9963 | .1317 | 1194 | 7.5958 | 8806 | 30 |
| 40 | .1334 | 1252 | .9911 | 9961 | .1346 | 1291 | 7.4287 | 8709 | 20 |
| 50 | .1363 | 1345 | .9907 | 9959 | .1376 | 1385 | 7.2687 | 8615 | 10 |
| 8° 00′ | .1392 | **9.**1436 | .9903 | **9.**9958 | .1405 | **9.**1478 | 7.1154 | **0.**8522 | 82° 00′ |
| 10 | .1421 | 1525 | .9899 | 9956 | .1435 | 1569 | 6.9682 | 8431 | 50 |
| 20 | .1449 | 1612 | .9894 | 9954 | .1465 | 1658 | 6.8269 | 8342 | 40 |
| 30 | .1478 | 1697 | .9890 | 9952 | .1495 | 1745 | 6.6912 | 8255 | 30 |
| 40 | .1507 | 1781 | .9886 | 9950 | .1524 | 1831 | 6.5606 | 8169 | 20 |
| 50 | .1536 | 1863 | .9881 | 9948 | .1554 | 1915 | 6.4348 | 8085 | 10 |
| 9° 00′ | .1564 | **9.**1943 | .9877 | **9.**9946 | .1584 | **9.**1997 | 6.3138 | **0.**8003 | 81° 00′ |
| | Nat. | Log. | Nat. | Log. | Nat. | Log. | Nat. | Log. | |
| Angles | Cosines | | Sines | | Cotangents | | Tangents | | Angles |

## TABLE II.—TRIGONOMETRIC FUNCTIONS.—(*Continued*)

| Angles | Sines | | Cosines | | Tangents | | Cotangents | | Angles |
|---|---|---|---|---|---|---|---|---|---|
| | Nat. | Log. | Nat. | Log. | Nat. | Log. | Nat. | Log. | |
| 9° 00′ | .1564 | 9.1943 | .9877 | 9.9946 | .1584 | 9.1997 | 6.3138 | 0.8003 | 81° 00′ |
| 10 | .1593 | 2022 | .9872 | 9944 | .1614 | 2078 | 6.1970 | 7922 | 50 |
| 20 | .1622 | 2100 | .9868 | 9942 | .1644 | 2158 | 6.0844 | 7842 | 40 |
| 30 | .1650 | 2176 | .9863 | 9940 | .1673 | 2236 | 5.9758 | 7764 | 30 |
| 40 | .1679 | 2251 | .9858 | 9938 | .1703 | 2313 | 5.8708 | 7687 | 20 |
| 50 | .1708 | 2324 | .9853 | 9936 | .1733 | 2389 | 5.7694 | 7611 | 10 |
| 10° 00′ | .1736 | 9.2397 | .9848 | 9.9934 | .1763 | 9.2463 | 5.6713 | 0.7537 | 80° 00′ |
| 10 | .1765 | 2468 | .9843 | 9931 | .1793 | 2536 | 5.5764 | 7464 | 50 |
| 20 | .1794 | 2538 | .9838 | 9929 | .1823 | 2609 | 5.4845 | 7391 | 40 |
| 30 | .1822 | 2606 | .9833 | 9927 | .1853 | 2680 | 5.3955 | 7320 | 30 |
| 40 | .1851 | 2674 | .9827 | 9924 | .1883 | 2750 | 5.3093 | 7250 | 20 |
| 50 | .1880 | 2740 | .9822 | 9922 | .1914 | 2819 | 5.2257 | 7181 | 10 |
| 11° 00′ | .1908 | 9.2806 | .9816 | 9.9919 | .1944 | 9.2887 | 5.1446 | 0.7113 | 79° 00′ |
| 10 | .1937 | 2870 | .9811 | 9917 | .1974 | 2953 | 5.0658 | 7047 | 50 |
| 20 | .1965 | 2934 | .9805 | 9914 | .2004 | 3020 | 4.9894 | 6980 | 40 |
| 30 | .1994 | 2997 | .9799 | 9912 | .2035 | 3085 | 4.9152 | 6915 | 30 |
| 40 | .2022 | 3058 | .9793 | 9909 | .2065 | 3149 | 4.8430 | 6851 | 20 |
| 50 | .2051 | 3119 | .9787 | 9907 | .2095 | 3212 | 4.7729 | 6788 | 10 |
| 12° 00′ | .2079 | 9.3179 | .9781 | 9.9904 | .2126 | 9.3275 | 4.7046 | 0.6725 | 78° 00′ |
| 10 | .2108 | 3238 | .9775 | 9901 | .2156 | 3336 | 4.6382 | 6664 | 50 |
| 20 | .2136 | 3296 | .9769 | 9899 | .2186 | 3397 | 4.5736 | 6603 | 40 |
| 30 | .2164 | 3353 | .9763 | 9896 | .2217 | 3458 | 4.5107 | 6542 | 30 |
| 40 | .2193 | 3410 | .9757 | 9893 | .2247 | 3517 | 4.4494 | 6483 | 20 |
| 50 | .2221 | 3466 | .9750 | 9890 | .2278 | 3576 | 4.3897 | 6424 | 10 |
| 13° 00′ | .2250 | 9.3521 | .9744 | 9.9887 | .2309 | 9.3634 | 4.3315 | 0.6366 | 77° 00′ |
| 10 | .2278 | 3575 | .9737 | 9884 | .2339 | 3691 | 4.2747 | 6309 | 50 |
| 20 | .2306 | 3629 | .9730 | 9881 | .2370 | 3748 | 4.2193 | 6252 | 40 |
| 30 | .2334 | 3682 | .9724 | 9878 | .2401 | 3804 | 4.1653 | 6196 | 30 |
| 40 | .2363 | 3734 | .9717 | 9875 | .2432 | 3859 | 4.1126 | 6141 | 20 |
| 50 | .2391 | 3786 | .9710 | 9872 | .2462 | 3914 | 4.0611 | 6086 | 10 |
| 14° 00′ | .2419 | 9.3837 | .9703 | 9.9869 | .2493 | 9.3968 | 4.0108 | 0.6032 | 76° 00′ |
| 10 | .2447 | 3887 | .9696 | 9866 | .2524 | 4021 | 3.9617 | 5979 | 50 |
| 20 | .2476 | 3937 | .9689 | 9863 | .2555 | 4074 | 3.9136 | 5926 | 40 |
| 30 | .2504 | 3986 | .9681 | 9859 | .2586 | 4127 | 3.8667 | 5873 | 30 |
| 40 | .2532 | 4035 | .9674 | 9856 | .2617 | 4178 | 3.8208 | 5822 | 20 |
| 50 | .2560 | 4083 | .9667 | 9853 | .2648 | 4230 | 3.7760 | 5770 | 10 |
| 15° 00′ | .2588 | 9.4130 | .9659 | 9.9849 | .2679 | 9.4281 | 3.7321 | 0.5719 | 75° 00′ |
| 10 | .2616 | 4177 | .9652 | 9846 | .2711 | 4331 | 3.6891 | 5669 | 50 |
| 20 | .2644 | 4223 | .9644 | 9843 | .2742 | 4381 | 3.6470 | 5619 | 40 |
| 30 | .2672 | 4269 | .9636 | 9839 | .2773 | 4430 | 3.6059 | 5570 | 30 |
| 40 | .2700 | 4314 | .9628 | 9836 | .2805 | 4479 | 3.5656 | 5521 | 20 |
| 50 | .2728 | 4359 | .9621 | 9832 | .2836 | 4527 | 3.5261 | 5473 | 10 |
| 16° 00′ | .2756 | 9.4403 | .9613 | 9.9828 | .2867 | 9.4575 | 3.4874 | 0.5425 | 74° 00′ |
| 10 | .2784 | 4447 | .9605 | 9825 | .2899 | 4622 | 3.4495 | 5378 | 50 |
| 20 | .2812 | 4491 | .9596 | 9821 | .2931 | 4669 | 3.4124 | 5331 | 40 |
| 30 | .2840 | 4533 | .9588 | 9817 | .2962 | 4716 | 3.3759 | 5284 | 30 |
| 40 | .2868 | 4576 | .9580 | 9814 | .2994 | 4762 | 3.3402 | 5238 | 20 |
| 50 | .2896 | 4618 | .9572 | 9810 | .3026 | 4808 | 3.3052 | 5192 | 10 |
| 17° 00′ | .2924 | 9.4659 | .9563 | 9.9806 | .3057 | 9.4853 | 3.2709 | 0.5147 | 73° 00′ |
| 10 | .2952 | 4700 | .9555 | 9802 | .3089 | 4898 | 3.2371 | 5102 | 50 |
| 20 | .2979 | 4741 | .9546 | 9798 | .3121 | 4943 | 3.2041 | 5057 | 40 |
| 30 | .3007 | 4781 | .9537 | 9794 | .3153 | 4987 | 3.1716 | 5013 | 30 |
| 40 | .3035 | 4821 | .9528 | 9790 | .3185 | 5031 | 3.1397 | 4969 | 20 |
| 50 | .3062 | 4861 | .9520 | 9786 | .3217 | 5075 | 3.1084 | 4925 | 10 |
| 18° 00′ | .3090 | 9.4900 | .9511 | 9.9782 | .3249 | 9.5118 | 3.0777 | 0.4882 | 72° 00′ |
| | Nat. | Log. | Nat. | Log. | Nat. | Log. | Nat. | Log. | |
| Angles | Cosines | | Sines | | Cotangents | | Tangents | | Angles |

TABLE II.—TRIGONOMETRIC FUNCTIONS.—(*Continued*)

| Angles | Sines | | Cosines | | Tangents | | Cotangents | | Angles |
|---|---|---|---|---|---|---|---|---|---|
| | Nat. | Log. | Nat. | Log. | Nat. | Log. | Nat. | Log. | |
| 18° 00′ | .3090 | 9.4900 | .9511 | 9.9782 | .3249 | 9.5118 | 3.0777 | 0.4882 | 72° 00′ |
| 10 | .3118 | 4939 | .9502 | 9778 | .3281 | 5161 | 3.0475 | 4839 | 50 |
| 20 | .3145 | 4977 | .9492 | 9774 | .3314 | 5203 | 3.0178 | 4797 | 40 |
| 30 | .3173 | 5015 | .9483 | 9770 | .3346 | 5245 | 2.9887 | 4755 | 30 |
| 40 | .3201 | 5052 | .9474 | 9765 | .3378 | 5287 | 2.9600 | 4713 | 20 |
| 50 | .3228 | 5090 | .9465 | 9761 | .3411 | 5329 | 2.9319 | 4671 | 10 |
| 19° 00′ | .3256 | 9.5126 | .9455 | 9.9757 | .3443 | 9.5370 | 2.9042 | 0.4630 | 71° 00′ |
| 10 | .3283 | 5163 | .9446 | 9752 | .3476 | 5411 | 2.8770 | 4589 | 50 |
| 20 | .3311 | 5199 | .9436 | 9748 | .3508 | 5451 | 2.8502 | 4549 | 40 |
| 30 | .3338 | 5235 | .9426 | 9743 | .3541 | 5491 | 2.8239 | 4509 | 30 |
| 40 | .3365 | 5270 | .9417 | 9739 | .3574 | 5531 | 2.7980 | 4469 | 20 |
| 50 | .3393 | 5306 | .9407 | 9734 | .3607 | 5571 | 2.7725 | 4429 | 10 |
| 20° 00′ | .3420 | 9.5341 | .9397 | 9.9730 | .3640 | 9.5611 | 2.7475 | 0.4389 | 70° 00′ |
| 10 | .3448 | 5375 | .9387 | 9725 | .3673 | 5650 | 2.7228 | 4350 | 50 |
| 20 | .3475 | 5409 | .9377 | 9721 | .3706 | 5689 | 2.6985 | 4311 | 40 |
| 30 | .3502 | 5443 | .9367 | 9716 | .3739 | 5727 | 2.6746 | 4273 | 30 |
| 40 | .3529 | 5477 | .9356 | 9711 | .3772 | 5766 | 2.6511 | 4234 | 20 |
| 50 | .3557 | 5510 | .9346 | 9706 | .3805 | 5804 | 2.6279 | 4196 | 10 |
| 21° 00′ | .3584 | 9.5543 | .9336 | 9.9702 | .3839 | 9.5842 | 2.6051 | 0.4158 | 69° 00′ |
| 10 | .3611 | 5576 | .9325 | 9697 | .3872 | 5879 | 2.5826 | 4121 | 50 |
| 20 | .3638 | 5609 | .9315 | 9692 | .3906 | 5917 | 2.5605 | 4083 | 40 |
| 30 | .3665 | 5641 | .9304 | 9687 | .3939 | 5954 | 2.5386 | 4046 | 30 |
| 40 | .3692 | 5673 | .9293 | 9682 | .3973 | 5991 | 2.5172 | 4009 | 20 |
| 50 | .3719 | 5704 | .9283 | 9677 | .4006 | 6028 | 2.4960 | 3972 | 10 |
| 22° 00′ | .3746 | 9.5736 | .9272 | 9.9672 | .4040 | 9.6064 | 2.4751 | 0.3936 | 68° 00′ |
| 10 | .3773 | 5767 | .9261 | 9667 | .4074 | 6100 | 2.4545 | 3900 | 50 |
| 20 | .3800 | 5798 | .9250 | 9661 | .4108 | 6136 | 2.4342 | 3864 | 40 |
| 30 | .3827 | 5828 | .9239 | 9656 | .4142 | 6172 | 2.4142 | 3828 | 30 |
| 40 | .3854 | 5859 | .9228 | 9651 | .4176 | 6208 | 2.3945 | 3792 | 20 |
| 50 | .3881 | 5889 | .9216 | 9646 | .4210 | 6243 | 2.3750 | 3757 | 10 |
| 23° 00′ | .3907 | 9.5919 | .9205 | 9.9640 | .4245 | 9.6279 | 2.3559 | 0.3721 | 67° 00′ |
| 10 | .3934 | 5948 | .9194 | 9635 | .4279 | 6314 | 2.3369 | 3686 | 50 |
| 20 | .3961 | 5978 | .9182 | 9629 | .4314 | 6348 | 2.3183 | 3652 | 40 |
| 30 | .3987 | 6007 | .9171 | 9624 | .4348 | 6383 | 2.2998 | 3617 | 30 |
| 40 | .4014 | 6036 | .9159 | 9618 | .4383 | 6417 | 2.2817 | 3583 | 20 |
| 50 | .4041 | 6065 | .9147 | 9613 | .4417 | 6452 | 2.2637 | 3548 | 10 |
| 24° 00′ | .4067 | 9.6093 | .9135 | 9.9607 | .4452 | 9.6486 | 2.2460 | 0.3514 | 66° 00′ |
| 10 | .4094 | 6121 | .9124 | 9602 | .4487 | 6520 | 2.2286 | 3480 | 50 |
| 20 | .4120 | 6149 | .9112 | 9596 | .4522 | 6553 | 2.2113 | 3447 | 40 |
| 30 | .4147 | 6177 | .9100 | 9590 | .4557 | 6587 | 2.1943 | 3413 | 30 |
| 40 | .4173 | 6205 | .9088 | 9584 | .4592 | 6620 | 2.1775 | 3380 | 20 |
| 50 | .4200 | 6232 | .9075 | 9579 | .4628 | 6654 | 2.1609 | 3346 | 10 |
| 25° 00′ | .4226 | 9.6259 | .9063 | 9.9573 | .4663 | 9.6687 | 2.1445 | 0.3313 | 65° 00′ |
| 10 | .4253 | 6286 | .9051 | 9567 | .4699 | 6720 | 2.1283 | 3280 | 50 |
| 20 | .4279 | 6313 | .9038 | 9561 | .4734 | 6752 | 2.1123 | 3248 | 40 |
| 30 | .4305 | 6340 | .9026 | 9555 | .4770 | 6785 | 2.0965 | 3215 | 30 |
| 40 | .4331 | 6366 | .9013 | 9549 | .4806 | 6817 | 2.0809 | 3183 | 20 |
| 50 | .4358 | 6392 | .9001 | 9543 | .4841 | 6850 | 2.0655 | 3150 | 10 |
| 26° 00′ | .4384 | 9.6418 | .8988 | 9.9537 | .4877 | 9.6882 | 2.0503 | 0.3118 | 64° 00′ |
| 10 | .4410 | 6444 | .8975 | 9530 | .4913 | 6914 | 2.0353 | 3086 | 50 |
| 20 | .4436 | 6470 | .8962 | 9524 | .4950 | 6946 | 2.0204 | 3054 | 40 |
| 30 | .4462 | 6495 | .8949 | 9518 | .4986 | 6977 | 2.0057 | 3023 | 30 |
| 40 | .4488 | 6521 | .8936 | 9512 | .5022 | 7009 | 1.9912 | 2991 | 20 |
| 50 | .4514 | 6546 | .8923 | 9505 | .5059 | 7040 | 1.9768 | 2960 | 10 |
| 27° 00′ | .4540 | 9.6570 | .8910 | 9.9499 | .5095 | 9.7072 | 1.9626 | 0.2928 | 63° 00′ |
| | Nat. | Log. | Nat. | Log. | Nat. | Log. | Nat. | Log. | |
| Angles | Cosines | | Sines | | Cotangents | | Tangents | | Angles |

TABLE II.—TRIGONOMETRIC FUNCTIONS.—(*Continued*)

| Angles | Sines | | Cosines | | Tangents | | Cotangents | | Angles |
|---|---|---|---|---|---|---|---|---|---|
| | Nat. | Log. | Nat. | Log. | Nat. | Log. | Nat. | Log. | |
| 27° 00′ | .4540 | 9.6570 | .8910 | 9.9499 | .5095 | 9.7072 | 1.9626 | 0.2928 | 63° 00′ |
| 10 | .4566 | 6595 | .8897 | 9492 | .5132 | 7103 | 1.9486 | 2897 | 50 |
| 20 | .4592 | 6620 | .8884 | 9486 | .5169 | 7134 | 1.9347 | 2866 | 40 |
| 30 | .4617 | 6644 | .8870 | 9479 | .5206 | 7165 | 1.9210 | 2835 | 30 |
| 40 | .4643 | 6668 | .8857 | 9473 | .5243 | 7196 | 1.9074 | 2804 | 20 |
| 50 | .4669 | 6692 | .8843 | 9466 | .5280 | 7226 | 1.8940 | 2774 | 10 |
| 28° 00′ | .4695 | 9.6716 | .8829 | 9.9459 | .5317 | 9.7257 | 1.8807 | 0.2743 | 62° 00′ |
| 10 | .4720 | 6740 | .8816 | 9453 | .5354 | 7287 | 1.8676 | 2713 | 50 |
| 20 | .4746 | 6763 | .8802 | 9446 | .5392 | 7317 | 1.8546 | 2683 | 40 |
| 30 | .4772 | 6787 | .8788 | 9439 | .5430 | 7348 | 1.8418 | 2652 | 30 |
| 40 | .4797 | 6810 | .8774 | 9432 | .5467 | 7378 | 1.8291 | 2622 | 20 |
| 50 | .4823 | 6833 | .8760 | 9425 | .5505 | 7408 | 1.8165 | 2592 | 10 |
| 29° 00′ | .4848 | 9.6856 | .8746 | 9.9418 | .5543 | 9.7438 | 1.8040 | 0.2562 | 61° 00′ |
| 10 | .4874 | 6878 | .8732 | 9411 | .5581 | 7467 | 1.7917 | 2533 | 50 |
| 20 | .4899 | 6901 | .8718 | 9404 | .5619 | 7497 | 1.7796 | 2503 | 40 |
| 30 | .4924 | 6923 | .8704 | 9397 | .5658 | 7526 | 1.7675 | 2474 | 30 |
| 40 | .4950 | 6946 | .8689 | 9390 | .5696 | 7556 | 1.7556 | 2444 | 20 |
| 50 | .4975 | 6968 | .8675 | 9383 | .5735 | 7585 | 1.7437 | 2415 | 10 |
| 30° 00′ | .5000 | 9.6990 | .8660 | 9.9375 | .5774 | 9.7614 | 1.7321 | 0.2386 | 60° 00′ |
| 10 | .5025 | 7012 | .8646 | 9368 | .5812 | 7644 | 1.7205 | 2356 | 50 |
| 20 | .5050 | 7033 | .8631 | 9361 | .5851 | 7673 | 1.7090 | 2327 | 40 |
| 30 | .5075 | 7055 | .8616 | 9353 | .5890 | 7701 | 1.6977 | 2299 | 30 |
| 40 | .5100 | 7076 | .8601 | 9346 | .5930 | 7730 | 1.6864 | 2270 | 20 |
| 50 | .5125 | 7097 | .8587 | 9338 | .5969 | 7759 | 1.6753 | 2241 | 10 |
| 31° 00′ | .5150 | 9.7118 | .8572 | 9.9331 | .6009 | 9.7788 | 1.6643 | 0.2212 | 59° 00′ |
| 10 | .5175 | 7139 | .8557 | 9323 | .6048 | 7816 | 1.6534 | 2184 | 50 |
| 20 | .5200 | 7160 | .8542 | 9315 | .6088 | 7845 | 1.6426 | 2155 | 40 |
| 30 | .5225 | 7181 | .8526 | 9308 | .6128 | 7873 | 1.6319 | 2127 | 30 |
| 40 | .5250 | 7201 | .8511 | 9300 | .6168 | 7902 | 1.6212 | 2098 | 20 |
| 50 | .5275 | 7222 | .8496 | 9292 | .6208 | 7930 | 1.6107 | 2070 | 10 |
| 32° 00′ | .5299 | 9.7242 | .8480 | 9.9284 | .6249 | 9.7958 | 1.6003 | 0.2042 | 58° 00′ |
| 10 | .5324 | 7262 | .8465 | 9276 | .6289 | 7986 | 1.5900 | 2014 | 50 |
| 20 | .5348 | 7282 | .8450 | 9268 | .6330 | 8014 | 1.5798 | 1986 | 40 |
| 30 | .5373 | 7302 | .8434 | 9260 | .6371 | 8042 | 1.5697 | 1958 | 30 |
| 40 | .5398 | 7322 | .8418 | 9252 | .6412 | 8070 | 1.5597 | 1930 | 20 |
| 50 | .5422 | 7342 | .8403 | 9244 | .6453 | 8097 | 1.5497 | 1903 | 10 |
| 33° 00′ | .5446 | 9.7361 | .8387 | 9.9236 | .6494 | 9.8125 | 1.5399 | 0.1875 | 57° 00′ |
| 10 | .5471 | 7380 | .8371 | 9228 | .6536 | 8153 | 1.5301 | 1847 | 50 |
| 20 | .5495 | 7400 | .8355 | 9219 | .6577 | 8180 | 1.5204 | 1820 | 40 |
| 30 | .5519 | 7419 | .8339 | 9211 | .6619 | 8208 | 1.5108 | 1792 | 30 |
| 40 | .5544 | 7438 | .8323 | 9203 | .6661 | 8235 | 1.5013 | 1765 | 20 |
| 50 | .5568 | 7457 | .8307 | 9194 | .6703 | 8263 | 1.4919 | 1737 | 10 |
| 34° 00′ | .5592 | 9.7476 | .8290 | 9.9186 | .6745 | 9.8290 | 1.4826 | 0.1710 | 56° 00′ |
| 10 | .5616 | 7494 | .8274 | 9177 | .6787 | 8317 | 1.4733 | 1683 | 50 |
| 20 | .5640 | 7513 | .8258 | 9169 | .6830 | 8344 | 1.4641 | 1656 | 40 |
| 30 | .5664 | 7531 | .8241 | 9160 | .6873 | 8371 | 1.4550 | 1629 | 30 |
| 40 | .5688 | 7550 | .8225 | 9151 | .6916 | 8398 | 1.4460 | 1602 | 20 |
| 50 | .5712 | 7568 | .8208 | 9142 | .6959 | 8425 | 1.4370 | 1575 | 10 |
| 35° 00′ | .5736 | 9.7586 | .8192 | 9.9134 | .7002 | 9.8452 | 1.4281 | 0.1548 | 55° 00′ |
| 10 | .5760 | 7604 | .8175 | 9125 | .7046 | 8479 | 1.4193 | 1521 | 50 |
| 20 | .5783 | 7622 | .8158 | 9116 | .7089 | 8506 | 1.4106 | 1494 | 40 |
| 30 | .5807 | 7640 | .8141 | 9107 | .7133 | 8533 | 1.4019 | 1467 | 30 |
| 40 | .5831 | 7657 | .8124 | 9098 | .7177 | 8559 | 1.3934 | 1441 | 20 |
| 50 | .5854 | 7675 | .8107 | 9089 | .7221 | 8586 | 1.3848 | 1414 | 10 |
| 36° 00′ | .5878 | 9.7692 | .8090 | 9.9080 | .7265 | 9.8613 | 1.3764 | 0.1387 | 54° 00′ |
| | Nat. | Log. | Nat. | Log. | Nat. | Log. | Nat. | Log. | |
| Angles | Cosines | | Sines | | Cotangents | | Tangents | | Angles |

## TABLE II.—TRIGONOMETRIC FUNCTIONS.—(*Continued*)

| Angles | Sines | | Cosines | | Tangents | | Cotangents | | Angles |
|---|---|---|---|---|---|---|---|---|---|
| | Nat. | Log. | Nat. | Log. | Nat. | Log. | Nat. | Log. | |
| 36° 00′ | .5878 | 9.7692 | .8090 | 9.9080 | .7265 | 9.8613 | 1.3764 | 0.1387 | 54° 00′ |
| 10 | .5901 | 7710 | .8073 | 9070 | .7310 | 8639 | 1.3680 | 1361 | 50 |
| 20 | .5925 | 7727 | .8056 | 9061 | .7355 | 8666 | 1.3597 | 1334 | 40 |
| 30 | .5948 | 7744 | .8039 | 9052 | .7400 | 8692 | 1.3514 | 1308 | 30 |
| 40 | .5972 | 7761 | .8021 | 9042 | .7445 | 8718 | 1.3432 | 1282 | 20 |
| 50 | .5995 | 7778 | .8004 | 9033 | .7490 | 8745 | 1.3351 | 1255 | 10 |
| 37° 00′ | .6018 | 9.7795 | .7986 | 9.9023 | .7536 | 9.8771 | 1.3270 | 0.1229 | 53° 00′ |
| 10 | .6041 | 7811 | .7969 | 9014 | .7581 | 8797 | 1.3190 | 1203 | 50 |
| 20 | .6065 | 7828 | .7951 | 9004 | .7627 | 8824 | 1.3111 | 1176 | 40 |
| 30 | .6088 | 7844 | .7934 | 8995 | .7673 | 8850 | 1.3032 | 1150 | 30 |
| 40 | .6111 | 7861 | .7916 | 8985 | .7720 | 8876 | 1.2954 | 1124 | 20 |
| 50 | .6134 | 7877 | .7898 | 8975 | .7766 | 8902 | 1.2876 | 1098 | 10 |
| 38° 00′ | .6157 | 9.7893 | .7880 | 9.8965 | .7813 | 9.8928 | 1.2790 | 0.1072 | 52° 00′ |
| 10 | .6180 | 7910 | .7862 | 8955 | .7860 | 8954 | 1.2723 | 1046 | 50 |
| 20 | .6202 | 7926 | .7844 | 8945 | .7907 | 8980 | 1.2647 | 1020 | 40 |
| 30 | .6225 | 7941 | .7826 | 8935 | .7954 | 9006 | 1.2572 | 0994 | 30 |
| 40 | .6248 | 7957 | .7808 | 8925 | .8002 | 9032 | 1.2497 | 0968 | 20 |
| 50 | .6271 | 7973 | .7790 | 8915 | .8050 | 9058 | 1.2423 | 0942 | 10 |
| 39° 00′ | .6293 | 9.7989 | .7771 | 9.8905 | .8098 | 9.9084 | 1.2349 | 0.0916 | 51° 00′ |
| 10 | .6316 | 8004 | .7753 | 8895 | .8146 | 9110 | 1.2276 | 0890 | 50 |
| 20 | .6338 | 8020 | .7735 | 8884 | .8195 | 9135 | 1.2203 | 0865 | 40 |
| 30 | .6361 | 8035 | .7716 | 8874 | .8243 | 9161 | 1.2131 | 0839 | 30 |
| 40 | .6383 | 8050 | .7698 | 8864 | .8292 | 9187 | 1.2059 | 0813 | 20 |
| 50 | .6406 | 8066 | .7679 | 8853 | .8342 | 9212 | 1.1988 | 0788 | 10 |
| 40° 00′ | .6428 | 9.8081 | .7660 | 9.8843 | .8391 | 9.9238 | 1.1918 | 0.0762 | 50° 00′ |
| 10 | .6450 | 8096 | .7642 | 8832 | .8441 | 9264 | 1.1847 | 0736 | 50 |
| 20 | .6472 | 8111 | .7623 | 8821 | .8491 | 9289 | 1.1778 | 0711 | 40 |
| 30 | .6494 | 8125 | .7604 | 8810 | .8541 | 9315 | 1.1708 | 0685 | 30 |
| 40 | .6517 | 8140 | .7585 | 8800 | .8591 | 9341 | 1.1640 | 0659 | 20 |
| 50 | .6539 | 8155 | .7566 | 8789 | .8642 | 9366 | 1.1571 | 0634 | 10 |
| 41° 00′ | .6561 | 9.8169 | .7547 | 9.8778 | .8693 | 9.9392 | 1.1504 | 0.0608 | 49° 00′ |
| 10 | .6583 | 8184 | .7528 | 8767 | .8744 | 9417 | 1.1436 | 0583 | 50 |
| 20 | .6604 | 8198 | .7509 | 8756 | .8796 | 9443 | 1.1369 | 0557 | 40 |
| 30 | .6626 | 8213 | .7490 | 8745 | .8847 | 9468 | 1.1303 | 0532 | 30 |
| 40 | .6648 | 8227 | .7470 | 8733 | .8899 | 9494 | 1.1237 | 0506 | 20 |
| 50 | .6670 | 8241 | .7451 | 8722 | .8952 | 9519 | 1.1171 | 0481 | 10 |
| 42° 00′ | .6691 | 9.8255 | .7431 | 9.8711 | .9004 | 9.9544 | 1.1106 | 0.0456 | 48° 00′ |
| 10 | .6713 | 8269 | .7412 | 8699 | .9057 | 9570 | 1.1041 | 0430 | 50 |
| 20 | .6734 | 8283 | .7392 | 8688 | .9110 | 9595 | 1.0977 | 0405 | 40 |
| 30 | .6756 | 8297 | .7373 | 8676 | .9163 | 9621 | 1.0913 | 0379 | 30 |
| 40 | .6777 | 8311 | .7353 | 8665 | .9217 | 9646 | 1.0850 | 0354 | 20 |
| 50 | .6799 | 8324 | .7333 | 8653 | .9271 | 9671 | 1.0786 | 0329 | 10 |
| 43° 00′ | .6820 | 9.8338 | .7314 | 9.8641 | .9325 | 9.9697 | 1.0724 | 0.0303 | 47° 00′ |
| 10 | .6841 | 8351 | .7294 | 8629 | .9380 | 9722 | 1.0661 | 0278 | 50 |
| 20 | .6862 | 8365 | .7274 | 8618 | .9435 | 9747 | 1.0599 | 0253 | 40 |
| 30 | .6884 | 8378 | .7254 | 8606 | .9490 | 9772 | 1.0538 | 0228 | 30 |
| 40 | .6905 | 8391 | .7234 | 8594 | .9545 | 9798 | 1.0477 | 0202 | 20 |
| 50 | .6926 | 8405 | .7214 | 8582 | .9601 | 9823 | 1.0416 | 0177 | 10 |
| 44° 00′ | .6947 | 9.8418 | .7193 | 9.8569 | .9657 | 9.9848 | 1.0355 | 0.0152 | 46° 00′ |
| 10 | .6967 | 8431 | .7173 | 8557 | .9713 | 9874 | 1.0295 | 0126 | 50 |
| 20 | .6988 | 8444 | .7153 | 8545 | .9770 | 9899 | 1.0235 | 0101 | 40 |
| 30 | .7009 | 8457 | .7133 | 8532 | .9827 | 9924 | 1.0176 | 0076 | 30 |
| 40 | .7030 | 8469 | .7112 | 8520 | .9884 | 9949 | 1.0117 | 0051 | 20 |
| 50 | .7050 | 8482 | .7092 | 8507 | .9942 | 9975 | 1.0058 | 0025 | 10 |
| 45° 00′ | .7071 | 9.8495 | .7071 | 9.8495 | 1.0000 | 0.0000 | 1.0000 | 0.0000 | 45° 00′ |
| | Nat. | Log. | Nat. | Log. | Nat. | Log. | Nat. | Log. | |
| Angles | Cosines | | Sines | | Cotangents | | Tangents | | Angles |

TABLE III.—POWERS AND ROOTS

| No. | Sq. | Sq. Root | Cube | Cube Root | No. | Sq. | Sq. Root | Cube | Cube Root |
|---|---|---|---|---|---|---|---|---|---|
| 1 | 1 | 1.000 | 1 | 1.000 | 51 | 2,601 | 7.141 | 132,651 | 3.708 |
| 2 | 4 | 1.414 | 8 | 1.260 | 52 | 2,704 | 7.211 | 140,608 | 3.733 |
| 3 | 9 | 1.732 | 27 | 1.442 | 53 | 2,809 | 7.280 | 148,877 | 3.756 |
| 4 | 16 | 2.000 | 64 | 1.587 | 54 | 2,916 | 7.348 | 157,464 | 3.780 |
| 5 | 25 | 2.236 | 125 | 1.710 | 55 | 3,025 | 7.416 | 166,375 | 3.803 |
| 6 | 36 | 2.449 | 216 | 1.817 | 56 | 3,136 | 7.483 | 175,616 | 3.826 |
| 7 | 49 | 2.646 | 343 | 1.913 | 57 | 3,249 | 7.550 | 185,193 | 3.849 |
| 8 | 64 | 2.828 | 512 | 2.000 | 58 | 3,364 | 7.616 | 195,112 | 3.871 |
| 9 | 81 | 3.000 | 729 | 2.080 | 59 | 3,481 | 7.681 | 205,379 | 3.893 |
| 10 | 100 | 3.162 | 1,000 | 2.154 | 60 | 3,600 | 7.746 | 216,000 | 3.915 |
| 11 | 121 | 3.317 | 1,331 | 2.224 | 61 | 3,721 | 7.810 | 226,981 | 3.936 |
| 12 | 144 | 3.464 | 1,728 | 2.289 | 62 | 3,844 | 7.874 | 238,328 | 3.958 |
| 13 | 169 | 3.606 | 2,197 | 2.351 | 63 | 3,969 | 7.937 | 250,047 | 3.979 |
| 14 | 196 | 3.742 | 2,744 | 2.410 | 64 | 4,096 | 8.000 | 262,144 | 4.000 |
| 15 | 225 | 3.873 | 3,375 | 2.466 | 65 | 4,225 | 8.062 | 274,625 | 4.021 |
| 16 | 256 | 4.000 | 4,096 | 2.520 | 66 | 4,356 | 8.124 | 287,496 | 4.041 |
| 17 | 289 | 4.123 | 4,913 | 2.571 | 67 | 4,489 | 8.185 | 300,763 | 4.062 |
| 18 | 324 | 4.243 | 5,832 | 2.621 | 68 | 4,624 | 8.246 | 314.432 | 4.082 |
| 19 | 361 | 4.359 | 6,859 | 2.668 | 69 | 4,761 | 8.307 | 328,509 | 4.102 |
| 20 | 400 | 4.472 | 8,000 | 2.714 | 70 | 4,900 | 8.367 | 343,000 | 4.121 |
| 21 | 441 | 4.583 | 9,261 | 2.759 | 71 | 5,041 | 8.426 | 357,911 | 4.141 |
| 22 | 484 | 4.690 | 10,648 | 2.802 | 72 | 5,184 | 8.485 | 373,248 | 4.160 |
| 23 | 529 | 4.796 | 12,167 | 2.844 | 73 | 5,329 | 8.544 | 389,017 | 4.179 |
| 24 | 576 | 4.899 | 13,824 | 2.884 | 74 | 5,476 | 8.602 | 405,224 | 4.198 |
| 25 | 625 | 5.000 | 15,625 | 2.924 | 75 | 5,625 | 8.660 | 421,875 | 4.217 |
| 26 | 676 | 5.099 | 17,576 | 2.962 | 76 | 5,776 | 8.718 | 438,976 | 4.236 |
| 27 | 729 | 5.196 | 19,683 | 3.000 | 77 | 5,929 | 8.775 | 456,533 | 4.254 |
| 28 | 784 | 5.291 | 21,952 | 3.037 | 78 | 6,084 | 8.832 | 474,552 | 4.273 |
| 29 | 841 | 5.385 | 24,389 | 3.072 | 79 | 6,241 | 8.888 | 493,039 | 4.291 |
| 30 | 900 | 5.477 | 27,000 | 3.107 | 80 | 6,400 | 8.944 | 512,000 | 4.309 |
| 31 | 961 | 5.568 | 29,791 | 3.141 | 81 | 6,561 | 9.000 | 531,441 | 4.327 |
| 32 | 1,024 | 5.657 | 32,768 | 3.175 | 82 | 6,724 | 9.055 | 551,368 | 4.344 |
| 33 | 1,089 | 5.745 | 35,937 | 3.208 | 83 | 6,889 | 9.110 | 571,787 | 4.362 |
| 34 | 1,156 | 5.831 | 39,304 | 3.240 | 84 | 7,056 | 9.165 | 592,704 | 4.380 |
| 35 | 1,225 | 5.916 | 42,875 | 3.271 | 85 | 7,225 | 9.220 | 614,125 | 4.397 |
| 36 | 1,296 | 6.000 | 46,656 | 3.302 | 86 | 7,396 | 9.274 | 636,056 | 4.414 |
| 37 | 1,369 | 6.083 | 50,653 | 3.332 | 87 | 7,569 | 9.327 | 658,503 | 4.431 |
| 38 | 1,444 | 6.164 | 54,872 | 3.362 | 88 | 7,744 | 9.331 | 681,472 | 4.448 |
| 39 | 1,521 | 6.245 | 59,319 | 3.391 | 89 | 7,921 | 9.434 | 704,969 | 4.465 |
| 40 | 1,600 | 6.325 | 64,000 | 3.420 | 90 | 8,100 | 9.487 | 729,000 | 4.481 |
| 41 | 1,681 | 6.403 | 68,921 | 3.448 | 91 | 8,281 | 9.539 | 753,571 | 4.498 |
| 42 | 1,764 | 6.481 | 74,088 | 3.476 | 92 | 8,464 | 9.592 | 778,688 | 4.514 |
| 43 | 1,849 | 6.557 | 79,507 | 3.503 | 93 | 8,649 | 9.644 | 804,357 | 4.531 |
| 44 | 1,936 | 6.633 | 85,184 | 3.530 | 94 | 8,836 | 9.695 | 830,584 | 4.547 |
| 45 | 2,025 | 6.708 | 91,125 | 3.557 | 95 | 9,025 | 9.747 | 857,375 | 4.563 |
| 46 | 2,116 | 6.782 | 97,336 | 3.583 | 96 | 9,216 | 9.798 | 884,736 | 4.579 |
| 47 | 2,209 | 6.856 | 103,823 | 3.609 | 97 | 9,409 | 9.849 | 912,673 | 4.595 |
| 48 | 2,304 | 6.928 | 110,592 | 3.634 | 98 | 9,604 | 9.899 | 941,192 | 4.610 |
| 49 | 2,401 | 7.000 | 117,649 | 3.659 | 99 | 9,801 | 9.950 | 970,299 | 4.626 |
| 50 | 2,500 | 7.071 | 125,000 | 3.684 | 100 | 10,000 | 10.000 | 1,000,000 | 4.642 |

## TABLE IV.—NATURAL LOGARITHMS

| N | 0 | 1 | 2 | 3 | 4 | 5 | 6 | 7 | 8 | 9 |
|---|---|---|---|---|---|---|---|---|---|---|
| **1.0** | 0.0 000 | 100 | 198 | 296 | 392 | 488 | 583 | 677 | 770 | 862 |
| 1.1 | 953 | *044 | *133 | *222 | *310 | *398 | *484 | *570 | *655 | *740 |
| 1.2 | 0.1 823 | 906 | 989 | *070 | *151 | *231 | *311 | *390 | *469 | *546 |
| 1.3 | 0.2 624 | 700 | 776 | 852 | 927 | *001 | *075 | *148 | *221 | *293 |
| 1.4 | 0.3 365 | 436 | 507 | 577 | 646 | 716 | 784 | 853 | 920 | 988 |
| 1.5 | 0.4 055 | 121 | 187 | 253 | 318 | 383 | 447 | 511 | 574 | 637 |
| 1.6 | 700 | 762 | 824 | 886 | 947 | *008 | *068 | *128 | *188 | *247 |
| 1.7 | 0.5 306 | 365 | 423 | 481 | 539 | 596 | 653 | 710 | 766 | 822 |
| 1.8 | 878 | 933 | 988 | *043 | *098 | *152 | *206 | *259 | *313 | *366 |
| 1.9 | 0.6 419 | 471 | 523 | 575 | 627 | 678 | 729 | 780 | 831 | 881 |
| **2.0** | 931 | 981 | *031 | *080 | *129 | *178 | *227 | *275 | *324 | *372 |
| 2.1 | 0.7 419 | 467 | 514 | 561 | 608 | 655 | 701 | 747 | 793 | 839 |
| 2.2 | 885 | 930 | 975 | *020 | *065 | *109 | *154 | *198 | *242 | *286 |
| 2.3 | 0.8 329 | 372 | 416 | 459 | 502 | 544 | 587 | 629 | 671 | 713 |
| 2.4 | 755 | 796 | 838 | 879 | 920 | 961 | *002 | *042 | *083 | *123 |
| 2.5 | 0.9 163 | 203 | 243 | 282 | 322 | 361 | 400 | 439 | 478 | 517 |
| 2.6 | 555 | 594 | 632 | 670 | 708 | 746 | 783 | 821 | 858 | 895 |
| 2.7 | 933 | 969 | *006 | *043 | *080 | *116 | *152 | *188 | *225 | *260 |
| 2.8 | 1.0 296 | 332 | 367 | 403 | 438 | 473 | 508 | 543 | 578 | 613 |
| 2.9 | 647 | 682 | 716 | 750 | 784 | 818 | 852 | 886 | 919 | 953 |
| **3.0** | 986 | *019 | *053 | *086 | *119 | *151 | *184 | *217 | *249 | *282 |
| 3.1 | 1.1 314 | 346 | 378 | 410 | 442 | 474 | 506 | 537 | 569 | 600 |
| 3.2 | 632 | 663 | 694 | 725 | 756 | 787 | 817 | 848 | 878 | 909 |
| 3.3 | 939 | 969 | *000 | *030 | *060 | *090 | *119 | *149 | *179 | *208 |
| 3.4 | 1.2 238 | 267 | 296 | 326 | 355 | 384 | 413 | 442 | 470 | 499 |
| 3.5 | 528 | 556 | 585 | 613 | 641 | 669 | 698 | 726 | 754 | 782 |
| 3.6 | 809 | 837 | 865 | 892 | 920 | 947 | 975 | *002 | *029 | *056 |
| 3.7 | 1.3 083 | 110 | 137 | 164 | 191 | 218 | 244 | 271 | 297 | 324 |
| 3.8 | 350 | 376 | 402 | 429 | 455 | 481 | 507 | 533 | 558 | 584 |
| 3.9 | 610 | 635 | 661 | 686 | 712 | 737 | 762 | 788 | 813 | 838 |
| **4.0** | 863 | 888 | 913 | 938 | 962 | 987 | *012 | *036 | *061 | *085 |
| 4.1 | 1.4 110 | 134 | 159 | 183 | 207 | 231 | 255 | 279 | 303 | 327 |
| 4.2 | 351 | 375 | 398 | 422 | 446 | 469 | 493 | 516 | 540 | 563 |
| 4.3 | 586 | 609 | 633 | 656 | 679 | 702 | 725 | 748 | 770 | 793 |
| 4.4 | 816 | 839 | 861 | 884 | 907 | 929 | 951 | 974 | 996 | *019 |
| 4.5 | 1.5 041 | 063 | 085 | 107 | 129 | 151 | 173 | 195 | 217 | 239 |
| 4.6 | 261 | 282 | 304 | 326 | 347 | 369 | 390 | 412 | 433 | 454 |
| 4.7 | 476 | 497 | 518 | 539 | 560 | 581 | 602 | 623 | 644 | 665 |
| 4.8 | 686 | 707 | 728 | 748 | 769 | 790 | 810 | 831 | 851 | 872 |
| 4.9 | 892 | 913 | 933 | 953 | 974 | 994 | *014 | *034 | *054 | *074 |
| **5.0** | 1.6 094 | 114 | 134 | 154 | 174 | 194 | 214 | 233 | 253 | 273 |

If given number $n = N \times 10^m$, then $\log_e n = \log_e N + m \log_e 10$. Find $m \log_e 10$ from the following table:

*Multiples of $\log_e$ 10*

| | |
|---|---|
| $\log_e 10 = 2.3026$ | $- \log_e 10 = 7.6974 - 10$ |
| $2 \log_e 10 = 4.6052$ | $-2 \log_e 10 = 5.3948 - 10$ |
| $3 \log_e 10 = 6.9078$ | $-3 \log_e 10 = 3.0922 - 10$ |
| $4 \log_e 10 = 9.2103$ | $-4 \log_e 10 = 0.7897 - 10$ |
| $5 \log_e 10 = 11.5129$ | $-5 \log_e 10 = 9.4871 - 20$ |

Table IV.—Natural Logarithms.—(Continued)

| N | 0 | 1 | 2 | 3 | 4 | 5 | 6 | 7 | 8 | 9 |
|---|---|---|---|---|---|---|---|---|---|---|
| **5.0** | 1.6 094 | 114 | 134 | 154 | 174 | 194 | 214 | 233 | 253 | 273 |
| 5.1 | 292 | 312 | 332 | 351 | 371 | 390 | 409 | 429 | 448 | 467 |
| 5.2 | 487 | 506 | 525 | 544 | 563 | 582 | 601 | 620 | 639 | 658 |
| 5.3 | 677 | 696 | 715 | 734 | 752 | 771 | 790 | 808 | 827 | 845 |
| 5.4 | 864 | 882 | 901 | 919 | 938 | 956 | 974 | 993 | *011 | *029 |
| 5.5 | 1.7 047 | 066 | 084 | 102 | 120 | 138 | 156 | 174 | 192 | 210 |
| 5.6 | 228 | 246 | 263 | 281 | 299 | 317 | 334 | 352 | 370 | 387 |
| 5.7 | 405 | 422 | 440 | 457 | 475 | 492 | 509 | 527 | 544 | 561 |
| 5.8 | 579 | 596 | 613 | 630 | 647 | 664 | 681 | 699 | 716 | 733 |
| 5.9 | 750 | 766 | 783 | 800 | 817 | 834 | 851 | 867 | 884 | 901 |
| **6.0** | 918 | 934 | 951 | 967 | 984 | *001 | *017 | *034 | *050 | *066 |
| 6.1 | 1.8 083 | 099 | 116 | 132 | 148 | 165 | 181 | 197 | 213 | 229 |
| 6.2 | 245 | 262 | 278 | 294 | 310 | 326 | 342 | 358 | 374 | 390 |
| 6.3 | 405 | 421 | 437 | 453 | 469 | 485 | 500 | 516 | 532 | 547 |
| 6.4 | 563 | 579 | 594 | 610 | 625 | 641 | 656 | 672 | 687 | 703 |
| 6.5 | 718 | 733 | 749 | 764 | 779 | 795 | 810 | 825 | 840 | 856 |
| 6.6 | 871 | 886 | 901 | 916 | 931 | 946 | 961 | 976 | 991 | *006 |
| 6.7 | 1.9 021 | 036 | 051 | 066 | 081 | 095 | 110 | 125 | 140 | 155 |
| 6.8 | 169 | 184 | 199 | 213 | 228 | 242 | 257 | 272 | 286 | 301 |
| 6.9 | 315 | 330 | 344 | 359 | 373 | 387 | 402 | 416 | 430 | 445 |
| **7.0** | 459 | 473 | 488 | 502 | 516 | 530 | 544 | 559 | 573 | 587 |
| 7.1 | 601 | 615 | 629 | 643 | 657 | 671 | 685 | 699 | 713 | 727 |
| 7.2 | 741 | 755 | 769 | 782 | 796 | 810 | 824 | 838 | 851 | 865 |
| 7.3 | 879 | 892 | 906 | 920 | 933 | 947 | 961 | 974 | 988 | *001 |
| 7.4 | 2.0 015 | 028 | 042 | 055 | 069 | 082 | 096 | 109 | 122 | 136 |
| 7.5 | 149 | 162 | 176 | 189 | 202 | 215 | 229 | 242 | 255 | 268 |
| 7.6 | 281 | 295 | 308 | 321 | 334 | 347 | 360 | 373 | 386 | 399 |
| 7.7 | 412 | 425 | 438 | 451 | 464 | 477 | 490 | 503 | 516 | 528 |
| 7.8 | 541 | 554 | 567 | 580 | 592 | 605 | 618 | 631 | 643 | 656 |
| 7.9 | 669 | 681 | 694 | 707 | 719 | 732 | 744 | 757 | 769 | 782 |
| **8.0** | 794 | 807 | 819 | 832 | 844 | 857 | 869 | 882 | 894 | 906 |
| 8.1 | 919 | 931 | 943 | 956 | 968 | 980 | 992 | *005 | *017 | *029 |
| 8.2 | 2.1 041 | 054 | 066 | 080 | 090 | 102 | 114 | 126 | 138 | 150 |
| 8.3 | 163 | 175 | 187 | 199 | 211 | 223 | 235 | 247 | 258 | 270 |
| 8.4 | 282 | 294 | 306 | 318 | 330 | 342 | 353 | 365 | 377 | 389 |
| 8.5 | 401 | 412 | 424 | 436 | 448 | 460 | 471 | 483 | 494 | 506 |
| 8.6 | 518 | 529 | 541 | 552 | 564 | 576 | 587 | 599 | 610 | 622 |
| 8.7 | 633 | 645 | 656 | 668 | 679 | 691 | 702 | 713 | 725 | 736 |
| 8.8 | 748 | 759 | 770 | 782 | 793 | 804 | 815 | 827 | 838 | 849 |
| 8.9 | 861 | 872 | 883 | 894 | 905 | 917 | 928 | 939 | 950 | 961 |
| **9.0** | 972 | 983 | 994 | *006 | *017 | *028 | *039 | *050 | *061 | *072 |
| 9.1 | 2.2 083 | 094 | 105 | 116 | 127 | 137 | 148 | 159 | 170 | 181 |
| 9.2 | 192 | 203 | 214 | 225 | 235 | 246 | 257 | 268 | 279 | 289 |
| 9.3 | 300 | 311 | 322 | 332 | 343 | 354 | 364 | 375 | 386 | 396 |
| 9.4 | 407 | 418 | 428 | 439 | 450 | 460 | 471 | 481 | 492 | 502 |
| 9.5 | 513 | 523 | 534 | 544 | 555 | 565 | 576 | 586 | 597 | 607 |
| 9.6 | 618 | 628 | 638 | 649 | 659 | 670 | 680 | 690 | 701 | 711 |
| 9.7 | 721 | 732 | 742 | 752 | 762 | 773 | 783 | 793 | 803 | 814 |
| 9.8 | 824 | 834 | 844 | 854 | 865 | 875 | 885 | 895 | 905 | 915 |
| 9.9 | 925 | 935 | 946 | 956 | 966 | 976 | 986 | 996 | *006 | *016 |
| **10.** | 2.3 026 | 036 | 046 | 056 | 066 | 076 | 086 | 096 | 106 | 115 |

## TABLE V.—EXPONENTIAL AND HYPERBOLIC FUNCTIONS

| $x$ | $e^x$ | $e^{-x}$ | sinh $x$ | cosh $x$ | tanh $x$ |
|---|---|---|---|---|---|
| .00 | 1.000 | 1.000 | .000 | 1.000 | .000 |
| .01 | 1.010 | .990 | .010 | 1.000 | .010 |
| .02 | 1.020 | .980 | .020 | 1.000 | .020 |
| .03 | 1.030 | .970 | .030 | 1.000 | .030 |
| .04 | 1.041 | .961 | .040 | 1.001 | .040 |
| .05 | 1.051 | .951 | .050 | 1.001 | .050 |
| .06 | 1.062 | .942 | .060 | 1.002 | .060 |
| .07 | 1.073 | .932 | .070 | 1.002 | .070 |
| .08 | 1.083 | .923 | .080 | 1.003 | .080 |
| .09 | 1.094 | .914 | .090 | 1.004 | .090 |
| .1 | 1.105 | .905 | .100 | 1.005 | .100 |
| .2 | 1.221 | .819 | .201 | 1.020 | .197 |
| .3 | 1.350 | .741 | .305 | 1.045 | .291 |
| .4 | 1.492 | .670 | .411 | 1.081 | .380 |
| .5 | 1.649 | .607 | .521 | 1.128 | .462 |
| .6 | 1.822 | .549 | .637 | 1.185 | .537 |
| .7 | 2.014 | .497 | .759 | 1.255 | .604 |
| .8 | 2.226 | .449 | .888 | 1.337 | .664 |
| .9 | 2.460 | .407 | 1.027 | 1.433 | .716 |
| 1.0 | 2.718 | .368 | 1.175 | 1.543 | .762 |
| 1.1 | 3.004 | .333 | 1.336 | 1.669 | .800 |
| 1.2 | 3.320 | .301 | 1.509 | 1.811 | .834 |
| 1.3 | 3.669 | .273 | 1.698 | 1.971 | .862 |
| 1.4 | 4.055 | .247 | 1.904 | 2.151 | .885 |
| 1.5 | 4.482 | .223 | 2.129 | 2.352 | .905 |
| 1.6 | 4.953 | .202 | 2.376 | 2.577 | .922 |
| 1.7 | 5.474 | .183 | 2.646 | 2.828 | .935 |
| 1.8 | 6.050 | .165 | 2.942 | 3.107 | .947 |
| 1.9 | 6.686 | .150 | 3.268 | 3.418 | .956 |
| 2.0 | 7.389 | .135 | 3.627 | 3.762 | .964 |
| 2.1 | 8.166 | .122 | 4.022 | 4.144 | .970 |
| 2.2 | 9.025 | .111 | 4.457 | 4.568 | .976 |
| 2.3 | 9.974 | .100 | 4.937 | 5.037 | .980 |
| 2.4 | 11.023 | .091 | 5.466 | 5.557 | .984 |
| 2.5 | 12.182 | .082 | 6.050 | 6.132 | .987 |
| 2.6 | 13.464 | .074 | 6.695 | 6.769 | .989 |
| 2.7 | 14.880 | .067 | 7.406 | 7.473 | .991 |
| 2.8 | 16.445 | .061 | 8.192 | 8.253 | .993 |
| 2.9 | 18.174 | .055 | 9.060 | 9.115 | .994 |
| 3.0 | 20.086 | .050 | 10.018 | 10.068 | .995 |
| 3.1 | 22.20 | .045 | 11.08 | 11.12 | .996 |
| 3.2 | 24.53 | .041 | 12.25 | 12.29 | .997 |
| 3.3 | 27.11 | .037 | 13.54 | 13.57 | .997 |
| 3.4 | 29.96 | .033 | 14.97 | 15.00 | .998 |
| 3.5 | 33.12 | .030 | 16.54 | 16.57 | .998 |
| 3.6 | 36.60 | .027 | 18.29 | 18.31 | .999 |
| 3.7 | 40.45 | .025 | 20.21 | 20.24 | .999 |
| 3.8 | 44.70 | .022 | 22.34 | 22.36 | .999 |
| 3.9 | 49.40 | .020 | 24.69 | 24.71 | .999 |
| 4.0 | 54.60 | .018 | 27.29 | 27.31 | .999 |
| 4.1 | 60.34 | .017 | 30.16 | 30.18 | .999 |
| 4.2 | 66.69 | .015 | 33.34 | 33.35 | 1.000 |
| 4.3 | 73.70 | .014 | 36.84 | 36.86 | 1.000 |
| 4.4 | 81.45 | .012 | 40.72 | 40.73 | 1.000 |
| 4.5 | 90.02 | .011 | 45.00 | 45.01 | 1.000 |
| 4.6 | 99.48 | .010 | 49.74 | 49.75 | 1.000 |
| 4.7 | 109.95 | .0090 | 54.97 | 54.98 | 1.000 |
| 4.8 | 121.51 | .0082 | 60.75 | 60.76 | 1.000 |
| 4.9 | 134.29 | .0074 | 67.14 | 67.15 | 1.000 |
| 5.0 | 148.41 | .0067 | 74.20 | 74.21 | 1.000 |
| 6.0 | 403.4 | .0025 | 201.7 | | 1.000 |
| 7.0 | 1096.6 | .00091 | 548.3 | | 1.000 |
| 8.0 | 2981.0 | .00034 | 1490.5 | | 1.000 |
| 9.0 | 8103.1 | .00012 | 4051.5 | | 1.000 |
| 10.0 | 22026.5 | .000045 | 11013.2 | | 1.000 |

# INDEX

# ANSWERS

## INTRODUCTION
### Arts. 1–5, pp. 6–7

**1.** (a) 2, 5; (c) 3, $-\frac{1}{2}$. **3.** (a) 3, $-\frac{5}{2}$; (c) $2 \pm 4i$. **4.** (a) 12; (c) $-10$.
**5.** (a) $x = -1, y = 4$; (c) $x = 1.6, y = 2.8$. **6.** (a) $x = 2, y = -1, z = 3$.
**8.** $2\frac{1}{80}$. **9.** $\frac{1}{4}$. **10.** $\frac{1}{5}$. **11.** 125. **15.** 5.1059. **16.** 2.2823.

### Arts. 6–17, pp. 13–14

**1.** (a) 1.5359; (c) 6.9813. **2.** (a) 80° 12′ 51″ (c) 120° 19′ 16″.
**4.** 38° 47′ 37″. **5.** 0. **6.** 3. **7.** $-3\frac{1}{2}$. **8.** $4\frac{1}{2}$.
**9.** 0 8192; $-0.4384$; $-5.671$. **14.** $\frac{24}{25}$; $\frac{7}{25}$; $\frac{1}{3}$. **15.** $-\frac{120}{169}$; $\frac{119}{169}$; $-\frac{120}{119}$.

**16.** $\frac{63}{65}$; $-\frac{33}{65}$. **17.** $\frac{3}{5}$; $\frac{4}{5}$. **18.** $\dfrac{2}{\sqrt{5}}$; $\dfrac{1}{\sqrt{5}}$. **23.** 30°, 90°, 150°, 270°.

**24.** 60°, 300°, 70° 32′, 289° 28′. **25.** 0°, 120°, 180°, 240°.
**26.** 0°, 120°, 180°, 240°. **27.** 36° 52′. **28.** 135°, 315°.

## CHAPTER I
### Arts. 1–2, pp. 19–20

**4.** (a) 24; (b) 20; (c) 16. **5.** (8, 4). **6.** (a) (11, 4), $(-5, 4)$, $(5, -4)$; 32.
**7.** $(-4, 3)$. **8.** $(\pm 3\sqrt{2}, \pm 3\sqrt{2})$. **9.** (a) 5; (b) 13. **14.** $(\frac{11}{5}, \frac{27}{5})$.
**15.** $(\frac{60}{13}, -\frac{25}{13})$; $(-\frac{60}{13}, -\frac{144}{13})$; $(0, -13)$; $(0, -\frac{13}{2})$.

### Arts. 3–5, pp. 26–28

**21.** $A = 10y - \frac{5}{8}y^2$. **22.** $L = 2\sqrt{36 - x^2}$. **23.** $V = 2\pi x^2(6 - x)$.
**24.** $A = x\sqrt{144 - x^2}$.

### Art. 6, p. 30

**1.** (4, 3). **2.** (1, $-2$). **3.** parallel. **4.** coincide. **5.** (1, $-4$); (4, $-4$).
**6.** (3, $-4$); $(-\frac{4}{9}, \frac{16}{9})$. **7.** (4, 4); (1, $-2$). **8.** (6, 2); $(-3, -4)$.
**9.** (1, $-6$); (2, $-4$). **10.** $(\pm\sqrt{12}, 2)$. **11.** $(\frac{1}{2}\sqrt{2}, \frac{1}{2}\sqrt{2})$.
**12.** (0, 0); (3, 3); (5, 5). **13.** (1, 3); (2, 4). **14.** (2, 1). **15.** (8, 4); (0, 0).
**16.** (1, 2). **17.** (2, 8). **18.** $(-1, -15)$; (2, 0).

## CHAPTER II
### Arts. 7–10, pp. 35–36

**9.** $(5\frac{1}{3}, 0)$. **10.** $(-10\frac{5}{8}, -3)$. **11.** (4, 3); 5.
**12.** $(5 + 5\sqrt{3}, 1 + 5\sqrt{3})$; $(5 - 5\sqrt{3}, 1 - 5\sqrt{3})$.
**13.** $x^2 + y^2 - 4x - 2y - 20 = 0$. **14.** $3x + 2y = 12$. **15.** $x - y = 2$.
**16.** $y^2 = 8x - 16$.

### Arts. 11–15, pp. 41–43

**1.** (a) (4, 8); (c) $(-5, -2)$; (e) $(3, -\frac{5}{2})$.

**2.** (a) $(5, -2)$; (c) $(-5, -1\frac{3}{2})$; (e) $(2, 0)$.

**3.** (a) $(4, 6)$; (c) $(11, 11)$; (e) $(11, -18)$.    **5.** $(6, 3)$.    **6.** $(1, 4)$, $(4, 2)$, $(7, 0)$.

**7.** $(1\frac{6}{3}, -\frac{5}{3})$.    **12.** $-1\frac{3}{4}$, $\frac{1}{5}$, $\frac{5}{2}$; $-1\frac{6}{7}$, $-\frac{1}{14}$, $\frac{14}{1}$.    **16.** $-6$.    **17.** $\frac{5}{7}$.

**19.** $\frac{56}{33}$; $-1\frac{3}{5}$    **20.** 7.

## Arts. 16–17, pp. 47–48

**1.** (a) 16; (c) 15.    **2.** (a) 26; (c) 97.    **3.** (a) 38; (c) 43.    **7.** $11\frac{5}{13}$.    **8.** 0.

**9.** 1.

## Art. 18, pp. 50–51

**1.** $x^2 + y^2 + 2x - 4y - 11 = 0$.    **2.** $x^2 + y^2 + 4x + 8y + 11 = 0$.

**3.** $3x + 2y - 13 = 0$.    **4.** (a) $3x - 4y - 7 = 0$;   (c) $4x + 3y - 1 = 0$.

**5.** $y^2 - 4y - 6x + 13 = 0$.    **6.** (a) $y^2 = 8x - 32$.

**7.** $x^2 + y^2 + 4x - 12 = 0$.    **8.** $x^2 + y^2 = 12x$.    **9.** $y = x$.    **10.** $x = 12$.

**11.** $2xy - 3y + x = 0$.    **12.** $3x^2 + 4y^2 - 32x + 64 = 0$.

**13.** (a) $x^2 + y^2 = 25$; (c) $x^2 + y^2 - 5x - 4y + 4 = 0$.

**14.** $y^2 - 12x - 2y + 13 = 0$.    **15.** $9x^2 + 25y^2 = 225$.

**16.** $44x^2 - 100y^2 = 275$.

## CHAPTER III

### Arts. 19–24, pp. 55–57

**1.** (a) $x + y = 6$; (c) $x - 2y = 2$; (e) $2x + y + 7 = 0$.

**2.** (a) $5x - 4y + 3 = 0$; (c) $11x + 16y = 31$; (e) $x = 4$.

**3.** (a) $2y - x = 5$; (c) $3y = 2x$; (e) $4x - 15y + 10 = 0$.

**6.** (a) $3x + y = 18$; (c) $4y - 16x = 45$.

**7.** (a) $5y - 3x = 5$; (c) $y - 2x = 3$.

**8.** (a) $x + 2y = 10$.    **9.** $y = 2x + 16$.

**10.** $(12, -2)$.    **11.** $(7, 13)$.    **12.** $(0, 1)$.    **13.** $(4, 1)$.

**15.** (a) $x + y = 5$; (c) $20x + 21y = 44$.    **16.** 30.

### Arts. 25–28, pp. 61–64

**1.** (a) $y = -\frac{1}{4}x + \frac{3}{2}$; (c) $y = \frac{1}{3}x + \frac{2}{3}$; (e) $y = -0.2x$.

**2.** (a) $a = -1\frac{1}{4}$, $b = \frac{22}{7}$; (c) $a = -\frac{7}{5}$, $b = -\frac{7}{2}$.

**3.** (a) $-6$; $\frac{2}{3}$.   (c) $-\frac{28}{3}$; $\frac{21}{4}$.

**4.** (a) $x - 2y + 11 = 0$, (c) $3x - 2y = 5$,

          $2x + y = 8$;      $2x + 3y = -1$.

**5.** $3x + 2y = 12$; $x - 3y = 15$.    **7.** (a) $\tan \theta = \pm 5$; (c) $\tan \theta = \pm 1$.

**8.** $\tan \theta = -2$.    **9.** (a) $\tan A = \frac{10}{11}$; $\tan B = 5$; $\tan C = \frac{5}{3}$.

(c) $\tan A = \frac{4}{3}$; $\tan B = \frac{4}{5}$; $\tan C = 32$.

**10.** (a) $\tan A = 1$; $\tan B = -1$.   (c) $\tan A = 7$; $\tan B = -7$.

**11.** $\tan \theta = \pm \frac{3}{8}$.    **14.** $A = 100 + 0.04t$.    **15.** $L = \sqrt{3}\, x$.    **16.** $F = 8x$.

**17.** concentration $= (20 + 3.75x)\%$.    **18.** $L = 30 + 0.000195(t - 50)$.

**19.** $D_1 = 300 - 40t$; $D_2 = 20t$.    **20.** 8:40 P.M.

### Arts. 29–32, pp. 71–73

**1.** (a) $\dfrac{\sqrt{3}}{2} x + \frac{1}{2}y = 4$; (c) $-\frac{1}{2}x + \dfrac{\sqrt{3}}{2} y = 0$;

(e) $-0.940x - 0.342y = 2$.

**2.** (a) $-\dfrac{x}{\sqrt{2}} - \dfrac{y}{\sqrt{2}} = \dfrac{1}{\sqrt{2}}$; (c) $\dfrac{x}{\sqrt{5}} + \dfrac{2y}{\sqrt{5}} = 4$; (e) $\dfrac{x}{\sqrt{26}} + \dfrac{5y}{\sqrt{26}} = 0$.

**3.** (a) $\tfrac{4}{5}x + \tfrac{3}{5}y = \tfrac{12}{5}$; (c) $\dfrac{x}{\sqrt{2}} - \dfrac{y}{\sqrt{2}} = \dfrac{3}{\sqrt{2}}$. **4.** (a) $\tfrac{12}{5}$; (b) $\dfrac{7\sqrt{5}}{2}$.

**5.** $3x - 4y = \pm 50$. **6.** $p = \pm \dfrac{ab}{\sqrt{a^2 + b^2}}$. **7.** $\dfrac{\pm b}{\sqrt{m^2 + 1}}$.

**9.** (a) $-\tfrac{28}{13}$; (c) $\sqrt{10}$. **10.** (a) $3\sqrt{2}$; (c) $\tfrac{1}{2}\sqrt{26}$. **11.** no intersection.
**13.** $7x - 56y + 228 = 0$; $8x + y - 18 = 0$. **14.** $(\tfrac{5}{2}, \tfrac{3}{2})$. **15.** $(1, 2)$; $\sqrt{2}$.
**16.** $12x - 5y + 101 = 0$;
$12x - 5y - 159 = 0$.
**17.** 75 lb. **18.** $116\tfrac{2}{3}$ lb. **19.** $20\tfrac{5}{8}$ lb. **20.** 26.8 lb.

### Arts. 33–35, pp. 77–78

**2.** $y = -2x + b$. **3.** (a) $2y - x = 8$; (b) $2x + 5y = 20$.
**4.** $x + 5y + 4 = 0$. **5.** $5x + 2y - 20 = 0$; $5x + 18y + 60 = 0$.
**6.** $x + y = 10$; $2x + 3y = 24$. **7.** $4x - 3y = 50$. **8.** $y = \pm 4x - 4$.
**9.** $2x + y = 9$. **11.** $y = x + 1$. **12.** $x + 2y + 2 = 0$.

### CHAPTER IV

### Arts. 36–37, pp. 83–85

**11.** $\pm 10$. **13.** (a) $y = 2x^2 - 3x + 4$; (c) $y = \tfrac{1}{2}x^2 - 6$. **18.** $S = 6x^2$.
**20.** $A = 300x - \tfrac{3}{2}x^2$; 100 by 150. **21.** $A = 400x - 2x^2$; 100 by 200.
**22.** $R = (18 + x)(30 - x)$; \$24. **23.** 50 ft. **24.** $80\sqrt{2}$ ft. per second.
**25.** 256 ft.

### Arts. 38–42, pp. 92–93

**15.** $V = 4x(6 - x)(9 - x)$. **16.** $V = \tfrac{5}{3}x^2(9 - x)$; $x = 6$.
**17.** $V = \dfrac{\pi y}{4}(36 - y^2)$.

### CHAPTER V

### Arts. 43–47, pp. 99–101

**21.** $V = 12\pi \dfrac{y^2}{y - 12}$. **22.** $C = 0.06\left(x^2 + \dfrac{432}{x}\right)$.

### CHAPTER VI

### Arts. 48–50, pp. 105–106

**1.** $y' = \tfrac{1}{2}x'$. **2.** $x' + y' = 0$. **3.** $y' = x'^2 - 3x'$. **4.** $y' = -x'^2$.
**5.** $y' = x'^3 - 4x'$. **6.** $y' = x'^3 - 2x'^2$. **7.** $y' = \dfrac{3}{x'}$. **8.** $y' = \dfrac{8}{x'^2 + 4}$.
**9.** $y' = \dfrac{x'}{x'^2 + 1}$. **11.** (a) $(4\sqrt{3} + 3, 3\sqrt{3} - 4)$; (c) $(5, 5\sqrt{3})$.
**12.** (a) $(7\sqrt{2}, -\sqrt{2})$; (c) $(5\sqrt{2}, 5\sqrt{2})$. **13.** (a) $(6, -8)$; (c) $(10, 0)$.
**14.** $x' = \dfrac{2}{\sqrt{5}}$. **15.** $y' = -4$. **17.** $(x' - y')^2 = \sqrt{2}(x' + y')$.
**18.** $x'^2 - y'^2 = 2$. **19.** $x' = x\cos\theta + y\sin\theta$; $y' = y\cos\theta - x\sin\theta$.

## CHAPTER VII
### Arts. 51–53, pp. 110–112

**1.** (a) $(x - 3)^2 + (y - 2)^2 = 1$; $x^2 + y^2 - 6x - 4y + 12 = 0$.
(c) $(x - 4)^2 + y^2 = 4$; $x^2 + y^2 - 8x + 12 = 0$.
(e) $(x + 8)^2 + (y - 1)^2 = 9$, $x^2 + y^2 + 16x - 2y + 56 = 0$.
**2.** (a) $(-4, 3)$; 0.   (c) $(2\frac{1}{2}, -3)$; $2\frac{1}{2}$.   (e) $(4, -\frac{5}{3})$; $\frac{13}{3}$.
**4.** (a) $(x - 2)^2 + (y - 3)^2 = 20$.   (b) $(x - 15)^2 + (y - 12)^2 = 225$.
(c) $(x - 4)^2 + (y - 4)^2 = 16$.   (d) $(x - 7)^2 + y^2 = 80$.
**5.** $x^2 + y^2 - 16x + 48 = 0$.   **6.** $x^2 + y^2 = 9$.   **7.** Two points.
**8.** (a) $(x - 3)^2 + (y - 9)^2 = 106$.   (c) $(x - 2)^2 + (y + 3)^2 = 5$.
**9.** $(x - 5)^2 + (y + 3)^2 = 9$.   **10.** $(x + 2)^2 + (y - 1)^2 = \frac{1}{2}$.
**11.** $(x - 3)^2 + (y + 5)^2 = 25$.   **12.** $(x - 7)^2 + (y - 1)^2 = 5$.
**13.** $(x + 2)^2 + (y + 1)^2 = 5$; $(x - 10)^2 + (y + 5)^2 = 125$.
**14.** $2x - y = 2$.

## CHAPTER VIII
### Arts. 54–57, pp. 118–120

**1.** (a) $(1, 0)$; $x = -1$.   (c) $(0, -\frac{1}{2})$; $y = \frac{1}{2}$.   (e) $(\frac{1}{2}, 0)$; $x = -\frac{1}{2}$.
**2.** (a) $8y = x^2$.   (c) $y^2 + 4y - 4x = 12$.
**4.** (a) $y = x^2 + 4x - 3$.   (c) $y = 1 + 2x - x^2$.   **5.** $\frac{2}{3}$ in. from vertex.
**6.** $x^2 + 25y + 100 = 0$.
**9.** (a) $(y - 1)^2 = x - 3$.   (c) $(y + 2)^2 = -4(x - 1)$.
**10.** $\left(x + \dfrac{b}{2a}\right)^2 = \dfrac{1}{a}\left[y - \left(c - \dfrac{b^2}{4a}\right)\right]$.   **11.** $A = 40x - x^2$.
**12.** $A = 120x - 2x^2$.   **13.** 200 by 80.   **14.** 200 ft.; 50 ft.

### Arts. 58–61, pp. 125–126

**1.** (a) $(0, \pm \sqrt{5})$; $e = \dfrac{\sqrt{5}}{3}$.   (c) $(0, \pm 1)$; $e = \frac{1}{2}$.
(e) $(\pm \sqrt{20}, 0)$; $e = \sqrt{\frac{5}{8}}$.
**2.** (a) $\dfrac{x^2}{64} + \dfrac{y^2}{48} = 1$.   (c) $\dfrac{x^2}{16} + \dfrac{y^2}{25} = 1$.
**3.** (a) $\dfrac{(x - 8)^2}{64} + \dfrac{(y - 4)^2}{48} = 1$.   (c) $\dfrac{(x - 4)^2}{16} + \dfrac{(y + 4)^2}{32} = 1$.
**4.** 0.866; 0.995.   **7.** $\dfrac{(x - 5)^2}{25} + \dfrac{y^2}{9} = 1$.   **8.** $\dfrac{(x - 3)^2}{36} + \dfrac{y^2}{27} = 1$.
**9.** 5.9, 5.5, 4.8, 3.6, 2.6.   **10.** $\dfrac{x^2}{256} + \dfrac{y^2}{64} = 1$.
**11.** (a) $\dfrac{x^2}{4} + \dfrac{(y - 3)^2}{9} = 1$.   (c) $\dfrac{(x + 3)^2}{9} + \dfrac{(y - 2)^2}{4} = 1$.
**12.** $(3, 2\frac{2}{5})$; $(-4, -1\frac{4}{5})$.   **13.** 94.5 and 91.3 million miles.
**14.** $(8, \frac{12}{5})$; $(5, -3)$.

### Arts. 62–64, pp. 131–133

**1.** (a) $(0, \pm 5)$; $(0, \pm \sqrt{34})$.   (c) $(\pm 4, 0)$; $(\pm 5, 0)$.   **2.** $\sqrt{2}$.
**4.** $xy = -2$.   **7.** (a) $\dfrac{x^2}{36} - \dfrac{y^2}{45} = 1$.   (c) $\dfrac{x^2}{16} - \dfrac{y^2}{48} = 1$.

**8.** (a) $\dfrac{(y-1)^2}{9} - \dfrac{(x-4)^2}{16} = 1.$  (c) $\dfrac{(y+3)^2}{9} - \dfrac{(x+2)^2}{27} = 1.$

**9.** $\dfrac{(x-3)^2}{9} - \dfrac{y^2}{16} = 1.$  **10.** $3x^2 - y^2 + 48x + 144 = 0.$

**12.** (a) $\dfrac{(x-2)^2}{4} - \dfrac{(y+1)^2}{1} = 1$  (c) $\dfrac{(x-4)^2}{16} - \dfrac{y^2}{20} = 1.$

(e) $\dfrac{(y-4)^2}{9} - \dfrac{(x+2)^2}{16} = 1.$  **19.** $x'y' + 3 = 0.$  **20.** $x'y' = 6.$

**21.** $3x'y' + 20 = 0.$  **22.** $2x'y' = 3.$

### Arts. 65–68, pp. 137–138

**2.** (a) parabola.  (c) hyperbola.  (e) hyperbola.

**3.** (a) ellipse; $\sin \theta = \dfrac{2}{\sqrt{5}}, \cos \theta = \dfrac{1}{\sqrt{5}}.$  (e) hyperbola; $\sin \theta = \dfrac{1}{\sqrt{17}},$

$\cos \theta = \dfrac{4}{\sqrt{17}}.$

**4.** (a) $4x'^2 - y'^2 = 4.$  (c) $y'^2 = 6x'.$  (e) $(x'-1)^2 = 4(y'-1).$

**7.** (a) two intersecting lines.  (c) ellipse.  **8.** $3x^2 + 4y^2 - 24x + 36 = 0.$

**9.** $x^2 - 2xy + y^2 - 2x - 2y - 1 = 0.$  **10.** $x^2 - 3y^2 - 12y + 36 = 0.$

### CHAPTER X

### Arts. 78–79, pp. 158–159

**9.** $x = 0, \dfrac{\pi}{3}, \pi, \dfrac{5\pi}{3}.$  **10.** $x = \dfrac{\pi}{6}, \dfrac{\pi}{2}, \dfrac{5\pi}{6}, \dfrac{3\pi}{2}.$  **11.** $x = 0, \dfrac{2\pi}{3}, \dfrac{10\pi}{3}, 4\pi, \dfrac{14\pi}{3}, \dfrac{22\pi}{3}.$

**12.** $x = \dfrac{\pi}{12}, \dfrac{\pi}{4}, \dfrac{5\pi}{12}.$  **14.** $\frac{1}{2}\sqrt{3}.$  **15.** $\dfrac{1}{\sqrt{2}}.$  **16.** $-\frac{3}{5}.$  **17.** $\frac{120}{119}.$  **18.** $\frac{1}{2}.$

**19.** 7.  **23.** $\theta = 2 \arctan \dfrac{8}{4+t}.$  **24.** $\theta = \arctan \dfrac{5}{x} - \arctan \dfrac{3}{x}.$  **31.** $x = \frac{1}{2}.$

**32.** $x = \frac{1}{6}.$  **33.** $x = \frac{3}{4}.$  **34.** $x = \frac{2}{5}.$

### CHAPTER XI

### Arts. 80–82, pp. 164–165

**29.** (a) 3.6323; (c) 6.7197; (e) 7.5349 − 10.  **30.** (a) 10.45; (c) 0.02834.

### Arts. 83–84, pp. 170–171

**21.** $x = \log_e (y + \sqrt{y^2 + 1}).$  **22.** $x = \log_e (y + \sqrt{y^2 - 1}).$

**23.** $x = \frac{1}{2} \log_e \dfrac{1+y}{1-y}.$

### CHAPTER XII

### Arts. 85–88, pp. 175–176

**1.** $y = 4 - \frac{1}{2}x.$  **3.** $x^2y = 2.$  **5.** $16y^2 - x^2 = 16.$

**7.** $\dfrac{(x-2)^2}{25} + (y+3)^2 = 1.$  **8.** $x^2 + y^2 = 25.$

**9.** $\dfrac{(x-4)^2}{9} + \dfrac{(y+2)^2}{25} = 1.$  **10.** $\dfrac{(x-8)^2}{64} + \dfrac{y^2}{16} = 1.$

**11.** $y = \dfrac{64}{x^2 + 16}$. **12.** $x^{\frac{1}{2}} + y^{\frac{1}{2}} = a^{\frac{1}{2}}$.

**13.** $x = 120t$; $y = -\frac{1}{2}gt^2$; distance $= 60\sqrt{\frac{2}{3}}$ ft.

**14.** $x = 248$ ft., $y = -59.5$ ft.

## CHAPTER XIII

### Arts. 92–95, pp. 188–189

**2.** $(a)$ $(3, -3\sqrt{3})$; $(-8, 0)$; $(-2, -2)$.

**3.** $(a)$ $\left(4\sqrt{2}, -\dfrac{\pi}{4}\right)$ and $\left(4\sqrt{2}, \dfrac{7\pi}{4}\right)$; $(3, \pi)$ and $(-3, 0)$; $\left(-12, \dfrac{\pi}{6}\right)$ and $\left(12, \dfrac{7\pi}{6}\right)$.

**5.** $x^2 + y^2 = 16$. **6.** $y = x$. **7.** $x = 2$. **9.** $x^2 + y^2 = 6y$.

**11.** $x^2 + y^2 - 8x - 6y = 0$. **12.** $y^2 = 4 - 4x$.

**13.** $4x^2 + 3y^2 + 12y = 36$. **14.** $x^2 - 3y^2 - 32y = 64$. **15.** $xy = 4$.

**16.** $x^2 - y^2 = 4$. **17.** $y^2 = 4a^2 - 4ax$. **18.** $\tan\theta = 2$. **19.** $\rho \sin\vartheta = 4$.

**20.** $\rho \cos\theta + 2 = 0$. **21.** $\rho = \pm 3$. **22.** $\rho = 10\cos\theta$.

**23.** $\rho + 9\sin\theta = 0$. **24.** $\rho^2 \sin 2\theta = a^2$. **25.** $\rho^2 \cos 2\theta = a^2$.

**26.** $\rho = 8\cos\theta + 6\sin\theta$. **27.** $\rho = \dfrac{9}{5 - 4\cos\theta}$.

### Arts. 99–104, pp. 201–203

**33.** $\rho' = \sqrt{8}\,(\cos\theta' - \sin\theta')$; $\rho' = 4\sin\theta'$. **40.** $(\frac{12}{5}, \arctan\frac{3}{4})$; origin.

**41.** $(5, \arcsin\frac{3}{5})$. **42.** $\left(2\sqrt{3}, \dfrac{\pi}{3}\right)$; $\left(2\sqrt{3}, \dfrac{2\pi}{3}\right)$. **43.** $\left(3, \pm\dfrac{\pi}{3}\right)$; origin.

**44.** $(2, \frac{1}{2}\pi)$; $(\frac{6}{5}, \arcsin\frac{3}{5})$; origin. **45.** $\left(\dfrac{\sqrt{3}}{2}, \dfrac{\pi}{3}\right)$; $\left(\dfrac{\sqrt{3}}{2}, \dfrac{2\pi}{3}\right)$; origin.

**46.** $(1, 0)$; $(1, \pi)$; $\left(\frac{1}{2}, \dfrac{7\pi}{6}\right)$; $\left(\frac{1}{2}, -\dfrac{\pi}{6}\right)$; $(0.219, -51°\,20')$ $(0.219, 231°\,20')$; origin.

**47.** $(\frac{2}{5}\sqrt{5}, 63°\,26')$; origin. **50.** $\rho = \dfrac{\cos^2\theta - 8\sin^2\theta}{2\sin^3\theta}$.

**51.** $\rho = \dfrac{\sin^2\theta(3\cos\theta - 2\sin\theta)}{\cos^4\theta}$.

## CHAPTER XIV

### Arts. 105–109, pp. 210–212

**1.** $y = 0.431x + 5.49$. **3.** $y = 0.584x - 1.88$.

**5.** $L = 0.2800P + 10.12$; $16.28$ lb. **7.** $y = 0.185x^2 + 0.460x - 5.64$.

### Arts. 110–111, pp. 217–219

**1.** $y = 0.522x^{1.4833}$. **3.** $y = 25.63x^{-1.4396}$.

**5.** $y = (40.67)10^{-0.1952x} = (40.67)e^{-0.4495x}$. **7.** $t = 0.2532s^{0.5178}$.

**9.** $R = 0.07495V^{2.011}$. **11.** $P = 365.5v^{-1.401}$.

### Arts. 112–114, pp. 222–223

**1.** $y = 1.303x - 4.161$. **3.** $y = 0.5895x + 2.3286$. **5.** $y = 2.483x^{1.6513}$.

**7.** $y = (2.605)10^{0.1806}$.

## CHAPTER XV

### Arts. 115–119, pp. 233–235

**1.** (a) $\cos \alpha = \cos \beta = \frac{1}{6} \sqrt{6}$; $\cos \gamma = \frac{1}{3} \sqrt{6}$. (c) $\cos \alpha = \frac{2}{13} \sqrt{26}$;

$\cos \beta = -\frac{3}{26} \sqrt{26}$; $\cos \gamma = \frac{1}{26} \sqrt{26}$. (e) $\cos \alpha = \dfrac{-3}{7}$; $\cos \beta = \frac{2}{7}$;

$\cos \gamma = \dfrac{-6}{7}$.

**2.** $\pm \frac{2}{3}$. **3.** $\frac{1}{3} \sqrt{3}$. **5.** (a) $(-x, -y, -z)$; (c) $(x, -y, -z)$.

**6.** (a) 9; (c) 12. **7.** (a) $\sqrt{41}$, $\sqrt{50}$, $\sqrt{141}$. **10.** $(4, 4, \frac{7}{3})$; $(6, 1, \frac{11}{3})$.

**11.** $x^2 + y^2 + z^2 = 25$. **12.** $(x-3)^2 + (y-2)^2 + (z-5)^2 = 25$.

**13.** $y^2 + z^2 - 8x + 16 = 0$. **14.** $12x - 8y + 10z = 71$.

**15.** $9x^2 + 25y^2 + 25z^2 = 225$. **16.** $(-\frac{3}{2}, 0, 0)$.

**17.** (a) $F_x = F_y = 66\frac{2}{3}$ lb.; $F_z = 33\frac{1}{3}$ lb.

(c) $F_x = 36$ lb. $F_y = 0$; $F_z = -48$ lb.

**18.** $F_x = -3$ lb.; $F_y = -2$ lb.; $F_z = 51$ lb.

$F = \sqrt{9 + 4 + 2{,}601} = \sqrt{2{,}614}$.

$\cos \alpha = \dfrac{-3}{\sqrt{2{,}614}}$; $\cos \beta = \dfrac{-2}{\sqrt{2{,}614}}$; $\cos \gamma = \dfrac{51}{\sqrt{2{,}614}}$.

**19.** $F_x = 20$ lb.; $F_y = 36$ lb.; $F_z = 8$ lb.

**20.** $F_x = 24$ lb.; $F_y = 31$ lb.; $F_z = -14$ lb.

### Arts. 120–122, pp. 242–244

**1.** (a) $4 : 5 : 3$; $\cos \alpha = \dfrac{4}{\sqrt{50}}$; $\cos \beta = \dfrac{5}{\sqrt{50}}$; $\cos \gamma = \dfrac{3}{\sqrt{50}}$.

(c) $0 : 4 : 3$; $\cos \alpha = 0$; $\cos \beta = \frac{4}{5}$; $\cos \gamma = \frac{3}{5}$.

(e) $2 : -2 : 1$; $\cos \alpha = \frac{2}{3}$; $\cos \beta = -\frac{2}{3}$; $\cos \gamma = \frac{1}{3}$.

**3.** $1, 0, 0; 0, 1, 0; 0, 0, 1$. **4.** $\dfrac{1}{\sqrt{2}}, \frac{1}{2}, \frac{1}{2}$. **5.** $(0, 2, 3)$; $(2, 0, 4)$.

**6.** $(13, 8, 0)$; $(1, 0, 4)$. **7.** $(2, 5, 0)$; $(-3, 0, -5)$; $(0, 3, -2)$.

**8.** (a) $\pm \frac{4}{21}$. (c) $\pm 0.1$. **9.** (a) $\frac{5}{14} \sqrt{7}$. (c) $\frac{1}{2} \sqrt{2}$.

**10.** $\cos \theta = \pm \frac{1}{3} \sqrt{3}$. **12.** 26.6 lb. **13.** 34.6 lb. **15.** $-2 : 1 : 2$.

**16.** (a) $3 : 2 : 3$, (c) $5 : 8 : 5$. **17.** $5 : 7 : 5$.

## CHAPTER XVI

### Arts. 123–127, pp. 251–252

**1.** (a) $x + \sqrt{2}\, y + z = 8$; (c) $y - \sqrt{3}\, z + 12 = 0$.

**2.** (a) $x + 2y + z = 12$; (c) $4x + 3y + 25 = 0$; (e) $x + y - z = 6$.

**3.** (a) $-\frac{2}{9}x - \frac{3}{9}y - \frac{6}{9}z = 3$. (c) $\frac{8}{9}x + \frac{4}{9}y - \frac{1}{9}z = 3$.

**5.** (a) $3x + 2y + z = 10$; (c) $x - 2y + z = 0$.

**6.** $2x - y + z = 4$. **7.** $3x + 2y + z = 22$. **8.** $5x + y + 3z = 15$.

**9.** $(0, \frac{14}{5}, 0)$. **10.** $(4, 3, 1)$; $r = 9$. **12.** (a) 3; (c) $\dfrac{14 \sqrt{2}}{5}$.

**14.** $y + z = 5$. **15.** $11x - 6y + 5z + 4 = 0$.

## Arts. 128–131, pp. 256–258

**1.** $(a)$ $x + y + 2z = 12$.    $(c)$ $2x + 3y - 2z = 12$.    **2.** $x - 6y + 3z = 18$.
**3.** $2x - 5y + 3z = 20$.    **4.** $3x - y + 7z = 14$.
**5.** $6x - 7y - 4z + 24 = 0$.    **6.** $(a)$ $45°$; $(c)$ $44°\,19'$.    **7.** $49°\,2'$.    **8.** $85°\,36'$.
**9.** $55°\,33'$.    **10.** $3x + y - 2z + 20 = 0$.    **11.** $k = 2$.
**12.** $(a)$ $38°\,57'$; $(c)$ $0$.    **13.** $(0, 0, 12)$.

## Arts. 132–135, pp. 264–266

**2.** $(a)$ $(4, 6, 0)$, $(1, 0, 4)$; $(c)$ $(1, 5\frac{1}{2}, 0)$, $(7, 0, -3\frac{1}{2})$.    **3.** $\frac{6}{7}, \frac{2}{7}, \frac{3}{7}$.

**4.** $(a)$ $\dfrac{x - 2}{4} = \dfrac{y - 1}{3} = \dfrac{z - 6}{-2}$; $3x - 4y = 2$, $x + 2z = 14$.

    $(c)$ $\dfrac{x + 2}{3} = \dfrac{y + 5}{2} = \dfrac{z + 2}{2}$; $2x - 3y = 11$, $2x - 3z = 2$.

**5.** $(a)$ $x - 8 = y - 10 = \frac{1}{2}(z - 8)$.    **6.** $19°\,28'$.    **8.** $(0, 0, \frac{18}{5})$.
**9.** $19°\,28'$ or $160°\,32'$.    **10.** $(1\frac{1}{2}, 2, 1)$.
**11.** $4x + 3y - 11 = 0$, $x - 3z + 16 = 0$.    **12.** $(5, 5, 2)$.    **13.** $3.86$.
**14.** $6.79$.    **15.** $53.9$ lb.    **16.** $4x - y + 2z + 20 = 0$.
**17.** $3x - 2y - 3z = 0$.    **18.** $6x - 8y + z = 0$.    **19.** $3x - 7y + 2z = 5$.
**20.** $x + 2y + z + 5 = 0$.

## CHAPTER XVII

### Arts. 136–140, pp. 271–272

**1.** $(c)$ $x^2 + (y - 3)^2 + (z - 4)^2 = 29$.    **3.** $6x + 2y + 3z = 61$.
**4.** $7x - 4y + 4z = 65$; $4x + 7y = 28$, $4x - 7z = 0$.    **6.** $x^2 + y^2 = 4z$.
**7.** $x^2 + y^2 + z^2 = a^2$.    **9.** $4x^2 + 4z^2 - y^2 = 0$.
**11.** $9x^2 + 9y^2 + 25z^2 = 225$.    **13.** $x^2 + y^2 + \log_e z = 0$.

### Arts. 148–151, pp. 281–282

**13.** $r^2 = 6$, $\rho^2 \sin^2 \phi = 6$.    **15.** $r^2 \sin 2\theta = 4$, $\rho^2 \sin^2 \phi \sin 2\theta = 4$.
**17.** $r^2 + z^2 = 16$; $\rho = 4$.
**19.** $r^2 \cos 2\theta - 2z^2 = 4$; $\rho^2(\sin^2 \phi \cos 2\theta - 2 \cos^2 \phi) = 4$.